GINN CUSTOM PUBLISHING
191 Spring Street
Lexington, Massachusetts 02173

W9-DAV-876

Management

Forum

A Collection of Writings
By
Dr. T.F. Gautschi, P.E.
Wellesley, Mass.

GINN
AND
COM-
PANY

FOUNDED IN 1867

This book has been published as part of the
GINN CUSTOM PUBLISHING PROGRAM.

The articles reprinted in this book appeared
in Design News from October 1974 to January
1979, and are reprinted by permission of
Design News, A Cahners Publication. Cahners
Publishing Co., Inc., 221 Columbus Avenue,
Boston, Massachusetts 02116.

Contents

CHAPTER 14:
CAREER PLANNING

CHAPTER 15:
TIME MANAGEMENT

INTRODUCTION

This book is a collection of over 120 articles that have appeared in the "Management Forum" series as published by Design News and the TAPPI journal. The articles are intended to be short, terse, and to the point. They are timely and useful because they are based upon current research, seminar discussions, undergraduate and graduate level teaching, reader feedback, consulting and selective culling from numerous texts, periodicals and journals.

The subjects covered in the series were not selected in accordance with some overall outline or plan. However, for this book they have been divided into twenty categories, as shown in the table of contents. As such they are useful for individual study or as a framework for an academic course of study at the college level.

Since management is such a dynamic and growing field, the "Management Forum", as published in Design News and the TAPPI journal series, will also continue to grow—new articles will be added to existing categories and new categories will be added. In this perspective, "Management Forum" is a living thing, and this book should be considered as an up-to-date "snapshot" of the entire panorama of what has been, what is, and what will be.

AUTHOR'S BIOGRAPHY

Dr. T. F. Gautschi has over 30 years' experience in management for some of the most respected high-technology companies and agencies in the United States. This experience encompasses the entire range of management skills, including R & D management, planning and program management, organization development, training motivation, communications, and utilization of human resources.

Before entering the academic world, he held the title of Director of Management and Organizational Development for Data Processing Operations with Honeywell Information Systems, Wellesley, Massachusetts. Previous to that position, he was Director of Planning and Coordination for Computer System Operations for Honeywell.

Dr. Gautschi has had extensive experience in on-line program management as Mission Operations Systems Manager for the Jet Propulsion Laboratory, Pasadena, California--a position he held during that laboratory's successful unmanned lunar landing (Surveyor). He has also worked for the Navy as Program Manager for the development of several major anti-submarine weapon systems.

Dr. Gautschi's educational background includes the Doctorate in Management from the University of Southern California, an M.S. in Industrial Management from Massachusetts Institute of Technology, and a B.S.E.E. from the University of California at Berkeley. He has served on five graduate school faculties, conducting courses in engineering and management.

In addition to his teaching and writing activities, Dr. Gautschi is frequently called upon to conduct seminars and lectures on management for companies and organizations across the country. He currently holds the rank of Associate Professor of Management at Bryant College and he is author of "Management Forum" in Design News.

He is a registered professional engineer, a member of the Sigma Xi honary scientific fraternity, and a Sloan Fellow to the Massachusetts Institute of Technology. Honors include the Meritorious Civilian Service Award from the U.S. Navy and a Group Citation from NASA.

The contingency theory of management

Dr. T.F. Gautschi, P.E.

There is a need for an integrating management theory that is more practical than the simplistic classical and behavioral models that managers and scholars have been struggling with almost since organizations first became a reality. The *classical model* achieves efficiency through emphasis on technical proficiency and its machine-like qualities. The *behavior model* asserts that effectiveness is achieved by arranging matters so that people feel that they count, that they belong and that work can be meaningful.

In essence the *contingency philosophy* is simply the application of the basic management process of:

- diagnosing the situation to define the problems, parameters, constraints, management objectives and a solution technique.
- isolating the key factors affecting the problem or situation.
- identifying alternative courses of action.
- evaluating each alternative course to determine which one best meets the requirements of the situation.
- implementing the appropriate alternative.

In other words, there is no one best way—*it all depends*.

Application—To apply the contingency philosophy it must be recognized that: 1) no one approach is equally appropriate and applicable in all situations. For example, not all people are comfortable in job enrichment programs whose purpose is to increase individual autonomy and discretion. Also, not all jobs, or tasks, lend themselves to job enrichment. 2) The tasks, the technologies

and people for a particular organization must be well understood. 3) The people performing the analysis must have a working knowledge of the important management tools and a basic understanding of the various alternatives and their consequences. All useful organizational forms can be viewed as falling along a continuum bounded at the extremes by mechanistic and organic orientations. The mechanistic orientation, at one extreme, views the organization as a machine-like system whose component parts are facilities, tools, materials, procedures and rules, and workers who are used basically as programmable robots. At the other extreme is the organic orientation, which stresses flexibility and the psychosocial aspects of the organization—human motivations and needs.

The decision maker should recognize that a rigid mechanistic organization is best when a firm is producing a standardized product in an established market, but that an organic-type orientation would be better for an organization that must continually adjust and respond to a dynamic external environment.

Production technology limits the amount of discretion a subordinate can be given, and it usually determines the extent to which a job can be programmed.

A functional type of organization is usually closer to the mechanistic end of the organic-mechanistic continuum, and the program (or project) type of organization is closer to the organic extreme.

The application of contingency theory is *not* just a matter of applying specific statements like the above to every situation. As with mathematical analysis we should not memorize or document the answers to specific problems and then search for the identical problem in real life. Rather, we should use the general tools of mathematics to solve the many different kinds of mathematical problems, and we must use the tools of management to solve management problems.

The contingency philosophy is *not* unique to any one area of management theory. It is a basic process which should be applied to all areas. Once a firm adopts a contingency philosophy, it should begin to look more closely at itself in terms of relevant variables and their interaction with one another.

Leadership—There are no universal guidelines for leadership activities—rather, the appropriate leadership style is that which should result from a consideration of the capabilities and the needs of the manager's, the subordinate's and the work group's, as well as an understanding of the task and the situation.

For example, some professionals prefer broad guidelines for direction, whereas others may be much more concerned about being sure that they comply with the detailed desires of the manager. These two types require different interfaces. The Surveyor Program (which soft-landed the first U.S. unmanned spacecraft on the moon) was made up of many highly skilled professional engineers and scientists whose productivity and morale were very high even though they had to work long hours within a highly structured organization system. Any other structure would have been inappropriate for the time scales and the command decisions that were required.

Training and development—The contingency philosophy would suggest that training and development activities be geared both to the participant's needs and learning abilities, and to the particular requirements and environment of the organization of which he is a part. For example, in-depth training experiences, such as sensitivity training, are probably more important for the organic-type organization in order to meet rapidly changing conditions. Skills-type training would be more appropriate to the mechanistic-type organization.

Performance evaluation—In organic-type organizations the jobs are less well defined—in a sense, they are what the person makes them. Performance criteria are not always clear, so innovative performance appraisal techniques may be required, such as the compilation and discussion of "critical incidents", or employer-employee evaluation systems.

In the mechanistic-type organization the primary task is one of matching a person with a job and then measuring to assure that the person is performing to the standard established for the job. The highly structured organization usually has clear, well-thought-out job descriptions along with standards for measuring performance, and performance evaluation is generally a straightforward task.

Exercising the contingency theory of management

Dr. T. F. Gautschi, P.E.

In the previous issue we stated that the contingency theory of management means implementing the appropriate management approach depending on the situation. Organization and planning in such a theory are now described.

Controls—The contingency philosophy suggests that each firm tailor its control system to its requirements.

- Key factors to be controlled should be identified.
- Standards for measuring performance against these key factors should be specified.
- The information required should be defined.
- A reporting structure should be developed that will flag "out-of-tolerance" trends and activities for those who have the responsibility for the performance of the task.

Organization—To be most effective, an organization should be designed to fit its managers, its market environment, its technology and its work force.

This may require that different departments in the same firm be organized differently. An organic orientation would be better for encouraging innovation and coping with a dynamic environment. But it would not be suitable for a standard mass-produced item—where quality, consistency and costs are important and innovation and change should be kept to a minimum.

The essence of the contingency approach seems to be that there is no one best organizational form for combining the four organizational subsystems—technological, structural, psychosocial and managerial.

Some firms attempt to keep their core activities standardized, and as mechanistic as possible. To do this they provide an organic interface activity between the core group and the outside dynamic environment. This interface function is often provided in the marketing organization by a program office or by special interface engineers. This type of organization is often used by those industries which require relatively large production runs over short periods of time—and yet require innovation, e.g. some aspects of the electronics industry or the toy industry.

When highly skilled and professional people are involved, organizational effectiveness can often be improved by adapting the structure to meet the psychological needs of the organization members.

For example, in our recent career survey the job factor that was rated as "most important" by most of the respondents was "being able to do enjoyable, challenging and creative work", yet many stated that "earnings, opportunity for promotion and job security" were the most important factors.

Thus, we must be careful not to assume that all engineers and engineering managers feel one way or the other. The specific situation must be carefully analyzed.

Quantitative—For the more structured and bounded situations, quantitative techniques are usually very appropriate, whereas the organic-type situation is usually less well defined and requires a much broader analysis than is currently available using quantitative techniques.

Sometimes quantitative practitioners get so involved with the mechanics of linear programming, game theory, etc., that they ignore the basic business problem—in a sense they cannot see the forest because the bugs on the trees are so interesting. "Satisficing"—the choosing of the first alternative that meets the constraints—tends to be organic in nature. Maximizing—the choosing of the best alternative—is more appropriate for mechanistic type activities.

Accounting—The contingency view would suggest that within overall legal and investor requirements the various tools, techniques and information be adapted to support the decision making needs of the situation, and not vice versa.

Planning—Planning is defined as a dynamic decision-making process involving the identification of opportunities and threats and the choosing among alternatives for the allocation of resources, all for the purpose of achieving the goals of the organization. Under the stable conditions that exist in a mechanistic-type organization, there tends to be greater reliance upon standing rules and policies. Plans are usually very detailed and forecasting techniques usually rely upon historical data.

Under the more open, dynamic conditions that characterize the organic organization, there is less reliance upon standing rules and policies. The plans are less detailed and tend to stress overall objectives rather than detailed activities; forecasting often involves a degree of intuition.

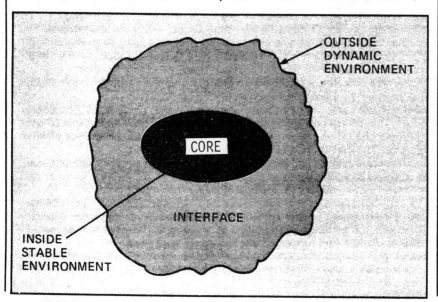

OUTSIDE DYNAMIC ENVIRONMENT

CORE

INTERFACE

INSIDE STABLE ENVIRONMENT

Consensus thinking can give the best decisions

*Some simple experiments
that show how powerful
consensus thinking really is*

Dr. T.F. Gautschi, P.E.

When the knowledge regarding a particular issue is spread among several people, the process of consensus thinking should be employed to assure the full utilization of such resources (see Mar. 3, 1975 Design Management Forum).

Other assessment techniques can be used (as shown below) but they will not be as effective as consensus thinking.

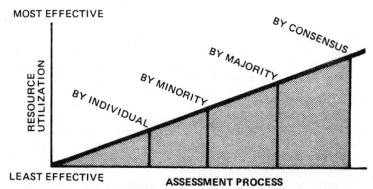

To provide some insight into the consensus process, we asked a number of groups to discuss and recommend solutions to a particular problem. The participants were told:

"Your spaceship has just crash-landed on the moon. You were scheduled to rendezvous with a mother ship 200 miles away on the lighted surface of the moon, but the rough landing has ruined your ship and destroyed all the equipment on board, except for the 15 items listed below. Your crew's survival depends on reaching the mother ship, so you must choose the most critical items available for the 200-mile trip. Your task is to rank the 15 items in terms of their importance for survival."

The priorities developed by the team were then compared with the priorities that were established by a panel of experts.

DISCUSSION PROCESS

Some groups used the "discussion process" and some used "consensus thinking". The "discussion" groups tackled the problems head on and spent a great deal of time and effort arguing about the relative merits of the various possible alternatives. Their solutions were generally far from optimal.

CONSENSUS THINKING PROCESS (1)

The consensus thinking groups took a different approach and their solutions were much closer to those of the experts. First, they defined the problem in terms that were specific and reasonably acceptable to everyone.

By the way, consensus does not require total agreement by all the contributors, but it does require general acceptance by everyone. When significant disagreement exists, it probably indicates that all of the inputs have not been adequately considered, and that further interaction should take place.

(2) Second, they pooled their information regarding the problem being considered. They were especially careful to include everyone's inputs to assure that they would develop a common data base.

(3) Next, they set about developing a hypothesis, or model, that would accommodate the information that they had.

(4) Finally, they "tested" their model to assure that it was compatible with the information they had and that it best addressed the problem they had defined.

Does this process sound familiar? It should. It is the process that anyone should go through when trying to solve a problem or make a decision.

The significant point here is that together the group should go through the same process an individual does, one step at a time. But what usually happens is that the participants assume that the first three steps are somehow covered and immediately skip to the fourth step—testing solutions. This often results in a great deal of argument and misunderstanding because everyone is pushing for his own solution in a win-lose contest. The problem has not been defined and the "contestants" are not working from a common data base.

FACILITATING CONSENSUS THINKING

In discussing the consensus thinking process, we always stress that the team should go through a four-step process, one step at a time. They are also urged to:

- **Avoid arguing for their own positions**
- **Avoid getting trapped by the win-lose syndrome**
- **Avoid changing their minds simply to reach agreement and harmony**
- **Avoid "cop-outs" like coin flipping, averaging and trading**
- **Seek out differences in opinion as being natural and helpful**
- **Present their information and other contributions as clearly and objectively as possible**
- **Perceive their team as one that could excel in the task that they're undertaking. They were urged not to let a negative self-concept defeat them before they could even get started.**

In another experiment, we asked teams to undertake a different task—to determine whether a particular defendent was innocent or guilty of a certain crime on the basis of given information.

All teams used the consensus thinking process and developed the correct solutions with little confusion even though some of the information was ambiguous and there were some subtle implications.

REAL-LIFE SITUATION

With this background, we took on a real-life situation:

A service organization that was diverse in character and having difficulty determining what their business really was decided to try the consensus thinking process. In a six-hour session involving the manager and his immediate reports, they were able to develop a realistic set of overall objectives, appropriate measurement criteria and an evaluation of how well they were achieving their objectives.

ADVANTAGES

Previous to this session, each subordinate manager had viewed the organization primarily from the point of view of his own unit. This, in turn, resulted in a series of suboptimizations without particular regard for the total organization and its objectives. As a result of participating in the consensus thinking process, the team was now able to view its individual organizations as part of a larger system and was willing to engage in tradeoffs that might even adversely affect their operations, in order to optimize the whole.

LIMITATION

In practice, the extent of such participation is limited by the perceived cost to the individuals involved. For example, if the tradeoff being considered would result in the elimination of the job of one of the participants, it would be difficult for that person to be objective.

We learned another thing:

Consensus thinking not only maximizes resource utilization, but it also increases the participants' commitment to any decisions that result from the consensus process. In the long run, this may be more important than any other aspect.

CAUTION

When the knowledge, or other inputs, are spread among several people, you might want to try consensus thinking. If this form of interaction is somewhat different from your usual style, proceed carefully, and be sure that everyone involved understands what you are trying to do. Consensus thinking can be a powerful tool when it is used correctly.

Planning

Dr. T.F. Gautschi, P.E.

Planning can be defined as a:
- dynamic decision-making process, involving
- the identification of opportunities and threats, and
- the selection of alternatives for the allocation of resources
- for the purpose of achieving the goals of the organization

Planning and its implementation is certainly one of management's most important responsibilities. Everything that a manager does—organizing, allocating resources, assigning personnel, leading, measuring and controlling—is in accordance with some sort of plan. Plans may be documented in some formal manner, or they may only be in the manager's mind. In any case, there is always some sort of plan for guiding or controlling the activities of the productive system in its quest toward meeting the goals of the organization.

The predominant characteristic of our environment is change. The successful managers are those who are sensitive and skillful in dealing with social/technological change and relating it to the other forces in the business environment as they do their planning. Flexibility and quick reaction are often required to assure timely and effective decision making. To be effective, the planning process must be dynamic. Plans at all levels must not be treated as if they were carved in stone. They must be responsive to change. Fortunately, some of the very forces, such as improved communication and data processing capabilities, that fuel the dynamic characteristic of our environment also provide the means for making the planning process more responsive to change.

There are three basic types of planning. *Strategic planning* involves the definition of objectives and the selection of strategies to fulfill those objectives. This requires value judgment, and answers to questions like: What business are we in?, What markets should we pursue?, and What general approach should we follow? *Appropriate answers to these kinds of questions are really what separate the successful from the unsuccessful firms.*

For example, if the railroads had recognized that they were in the transportation business, and not simply in the railroad business, they would have become one of the most powerful forces in our economy. Instead, most of them are struggling just to remain solvent and operational!

Strategic planning is primarily concerned with what *might* be, not what *is*. It is expressed in broad terms, and does not designate specific action plans. Strategic plans seek to provide direction within overall internal and external constraints.

Typically, strategic objectives involve broad subjective judgment statements. They specify what management believes to be the important characteristics of their productive organization. These may include:
- growth, stability and profit levels and be measured by one or more of the following: annual percent increase in sales, annual percent increase in profit, profit margins, market share, earnings per share, price to earnings ratio, asset turnover, debt/equity ratios and personnel turnover rates.
- image—how customers, and perhaps the general public, view the organization.
- quality of service
- employment security—some firms view employment security as being vital to their success, whereas others simply adjust staff to meet their requirements.
- distribution channels
- markets served
- products and product mix
- diversification
- technology level—the firm should decide whether it will be a technological leader or follower.

Long-range planning is the search for life-cycle solutions that will fulfill the strategic objectives of the organization. The long-range plan usually covers a three to five-year time period and considers product lines and products. Many firms use computer simulation models for relating the various business variables. Such variables include revenue, price, R&D investment, production cost, sales and service cost, return on investment, cash flow, etc. Such models can be used to iterate the variables until an acceptable solution is obtained in terms of profit, earnings per share, market share, gross revenue or whatever is indicated by the corporate goals. Long-range models are usually updated annually with the most recent year being the operational plan for the current year.

Operational planning is the identification of the specific activities and resources on an annual basis that are required to implement the long-range plan. This is the type of planning with which most managers are involved. It generally includes detailed product specifications, tasks to be performed, their schedule, and fund allocations. It states the relationship between resources, schedule and product performance requirements. The level of detail is a function of the product complexity, its magnitude, the number of organizations involved, etc. Generally, status vs. the operational plan are measured monthly and trade-offs and plan changes are made as required to meet the goals of the organization.

The planning process has a hierarchical relationship. All management levels should have stated objectives, and plans to implement them. The plans at the lower levels are detailed and usually cover a relatively short time span. As one moves up the planning hierarchy the plans and objectives are broader in scope, less detailed, and cover a longer time span. All levels must be alert for new inputs that might indicate a change in plans. The planning process should be dynamic. That is, it should involve the refinement of prior decisions concerning objectives, goals and strategies based upon new or improved information and actual performance measured against previous plans.

Planning: recognizing the uncontrollable factors

Dr. T. F. Gautschi, P.E.

The preparation of strategic and long-range plans requires the consideration of a number of uncontrollable factors. The following is a partial listing of such factors.

Rate of technology change

No corporation or product line is immune to obsolescence, and a firm can fail quickly if its management is not sensitive and skillful in recognizing and dealing with technological change, and relating it to the other forces in the environment. A single technological improvement can overpower almost any degree of productivity or even make a product line obsolete. Computers, nuclear power, the transistor, large-scale integrated circuitry are all examples of this.

The state-of-the-technological art

Since it usually takes three to five years to develop a product, the planner must be fully aware of what will be technically available when the product is introduced to the market. A wrong estimate in this area can result in a product that is either too advanced technically (the result can be high cost and low reliability) or does not take full advantage of what is technically practical (here the result can be low performance, limited flexibility, limited capability and probably higher cost).

Economic climate

Management should learn to carefully review economic forecasts before using them as a basis for planning, particularly during periods of sharp cyclical swings. The methodology of computer forecasting often gives a false impression of accuracy and certainty, especially when the numbers are stated to a decimal point or two.

Industrial climate

Long-range planners must take into account the fact that the structure of employment by industry is projected to change substantially between now and 1985. Employment in the public sectors will continue to expand. Retail trade and finance services will continue their relative expansion. Employment in the goods-producing sectors—manufacturing, transportation, public utilities, mining and construction—will continue their relative decline.

Population trends

Characteristic trends in the population and in the labor market must be considered in any long-range planning activity. The projected decline of the population aged 16 to 24 from 16.7% in 1980 to 12.8% in 1990 has important implications for education and training needs through the 1980's. During this same period there will be an increase in the participation of women in the workforce as well as a rise in the proportion in the group aged 25 to 44 from about 28% to 32%.

Competition

The dynamic nature of most market areas makes the assessment of competitive activities more difficult, yet more important than ever—especially as related to proposed introduction schedules and price/performance factors.

Customer desires, needs or wants

The ultimate criterion for every company should be how well they service their customers. We should never underestimate the power of an irate or dissatisfied customer, or the importance of a happy, satisfied customer.

Government regulations

In addition to the growth of direct government economic influence, our times are characterized by an accelerating framework of government control and regulation on the activities of private enterprise. Although most of us probably agree with the concept of "the regulation of some for the benefit of many", the impact of the collective body of these controls can become very significant to the management of a firm.

Managers must be aware of these and other uncontrollable factors, as they do their planning. Their success will depend upon how well they respond. But as with any decision-making process, planning involves:

A statement of goals or objectives. Sometimes these are derived in response to cues from the situation, by directives from higher management or in response to the firm's stated strategic objectives. This is often a time-consuming task, but there is no substitute for a well-defined goal.

Assembling relevant information. Great care must be exercised to assure that this data gathering process is fair and as objective as possible.

Identification of alternatives. The decision maker should *not* confine his analysis to one "best" solution. The development of alternatives is the step in the planning process where the manager can be most creative and innovative. Brainstorming either with a group or as an individual can help break the "brain-cramp" that sometimes occurs at this step. Also, this step can be enhanced by an incubation period—that is, a period of time where the planner simply mulls the situation, and possible alternate solutions, over in his mind, sometimes consciously and sometimes unconsciously.

Selecting an alternative. Making the best choice is not an easy task. Most managers will rely upon their mental model of the productive system, which has been developed through a combination of experience, advice from others, prejudice, intuition and the application of certain decision making techniques. (Discussed in *Design News* 1-3-77, 1-17-77, 2-7-77 and 2-21-77.)

The selection of the path to be followed is the responsibility of the manager—he must ultimately make the decision. Most managers do not try to maximize. This requires the identification of all possible solutions along with each of their consequences. Most managers do "satisfice". That is, they choose the first alternative that complies with the constraints of the situation. These constraints are usually related to (1) whether the plan will contribute to the attainment of the stated objective, (2) whether it makes the best use of resources and (3) whether it is really practical and capable of execution.

Planning: Key to successful management

Dr. T.F. Gautschi, P.E.

"Would any of you think of building a tower without first sitting down and calculating the cost, to see whether he could afford to finish it?"

Luke 14:28

In a sense, management is planning and communication. Everything that a manager does—organizing, allocating resources, assigning, measuring or controlling—must be part of a plan, whether on paper or in the mind . . . and it must be communicated.

During the past 20 years the planning process has become an accepted part of management in most companies. There is considerable evidence that when planning is well done, it can give any one company a definite edge over one that has no planning process.

Planning can be defined as a dynamic decision-making process involving the identification of opportunities and threats and the choosing among alternatives for the allocation of resources, all for the purpose of achieving the goals of the organization.

There are three basic kinds of planning:

DEFINITIONS

Strategic planning: The definition of objectives and the selection of strategies to fulfill the objectives. This involves value judgment, and answers to questions like: "What business are we in?", "What markets should we pursue?", "What general approach should we follow?".

Strategic planning is primarily concerned with what might be, not what is. It is expressed in broad terms, and does not designate specific action plans. Strategic plans seek to provide direction within overall internal and external constraints.

Many firms do not lay out strategic plans, they just seem to react to the situation. These firms are like a ship without a compass—they can do very well as long as they remain in familiar surroundings and can see the shore or other landmarks, but they would be lost in a heavy fog.

Long-range planning: The search for life cycle solutions that will fulfill the strategic objectives of the organization. The LRP usually covers a 3 to 5-year time period and considers product lines and products. Many firms use a computer simulation model for relating the various business variables. These include revenue, price, R & D investment, production cost, sales and service cost, return on investment, cash flow, etc. The model iterates these variables until an acceptable solution is obtained in terms of profit, earnings per share, market share, gross revenue or whatever is indicated by the corporate goals.

Operational planning: The identification of specific activities and resources on an annual basis to implement the Long Range Plan. This is the type of planning with which most engineers and engineering managers are involved. It generally includes detailed product specifications, tasks to be performed, their schedule, and fund allocations. The level of detail is a function of the product complexity, its magnitude, the number of organizations involved, etc. Generally, status vs. plan is measured monthly and trade-offs and plan changes are made as required to meet the goals of the organization.

PLANNING HIERARCHY

All management levels should have stated objectives and plans to implement them. As one moves down the planning hierarchy the objectives become more specific with fewer long-term implications and cover a shorter time span.

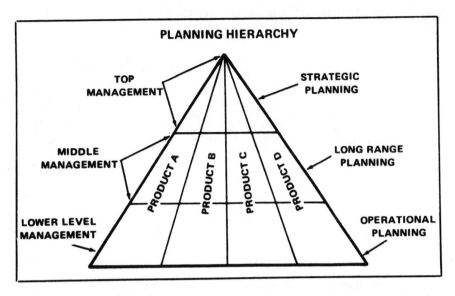

All levels must be alert for new inputs that might indicate a change in plans. The planning process should be adaptive. It should involve the continuous refinement of prior decisions concerning objectives, goals and strategies based upon new, or improved information and actual performance measured against previous plans.

ADAPTIVE

Typical strategic objectives:

growth	public service
stability	employment security
flexibility	distribution channels
market sensitivity	markets served
profit consciousness	products
image	diversification

Typical strategic goal measures:

annual % increase in sales	price to earnings ratio
annual % increase in profit	asset turnover
profit margins	debt/equity ratios
earnings per share	personnel turnover rate
market share	

Factors usually considered in the Strategic and Long Range Planning Process:

rate of technology change
state-of-the art
competition
customer desires
economic conditions
social factors—ecology, war/peace attitude, social values
taxes
government regulations

Resources in planning:
trained manpower
(technical, production, marketing, management)
facilities
financial

CHALLENGE

If you are a manager you should understand the planning process as used in your organization, and you should know what the overall strategy is. If you don't know these things, take steps to learn about them. It will make you a more effective manager.

Why product planning is so important

**R&D BECOMING
EXPENSIVE**

According to a recent industry-wide survey, business is not increasing its R & D expenditures. Furthermore, they are being used more for improving existing products and processes and less for developing new ones.

Of the manufacturers surveyed, 44% stated that their main R & D goal was to improve an existing product. At this rate only 13% of industrial sales will be new products in 1976. Only three industries expect 20% or more of their sales to come from new products—instruments, machinery, and electrical machinery and communications.

Perhaps one reason for this trend is that R & D is getting too expensive. As engineers and engineering managers, we are responsible for assuring that the R & D dollar is spent efficiently and effectively through better management and realistic product planning. Otherwise, our companies may be forced into sacrificing long-term potential in order to meet short-term profit goals.

So first, let's agree on what a product is. Our definition should include the customer or user, and the producer. Also remember that a product can be a service as well as a concrete object. With this in mind I'd like to propose the following definition:

PRODUCT DEFINITION

A product is a bundle of satisfactions or benefits to its user, which may or may not offer business opportunity to a firm for developing, producing and marketing it.

Product planning thus involves the integration of all the elements that enhance the product's satisfaction or benefit to its user: functionality, price, reliability, availability, maintenance/service, simplicity, timeliness, economical operating cost, acceptable environmental and safety features.

And, at the same time, it must identify an acceptable business opportunity to the firm in terms of sales forecasts, return on invested capital, cash flow, profit level, resource requirements, life cycle, technological risk, knowledge of business competition, and compatibility with the corporate image and long-range plans.

FOUR VARIETIES

New products come in four varieties:
- A new model involving an incremental improvement on an existing product
- A new product in a familiar market
- A new product to the company in an existing but unfamiliar market
- A totally new product in a totally new market

**DYNAMIC
ENVIRONMENT**

The planning process is further complicated when it must take place in fast-changing technologies and in an environment of rapidly changing user attitudes and expectations.

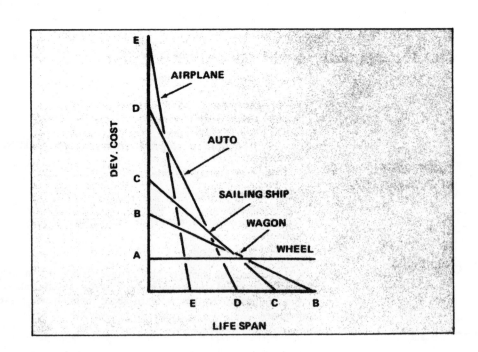

- Fewer than 10 of our 1000 ideas result in a commercially successful product.
- Most companies report that about one-third of their current sales are for products first marketed by the company within the preceding five years.
- Development costs are increasing and product life spans are getting shorter.

OPPORTUNITY WINDOW

The opportunity window gives us further insight into this complex situation.

The opportunity window is constrained at both ends at the point where costs exceed values. These costs are usually directly related to the technical state-of-the-art. It is getting narrower for many industries—especially those that depend upon a rapidly changing technology. The narrower window increases the pressure for starting and completing product development at the proper time. If it is started too soon, excessive costs result. If it is started too late, or takes too long, the product life is too short to recover the investment.

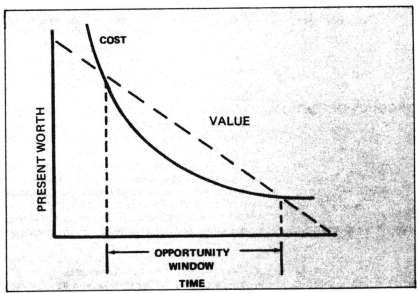

TIMING IS IMPORTANT

This is where management judgment comes in, based upon valid technological assumptions. We as engineers and managers must be prepared to provide these technological assumptions as they are required to assure that the opportunity window is met in the best way.

The logical way to set up a product plan

In designing a specific component or system, we often become involved in the design process—in fabricating and testing models and prototypes, in providing initial product support, in testing and evaluating customer acceptance. All of these are done according to predetermined performance, schedule, and resource specifications and restraints.

FUNCTIONAL REQUIREMENTS

In any new venture, however, we should also be involved in a prerequisite product planning process: the establishment of functional requirements in response to present and future needs of the market place; and what is considered technically and financially feasible. This interactive phase involves exploratory development, trade-off and business analysis, simulations, market studies and development of experimental hardware. It ends with the approval of a project plan that documents the functional requirements and schedule and resource commitments.

Product planning phase on this scale and commitment of resources is a comparatively recent innovation. It is important because new product decisions usually involve allocations of large resources that can have strong, sometimes irreversible effects upon a firm's future.

The initial step in product planning is a kind of "chicken and egg" thing between perceived market requirements and new product concepts; its output is a product concept that responds to user requirements. Clearly the marketing and engineering planners must work closely together at this point since neither can do his job properly without the other.

Marketing approaches this step by trying to predict what the customer will buy. Basically, this is an effort to define the product opportunity window from the user's point of view in terms of price, performance, and schedule. On the other hand, engineering approaches this step by trying to define what can be accomplished in terms of cost, performance and schedule.

To be successful, they must get together on a product definition that meets the user requirement and can be developed by engineering. By its very nature, this process must be innovative and involve the integration of conflicting ideas.

SCENARIO

A scenario that states key assumptions relating to user satisfactions and benefits enhances this interaction and provides a basis for long-range product strategies.

The probability of developing a successful product will be significantly decreased if both marketing and engineering do not do their part during this phase. Marketing often agrees to a general definition of requirements and leaves the details to

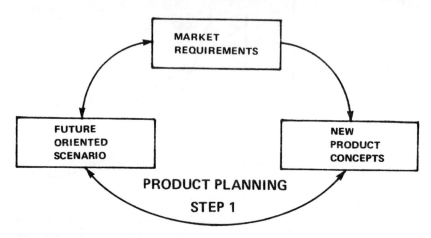

PRODUCT PLANNING
STEP 1

engineering. This can prove fatal because we engineers tend to be perfectionists; since we sometimes don't know what the customer really needs, we tend to provide more than he is willing to pay for.

CAUTION

At the same time we must be careful to be compatible with the long-range product strategy. This may indicate a product concept that can be enhanced as it matures to keep it competitive. Or it may require an inexpensive one-shot kind of product design that should be abandoned or completely redesigned at a later date. Negligence in this area can be costly to a firm in terms of timing and resources.

STEP 1

After the product concept is defined, both a technological assessment and a planning venture analysis should be made:

STEP 2

1. The predicted technological assumptions should be judged applicable at the time of market introduction. (This is especially important in a dynamic technological environment.)
2. The product concepts should be ranked in terms of their potential investment requirements. This insures that the best investment opportunity is chosen.

STEP 3

Next, the information required for decision-making should be assembled into a new venture package that includes the following elements:

1. Product objectives and relationship to overall strategies
2. Product description (marketing: functional spec)
3. Major business considerations
4. Pricing plan: product cost and service
5. Product justification: market need and forecast
6. Financial analysis (including life cycle considerations)
7. Competitive analysis
8. Results of engineering feasibility study
9. Impact on other company products
10. Schedule of key events
11. Implementation tasks with appropriate costs and schedules: engineering, marketing sales, production, field service installation

STEP 4

Finally, management should review the Step 3 new venture package, make its decision concerning resource investment and allocation, and communicate it to the implementers.

Product planning is such an important process that we as engineers and engineering managers should participate in it to make sure it is technologically realistic and rational.

This participation has two other important benefits:
1. The implementer has a better basis for making trade-off decisions that arise during the design and implementation phase.
2. The implementer is usually much more motivated to do a good job if he has participated in the planning.

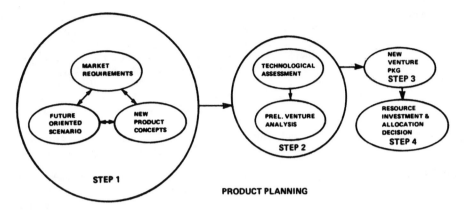

PRODUCT PLANNING

"The art of life consists in making correct guesses on insufficient information; insufficient because we can never know all the elements that enter into a right decision."

Justice Oliver Wendell Holmes

Understanding product life cycles

In some ways, products are like people—they are born, grow, mature and decline. Products have their own life cycle, which starts with their initiation of development and ends when the product can no longer be shipped to the customer profitably. To understand this cycle, refer to the chart below:

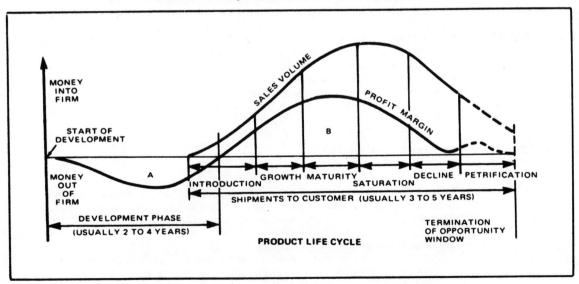

PRODUCT LIFE CYCLE

New development costs should be treated like capital expenditures—the firm is investing present dollars for anticipated future gain. The objective is to make area B (above) significantly larger than area A. The development phase ususally takes from two to four years, depending upon the complexity of the product, its uniqueness, its priority and its feasibility.

OTHER COSTS

This sounds like a long time until one is actually involved in a development! Also, since the natural tendency of many engineers is to develop the best product possible, management must be alert to the danger of product overdesign. Then, depending on customer acceptance and competition, shipment begins. Shipments often taper off just about when the producer is starting to achieve some real manufacturing efficiency.

In addition to engineering costs, development costs include marketing preparation (training, documentation, etc.) as well as field service and production planning.

By the way, long lead item procurement is becoming an especially critical problem. For example, electrical components are currently being quoted with as much as 50 to 60 weeks lead time. Also when some unique processing is involved—such as in LSI chip manufacture—the vendor doesn't want to manufacture so large an inventory that it could become obsolete. Since it is also difficult to predict process yields, the vendor may unintentionally underrun a particular lot.

SIX PHASES

Product planning should consider the total investment in development on a life-cycle basis. The shipment period as shown above can be divided into six distinct phases:

1. **Introduction.** Here quality has the biggest influence upon current and future customer acceptance. Other influences: advertising, price and service.

2. **Growth.** During this phase advertising becomes the dominant influence upon sales, with quality assuming a lesser role. Profit margins are usually on the increase as the result of reduced production costs.

3. **Maturity.** In this phase competition for customers increases and the price is lowered to attract the price-sensitive customer in a attempt to sustain or increase the shipment rate. The profit margin starts to get smaller. This is also the time to bring out any inherent or built-in product performance enhancements.

4. **Saturation.** At this point there is little remaining price elasticity (the firm cannot increase the sales rate by lowering price). The various sellers will often try to differentiate their product from their competitors' products by using alternate or unique packaging and any residual performance capabilities. Profit margins are drastically reduced.

5. **Decline.** Here the primary emphasis is upon identifying alternate uses and increased advertising. There still may be some impact from quality and service, but price reduction has little or no effect, and profit margins approach zero.

6. **Petrification.** In this phase little can be gained from further increases in advertising, packaging, quality or service. If higher-priced substitute products are available, the firm may actually be able to increase the price without sales rate deterioration. This phase can be continued to the point where the incremental costs of production are no longer covered.

WHAT WE CAN DO

The product life cycle varies in detail depending upon the product and the market. However, almost every product experiences all of the six phases described above. As engineering managers we should be fully aware of the product life cycle for our business so that we can properly relate to the marketing, manufacturing and field service functions in our effort to achieve fully our company's goals.

How to set up a product calendar

When a company has several related product lines that are subject to periodic upgrade and modification, or when its engineering and marketing is geographically dispersed, the company usually has coordination difficulties. The Product Calendar concept can be very helpful in such situations.

PURPOSE

It is basically an interface document that:

1. Identifies all new and existing products and their associated developments and enhancements that have been authorized by the appropriate management level.

2. Serves as a coordinating device between planning, engineering, marketing, program management, production and management.

3. Provides a vehicle for establishing product priorities that are in agreement with long-range planning and product planning requirements.

4. When extended over a time span of several years, can serve as an input to Long-Range and Operating plans.
5. When periodically updated, can provide information on the status and progress of current developments.
6. Can serve as a basis for product announcements.

To be most useful, the Product Calendar must be rigidly controlled—the initial issue and all subsequent changes. It can be prepared and updated manually or with computer assistance. It should include hardware, firmware and software. The various line items should be designated as new development, cost reduction, continuation, etc. Sometimes it is useful to designate those items that are funded and those that are not funded. There should be a brief description or title in the

CONTENT

PROGRAM MGT.

MARKETING

MANAGEMENT

PRODUCT CALENDAR

PRODUCT ENHANCEMENTS
PRODUCT DEVELOPMENTS
PRIORITIES
CAPABILITIES/FUNCTIONS
SCHEDULE
MGT. APPROVAL

PRODUCTION

ENGINEERING

PLANNING   ADVANCED TECHNOLOGY

Product Calendar that is referenced to more complete descriptions or specifications in other documents.

Priority designation is often a problem. I have found the following categories to be generally useful:

PRIORITY DESIGNATION

P 1 Mandatory/committed. Reflects an announced capability, or some sort of committment to customers of a product capability. Critical to achieve business goals, no schedule leeway can be permitted.

P 2 Mandatory/planned. Not yet committed to customers or to the marketplace. A planned capability that is critical to achieve business goals. No schedule leeway can be permitted. Deletion would result in significant reduction in forecasted revenue or profit.

P 3 Essential. Required to achieve near-term business goals. Limited flexibility in scheduled date. Deletion would result in some reduction in forecasted revenue or profit.

P 4 Desirable. Necessary to improve or maintain image as a responsive vendor. Will improve probability of achieving business goals. Deletion would result in a minimal reduction in forecasted revenue or profit.

TEAMWORK

The Product Calendar, as an interface document, should be the result of interaction between the various organizational segments involved—this should include engineering, marketing, planning, production, field maintenance, program management and perhaps advanced technology. The detailed implementation document that each of these functions may prepare in support of their product calendar commitments should in turn be compatible with, and responsive to, the Product Calendar.

The Product Calendar concept should be helpful in all organizations to assure that the various product activities are coordinated. It is essential to large, complex or geographically-dispersed organizations.

Some comments on survival planning

Recently after I was lecturing to a high school class one of the boys came up to me and asked what computer courses I took in college. It never occurred to him that computers, as we know them today, had not even been invented when I was in college! Thirty years ago hardly anyone would have even bet that in the 1970's spacecraft would be landing on the moon and returning to Earth, that man would walk in outer space, or that computers would be squeezing the work of months into seconds. These are only a few of the accomplishments of the 1970's and many more are on the way.

The task of managing the technology upon which these and underlying developments rest is becoming more difficult with each passing year. Not even a company's size can ensure its survival.

This age of computers, solid state electronics, TV, atomic energy, and the like has seen the birth and expansion of some major businesses, and the decline and death of many others. Both GE's and RCA's withdrawals from the computer business are current examples of this situation. As the time scale for technological development continues to grow shorter, more and more companies will face this problem.

FURTHER COMPLICATION

A complicating factor is that oftentimes profitable opportunities and many serious threats can arise in other fields. Witness the replacement of natural textiles and rubber by the products of basic chemistry (whoever heard of silk panty hose) and the way in which machinery is being affected by numerical controls or the influence of solid state electronics upon communications.

Most businesses have what can be called a critical mass for R&D expenditures. Below the critical mass, effectiveness falls off rapidly, and above the critical mass the firm receives diminishing returns from its R&D expenditures.

CRITICAL MASS

In the electronics industry for example, a company must keep up with the technical changes in components, introduce a flow of improvements and be able to bring out a completely new model when competition demands it. This requires a certain threshold of effort—the critical mass. This threshold is not directly related to sales revenue, and it may be too high for some firms. When you are in a poker game where there is a 25-cent limit and you only have $3.00 and the other participants have a minimum of $100 each, the best thing you can do is to get out while you still have your $3.00 and find a cheaper game.

The Independent Product Review

The Independent Product Review (IPR) is a process for evaluating program risk and for providing timely resolution of program and/or technical inadequacies. Its goal is to assure management that the product opportunity window will not be missed. The IPR is much broader than the usual Design Review because the risks depend not only on the actual product design, but also on the adequacy of planning and the integrated support by all functional organizations.

BACKGROUND

As we have already mentioned, the development portion of a product life cycle usually takes from two to four years and requires a substantial investment of present dollars in anticipation of future profits. This development phase involves engineering, marketing, field service training and documentation, and production planning, tooling, long lead item procurement, etc.

EVALUATE RISK

It should be periodically assessed against the current market situation to make sure that you are still developing a viable program. Nothing could be worse than for a firm to take so much time developing a product that cost exceeds value when the product finally makes it to the marketplace.

TIMELINESS

To avoid this possibility, the IPR should be scheduled at the request of the manager who has the overall product responsibility, and it should be conducted by qualified persons who are *not* responsible for implementing the project plan. Timeliness is of utmost importance. IPR's should take place before further investment of significant resources is required and before program risk increases substantially. The points for decision that generally meet this criteria, and the appropriate Reviews are shown in the table below and in Fig. 1. For completeness, both IPR's and Design Reviews are noted.

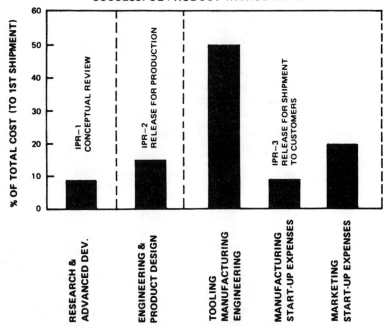

TYPICAL DISTRIBUTION OF DEVELOPMENT COSTS IN A SUCCESSFUL PRODUCT INTRODUCTION.

MULTIFUNCTION

The independent review team should be multifunctional, i.e., composed of representatives from those major functional areas of responsibility that are necessary to evaluate the major risk areas. The depth of review and specific team organization will vary between products and type of review. Therefore, the team chairman should determine the organization as part of his review plan.

EXPERIENCED PEOPLE

The team should be composed of experienced senior personnel from the responsible product organization, the supporting functional organizations, and the systems development organization directly concerned with the product. They *should not be* the same people who were directly involved in implementing the project plan.

The project manager should serve as a consultant to the chairman and provide liaison to the operating sections for obtaining information and scheduling detailed reviews or special tests. The project manager *should not be* an active member of the review team.

APPLICATION

The review process as discussed may not be for you, or for your project, or for your organization, but every product development team should consider the decision points as reviewed.

Remember, only one out of every five new products achieves sales whose profits provide a break-even return on the investment that has been made.

INDEPENDENT PRODUCT REVIEW

TYPE	WHEN	WHY	BASIS FOR REVIEW
Conceptual IPR-1 Review	Prior to program authorization.	To confirm that this conceptual design and the initial project plan represent the requirements and capabilities of the respective organizations.	Functional requirements as described by marketing vs. draft versions of the conceptual design specifications and initial project plan.
Preliminary Design Review	After completion of engineering model and prior to release of documentation for pre-production prototype (pre-production prototype design freeze).	To disclose risks in achieving goals of product design so that plans can be modified and resources reallocated to reduce risks.	Engineering test results vs. design specifications.
Intermediate Design Review	After completion of pre-production prototype, but prior to release of documentation for production prototype (production prototype design freeze).	To disclose risks in achieving goals of product design and support so that plans can be modified and resources reallocated to reduce risks.	Pre-production prototype test results vs. design specifications.
IPR-2 Review For Release For Production	Prior to product announcement and/or release to production.	Evaluate product performance and scheduled delivery dates, and verify product profitability.	Prototype qualification tests vs. design specifications, customer expectations project plan.
IPR-3	Prior to initial customer shipment.	To evaluate: the adequacy of the product as manufactured in production environment to meet announced performance and engineering design requirements, the adequacy of product support resources to meet customer expectations, the ability to meet product cost and profitability targets.	Pilot a production qualification test, using "hard tooling" and released documentation, cost estimates, and product support plans.
IPR-4	As soon as practicable after product has been used in customer environment.	To assure that product meets customer expectations in his environment in terms of function, availability, reliability and maintainability, and that cost and profitability targets are being achieved.	Actual field results and production records.

Planning and organizing
for the most productive operation

Dr. T. F. Gautschi, P.E.

The purpose of management is to make productive organizations both efficient (doing things right) and effective (doing the right things). To accomplish this purpose the management of every organization, regardless of technology or structure, must perform a number of the same key functions (or tasks). These are: Planning, Organizing, Staffing, Decision Making and Directing, Communications and Controlling, Responsibility, and Budgeting.

When a person is performing any of these tasks he/she is carrying out a management task. Not all managers do only management tasks—some managers, especially in the lower levels of management, are often involved in non-management tasks, e.g. the sales manager sells, and the engineering manager designs.

PLANNING can be defined as a dynamic decision-making process involving the identification of opportunities and threats and the choosing among alternatives for the allocation of resources, all for the purpose of achieving the goals of the organization.

Planning is dynamic because it is never completed—change is the one constant in every productive organization. Most experts say that planning is the most important and probably the most neglected of the management tasks.

There are generally three basic time-related plans—strategic, long range and operational. *Strategic planning* is the responsibility of top management, it involves value judgments and concerns declarations regarding what the basic purpose of the business is. The strategic plan provides guidelines for the total planning process, and as such it is timeless. Yet at the same time, it should be periodically reviewed to assure its continuing relevance.

The long-range plan documents the product life cycle solutions that will fulfill the strategic objectives. They usually cover a three to five-year period. Long-range plans are a relatively recent innovation, but they are rapidly becoming a necessary ingredi-

ent for most organizations. Many firms use computer simulation models to assist them in the preparation of their LRP.

The operational plan provides detailed guidelines for the day-to-day operations. This type of plan generally includes product specifications, tasks to be performed, their schedule, and resource allocations. The level of detail is determined by a number of factors, such as: product complexity, the size of the organization, the geographical dispersion of the transformation facilities, etc. The operational plan is usually the first year of the LRP as illustrated in Fig. 1. Then, as the operational plan year is completed, the next year is "spelled out" in greater detail and another year is added to the end of the LRP, and so on (Fig. 2).

Operational plans are usually prepared in response to the sales forecast and are often divided into detailed plans covering the functions of sales, production and finance (Fig. 3). Functional plans relate to LR and strategic

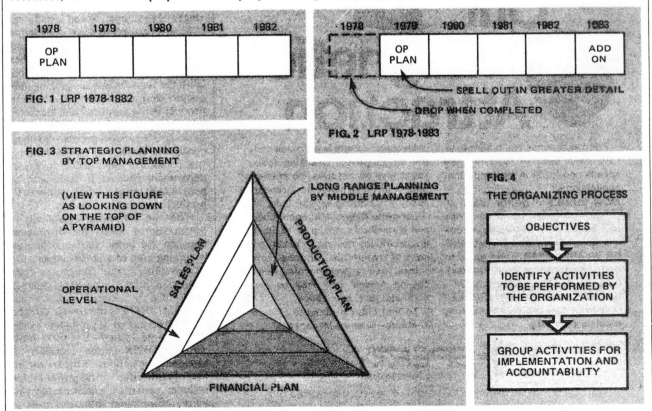

FIG. 1 LRP 1978-1982

FIG. 2 LRP 1978-1983
SPELL OUT IN GREATER DETAIL
DROP WHEN COMPLETED

FIG. 3 STRATEGIC PLANNING BY TOP MANAGEMENT

(VIEW THIS FIGURE AS LOOKING DOWN ON THE TOP OF A PYRAMID)

LONG RANGE PLANNING BY MIDDLE MANAGEMENT

OPERATIONAL LEVEL

SALES PLAN
PRODUCTION PLAN
FINANCIAL PLAN

FIG. 4 THE ORGANIZING PROCESS

OBJECTIVES

IDENTIFY ACTIVITIES TO BE PERFORMED BY THE ORGANIZATION

GROUP ACTIVITIES FOR IMPLEMENTATION AND ACCOUNTABILITY

plans as shown in Fig. 3.

ORGANIZING is the blending together of the efforts of many people in a meaningful and coordinated fashion to meet the objectives of the organization (Fig. 4).

The activities may be grouped by:
- function (marketing, production, engineering, etc.)
- product (A, B, C, etc.)
- geography (eastern, central, southern, etc.)
- project, program, or product

There are two main organizational philosophies:
- DECENTRALIZED — decision making by the lower management levels
- CENTRALIZED — decision making mostly by top management

During the 1950's and 1960's there was a strong trend towards decentralized operations to accommodate the increasing size and complexity of most organizations. But now many believe that in the 1970's there is a new trend towards recentralization in an effort to give top management more control and to improve both efficiency and effectiveness. This trend is for a discussion of the MATRIX supported by the giant steps that are being made in terms of improved data processing and communications. However, few people now predict the elimination of middle management levels with basically only top management and first level managers as was predicted in the mid-1950's when computers were in their early stages of development and installation.

Most organizations are depicted, or documented, by organization charts and position descriptions. Often these charts indicate line and staff functions. With the former term designating those people who contribute *directly* to the product being produced and marketed; and the later term being used as a noun to designate support people who do not contribute directly to the product, e.g. the personnel department is a staff department because it deals with the people in the organization, not with the product.

With the increasing complexity of organizational forms the distinctions between the terms staff and line are becoming blurred and less important.

Two other terms sometimes cause confusion in organizations—authority and power.

AUTHORITY is the *right* to direct or command, and it is assigned by the formal organization—it flows downward. *POWER* is the *capability* to influence the actions of others regardless of authority; typical power factors include: expertise, charisma, accessibility, information, authority.

Dr. T.F. Gautschi, P.E.

What you can learn from the recent recession

Recent hard times have taught us some valuable lessons

**ECONOMIC
FORECASTING IS
NOT ALWAYS
RELIABLE**

Because the present recession appears to be bottoming out I thought it might be helpful to reflect upon some of its lessons—lessons that should help us to better cope with the post-recession era.

Lesson #1:

The record in recent years clearly demonstrates the uncertainties and consequent unreliability of economic forecasting using the models available. Although the models are reasonably valid when the various factors are stable, they do not predict large perturbations like the one that resulted from the oil embargo.

Short-term forecasts covering only a few months are often wrong—at times economists even have difficulty describing *current* economic conditions!

The methodology of computer forecasting often gives a false impression of accuracy and certainty, especially when the numbers are stated to a decimal point or two. However, as most of us know, when we put garbage into a model, we get garbage out, no matter how fine we grind it.

**THE CHALLENGE IS
TO DEVELOP A
STABLE ECONOMIC
ENVIRONMENT**

Another limitation of most economic forecasting is that it provides only one estimate and not a range. Yet for most policy decisions it is more important to know the range of possible results and their probabilities than it is to have a single estimate.

Hopefully, management has learned to carefully review economic forecasts before using them as a basis for policy decisions, particularly during periods of sharp cyclical swings.

The real challenge for government and industry is to create a reasonably stable economic environment in which the private sector recovery can accelerate. This requires a great deal of attention to building consumer and business confidence.

Lesson #2:

The U.S. has the premier economy of the world and significant, though erratic, expansion continues to occur. But it cannot satisfy every new claim on its resources. Consequently, resource allocation should be a major concern to assure that government spending does not go beyond the willingness of society to pay for the programs provided.

**MATCH RESOURCE
ALLOCATION WITH
THE DESIRES &
CAPABILITIES
OF SOCIETY**

Most of us are aware the government's role is not limited to simply balancing the Federal budget over time. Federal decisions influence the entire economy through direct purchases, taxes, transfer payments and a variety of research programs, which serve as seed capital for private sector activities. In fact, total government spending now comprises over one-third of the total economy!

Since the U.S. has a finite, though increasing, production capacity, decisions on national economic priorities must include the private as well as the public sector expenditures, and tradeoff decisions should be made when new government programs are being considered. Otherwise, the new program will result in additional inflationary pressure. As it is, significant increases in productivity and massive amounts of private capital investment are required to meet future capacity employment needs.

During the 1966-1975 time period the G.N.P. increased by 100% (from $749.9 billion to $1.5 trillion) and government expenditures increased by 160% (to $350 billion). This indicates a strong shift from private to public expenditure, and a need for identifying national economic priorities.

**CONTROL &
REGULATION BY THE
GOVERNMENT IS
ACCELERATING**

For example, twenty years ago it was apparent that we were heading for an energy crisis, yet no substantial resources were allocated to the solution of this problem until recently. We will be paying for this mistake for some time.

Lesson #3:

In addition to the growth of direct government economic influence, our times are characterized by an accelerating framework of government control and regulation on the activities of private enterprise. (For example, consider the areas of equal employment opportunity and safety and health regulations.) Although most of us probably agree with the concept of "the regulation of some for the benefit of many", the impact of the collective body of these controls can become very significant. In fact, if this trend continues, there is a strong likelihood that by the year 2000, private institutions as we know them today will cease to exist.

Lesson #4:

Recognizing the characteristic trends of the labor market can help us prepare for the future.

THE AGE BREAKDOWN OF THE WORKFORCE IS CHANGING

The proportion of the population age 16 to 24 is projected to decline from an estimate of 16.7% in 1980 to 12.8% in 1990.[1]

This doesn't seem like much of a change until we realize that during the 1950-1970 time period significant teenage unemployment, and the growth of our education facilities, were caused by a 3% increase in the 16 to 24 age categories.

This projected decline has important implications for education and training needs through the 1980's.

During this same period there will be an increase in the participation of women in the workforce as well as a rise in the proportion in the group aged 25 to 44 from about 28% to 32%. This is the consequence of the passing on of the bulge in the birth rate that occurred after 1945. The education, maturity, energy and iconoclastic outlook of this group will provide some unusual opportunities—and problems—for increasing the productivity of the U.S. economy.

EXPECTATIONS OF THE WORKFORCE ARE CHANGING

The historical trend towards more white-collar and skilled employment will continue. This is a direct result of the utilization of increasingly complex technology, high education attainment and a diminishing interest in menial jobs.

In agreement with our recent employee loyalty survey (1-20-75 DN), more people want jobs that provide good pay and benefits; challenging and rewarding job content; opportunities for advancement; and pleasant and safe working conditions.

Lesson #5:

INDUSTRIAL STRUCTURE IS CHANGING

The structure of employment by industry is projected to change substantially between now and 1985.

Employment in the public sectors will continue to expand.

Retail trade, finance and services will continue their relative expansion.

Employment in the goods-producing sectors—manufacturing, transportation, public utilities, mining and construction will continue their relative decline.

Lesson #6:

RECRUIT & EXPAND PER A PLAN

The recession forced many companies to make a number of economy moves, including eliminating marginal personnel and production facilities. As a result, they are probably operating in an efficient, but understaffed mode, and will need to expand to take on much additional work. Don't let this growth take place in some non-controlled form. Use this as an opportunity to rethink your long-range objectives amd clearly identify and plan for the type of growth you want. This is basically a buyer's market, so act accordingly.

Lesson #7:

EMPHASIS IS TURNING TO NEW VENTURE PLANNING & ECONOMIC ANALYSIS

In the past, many firms rushed new products out the door, hoping that enough would catch on to keep the company growing. As a result of the recession, the market-place has changed. Product planning should now be a major consideration. Key elements of this approach are discussed in previous DN articles, and assembled as chapter 5 in the Management Forum booklet. The new venture package is central and must include a realistic financial analysis based upon predicted life cycle considerations.

There are many lessons that should be learned. Hopefully, the above will provide some food for thought and motivate all of us to be more aware of, and responsive to, our changing environment.

[1]Source: *Manpower Report of the President, 1975*

A model for looking into the future

How to prepare for changing trends

Dr. T. F. Gautschi, P.E.

Change is inevitable in the modern-day world. Change coupled with competition are the forcing functions in our dynamic environment.

> *"There is no sure way to corporate security and sustained success in this kind of environment . . . and a company can fail quickly if its management is not sensitive and skillful in recognizing and dealing with technological change, and relating it to the other forces in the business environment."*[1]

The results of change are problems for some and opportunities for others. Those who perceive change and its impact on their organization are able to recognize the opportunities; those that do not only see the problems.

In this article we will discuss a model that might help you relate a little better to changes taking place and predicted for the future. We will not present any answers, but we will certainly raise a lot of questions for you to ponder.

Our model has four major elements: the social and technological **TREND INFORMATION** gleaned from the environment; the **RELEVANT AREAS** of engineering management that should be considered; the **IMPACT** of the trends on relevant areas; and finally, the **STRATEGIES** that should be developed as a consequence.

There are a number of methods that can be used to study and predict changes.[2]

(1) EXTRAPOLATION PROCEDURES	(6) MORPHOLOGICAL ANALYSIS
(2) HISTORICAL ANALOGY	(7) NETWORK METHODS
(3) INTUITIVE REASONING	(8) MODEL BUILDING
(4) SCENARIO BUILDING	(9) DELPHI TECHNIQUE
(5) CROSS-IMPACT MATRICES	(10) MISSING LINK APPROACH

However, unless a firm's operations are extensive or extremely complex, it need not resort to these methods. Secondary sources are usually adequate to compile a listing. The Rand Corp., the World Future Society, the Club of Rome and the Stanford Research Institute all produce publications in this area.

The basic approach of just asking a number of knowledgeable people can also be used—the material presented in this article was generated by such a group through the use of a combination of brainstorming and DELPHI techniques. This process should be adequate for most of you also.

Once we have arrayed the pertinent information, the challenge becomes one of trying to predict the impact on engineering management that will result from the interaction of the TRENDS and the RELEVANT AREAS. Even a quick examination will reveal that this is no mean task. A complete analysis could easily fill a large book. To make the analysis more practical, you should concentrate on those TRENDS and RELEVANT AREAS that pertain to your organization and its environment. Then just sit and ponder about the various possibilities. For example: the greater emphasis upon personal creativity, and meaningful work coupled with the rapid expansion of computer and communication facilities will certainly have an impact upon organizational structure, the work environment and leadership requirements. And how about the impact of zero population growth, more government control and the greater loss of individual liberties on the workforce and the marketplace? There are many combinations that should stimulate our thinking and encourage innovative approaches to the changes that are taking place.

At minimum this model will provide an almost inexhaustible list of questions for debate in the work, educational or even social environment. Hopefully, it will also motivate each of us to think about, and be better prepared for the future—which, by the way, is very near at hand!

1. Gautschi, T.F., **Management Forum**, 1975, Cahners Publishing Co., p. 17.
2. This list was compiled by David T. Kollot, "Environmental Forecasting and Strategic Planning: Perspectives on the Methodology of FUTUROLOGY", in Neil Borden's (editor) *Relevance of Marketing*, Proceedings of the Fall Conference (Chicago: American Marketing Assn. 1972).

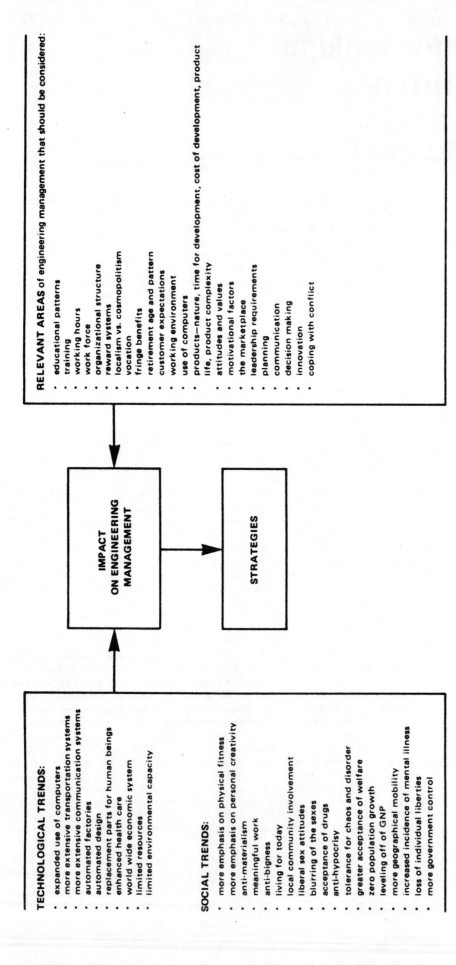

RELEVANT AREAS of engineering management that should be considered:

- educational patterns
- training
- working hours
- work force
- organizational structure
- reward systems
- localism vs. cosmopolitism
- vocation
- fringe benefits
- retirement age and pattern
- customer expectations
- working environment
- use of computers
- products—nature, time for development, cost of development, product life, product complexity
- attitudes and values
- motivational factors
- the marketplace
- leadership requirements
- planning
- communication
- decision making
- innovation
- coping with conflict

IMPACT ON ENGINEERING MANAGEMENT

STRATEGIES

TECHNOLOGICAL TRENDS:

- expanded use of computers
- more extensive transportation systems
- more extensive communication systems
- automated factories
- automated design
- replacement parts for human beings
- enhanced health care
- world wide economic system
- limited resources
- limited environmental capacity

SOCIAL TRENDS:

- more emphasis on physical fitness
- more emphasis on personal creativity
- anti-materialism
- meaningful work
- anti-bigness
- living for today
- local community involvement
- liberal sex attitudes
- blurring of the sexes
- acceptance of drugs
- anti-hypocrisy
- tolerance for chaos and disorder
- greater acceptance of welfare
- zero population growth
- leveling off of GNP
- more geographical mobility
- increased incidence of mental illness
- loss of individual liberties
- more government control

A MODEL TO HELP PLAN FOR THE FUTURE

Epilogue: Management challenges for the '70s

Dr. T.F. Gautschi, P.E.

A look at critical trends in the years ahead

While thumbing through one of the weekly news magazines I happened to come across the following:

> "The A-to-Z list of shortages in America's interlocking economy seems to lengthen with every passing day. As winter approaches, chilling headlines warn of inadequate supplies of antifreeze for autos, zinc and aluminum for storm windows and doors, cotton and synthetic fibers for clothing. Indeed, major companies in nearly every industrial sector—from steel, autos and rubber to petrochemicals, paper and plastics—are unable to get sorely needed goods from their suppliers or to supply their own customers in the quantities they seek."—**Newsweek, Nov. 19, 1973.**

The passage quoted above set me to thinking about the kinds of pressures that we, as managers, will have to face this coming year. Clearly, they are pressures we have not faced before, and if we don't take appropriate action we could find ourselves on the "managerial sidelines" and never quite know why.

HISTORICAL PERSPECTIVE

If we look back over our relatively brief history, from about 1650 to the present, we can identify five important eras. We've seen periods in our early history where rule was by absolute fiat, where a passion for money led to shrewd, tricky trading. We've seen an era in the mid-1800's where the speculative, promotional kind of personality dominated, a period of crude, hard fighting. Next came the beginning of mass production, the introduction of line and staff concepts, and large capitalization. Then, in the early years of this century the corporation and holding company dominated, bringing with it widespread share holding, manipulation, low-priced mass production and the recognition of labor as a force competing against executive management. The second third of this century gave us fantastic scientific achievement, large-scale decentralization, closer government regulation, wide application of the merit system, and new concepts in professional management.

As 1974 begins, we will see the ushering in of a new era, and I'd like to present what I think are major influences at work in this new era.

SPACESHIP EARTH

First, there is a recognition that our planet is a closed system with a finite environment that cannot sustain continued economic growth indefinitely. The major constraints imposed by this closed system are limited supply of land; a limited supply of natural resources such as fresh water, metals and fuels, and a limited capacity for absorbing thermal pollution (when this capacity is exceeded regardless of energy source, we will experience major climatic changes); and a limited capacity for absorbing the total emissions resulting from human activity without destroying our life-supporting ecology.

RESPECT FOR HUMAN DIGNITY

Second, there is recognition of the need for dignity and respect for all people in all parts of the world. The hard, stern, inhuman autocratic rule of the past is no longer a thinkable, much less practical management philosophy. Witness the progress being made in civil rights, women's liberation, job enrichment and the whole field of human motivation.

SNOWBALLING PROGRESS

Third, there is the exponential rate of technological progress that we are experiencing. This was discussed in my previous article, where engineering and scientific progress was compared to a snowball rolling downhill, gathering mass and momentum at an accelerating rate.

FUTURE TRENDS

How will these trends influence our decisions as managers? The serious and long-term petroleum shortage will require more efficient use of energy. We'll see more use of lightweight materials and more efficient energy conversion systems. We'll have to identify alternate energy sources such as oil from shale, solar power and nuclear energy. We'll have to develop alternatives to petrochemical products such as plastics and solvents.

We'll see more and more material shortages, requiring substitute materials, longer lead times, careful labor management, recycling and additional federal regulation. New federal standards will affect health and safety in the work place; product safety and reliability requirements; environmental pollution allowances; allocation of resources; even the switch to the metric system.

The data processing industry will become more mature with the widespread use of computer systems and the seeking out of new fields to automate, such as factories and even the food checkout line at the supermarket. It will also approach maturity in a technological sense—the various configurations will now grow by evolution as contrasted with the revolutionary trends of the past.

The whole area of Equal Opportunity Employment and Affirmative Action programs will gain importance. The latest goal, for instance, is to have 17% of the work force at all levels, and in all locations, manned by minority group employees.

We'll see a changing work force. White collar workers will outnumber blue collar workers. Vested rights between employers will be transferable. There will be pressure for white collar unions and a shorter work week. A better-educated work force will demand a "people" orientation along with the "production" orientation, where there will be greater emphasis on freedom, achievement and self-fulfillment. The multi-national environment will expose our work force to work cultures of other countries; we will have to work out new relationships and learn to operate organizations with extensive geographical dispersion. This will further require certain regulations and policies to be instituted on a world-wide basis.

The relationship between industry and educational institutions will have to become closer in order to help both operate in the dynamic environment they share.

Above all there will have to be commitment to the future in terms of investment in R&D, management training, product life cycle profit return and the like.

PLAN FOR THE FUTURE

You should think about these trends, because your success as a manager will depend on how well you respond to them in terms of analysis, planning and implementation. For example, as this article is being written, the shortage of gasoline is causing the public to ignore full-size automobiles (which are in over-supply) in preference to economy models (which are in short supply). In response, manufacturers are frantically trying not only to make large cars more economical but also transfer production over to economy models. Due to the interlocking nature of our economy, the waves and ripples resulting from this activity will reverberate through our economy for some time.

As we usher in this era, we might well ask ourselves if we're prepared to meet the challenges that lie ahead.

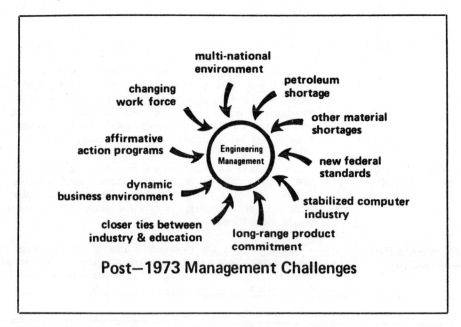

Post—1973 Management Challenges

3

Communications for the engineering manager

Dr. T. F. Gautschi, P.E.

ONE-TO-ONE MAPPING

We can define communication as the process of passing information and understanding from one person to another.

Understanding means that the receiver will interpret the message exactly as the sender intended: one-to-one mapping.

BASIC MODEL

In the diagram shown below communication is the process of reproducing T's thought in R. It is not as simple as you first might assume.

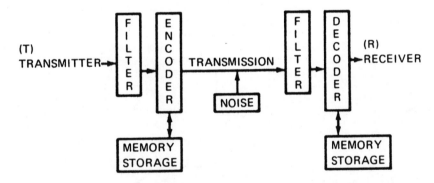

FILTER

Both fact and feeling are involved and there is content. T's thought is about something like baseball, sex, business, politics, etc. This thought must pass through T's filter where it is subjected to the many biases that he may have regarding the subject matter and the receiver, R. (We will discuss the determinents of these biases, along with the concept of perception, in the next issue of the Management Forum.)

ENCODING

Then T must put his thought into words or some nonverbal means of communication. This process is known as encoding and draws upon T's memory storage for a suitable expression for his thought. T must be careful at this point to select expressions that R will understand. Take the simple word slip. It can have many meanings – to fall on the ice, a verbal indiscretion, a woman's garment, a small piece of paper, a space for a ship, fabric cover for furniture, the deformation of metal crystals along certain plains, not meeting a scheduled date, etc.

I read somewhere that there is an average of 28 separate meanings for each of the 500 most used words in the English language.

SYMBOLS

We also have the problem of abbreviations and collections of letters that represent certain thoughts. For example, a nurse recently told me that SOB on an in-patient's form means short of breath – this is not the only interpretation that I have heard for this expression. These special symbols are very useful to those that are involved, but to outsiders they can be very confusing. I think that those of us who work in technical areas are especially prone to use this kind of expression. In fact, we sometimes forget the real meaning of its own – e.g., PERT.

I have also found that it usually takes me a few weeks to decipher the unique symbology in a new organization even when I work at it.

NOISE

After T encodes his thought it must be transmitted to R— and there usually is some "Noise" involved. That is, things that interfere with the transmission. This noise falls into two major classes: physical and psychological.

• Physical noise includes things like telephone static, print illegibility, a nearby noisy typewriter, etc.

• Psychological noise is more subtle – R might be thinking about something else. T or R may be using face-saving devices (we will cover face-saving in a later issue of Forum.) R may be so afraid of T that it is difficult for R to hear what T has to say, or T may be trying to impress R with his importance.

DECODING

Once T's thought gets through the noise, it must get through R's filter and its biases, and then be decoded by R using his memory storage as a reference.

After all of this, the thought that is formed in the mind of R may bear little resemblance to the thought that was initiated in T's mind.

ONE-WAY COMMUNICATION

The process that I have just described is called one-way communication.

To test your understanding of this process I suggest that you conduct a simple test. Gather a small group of your associates and ask one of them to verbally communicate diagram (A), shown below, to the others so that they can draw it on a piece of paper. Use only one-way communication.

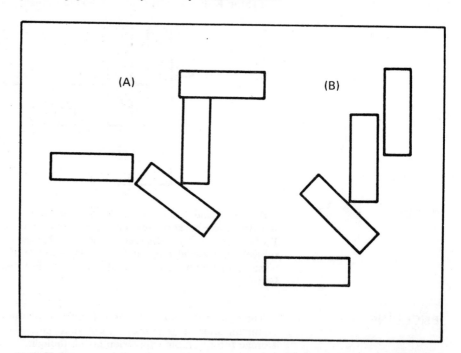

Even though the complexity of this communication is not all that great, I usually find that none of the receivers will be able to accurately reproduce the pattern.

FEEDBACK

The problem is that much of our communication activity is just too complicated to run open loop. To correct this situation we must add the well-known engineering concept of feedback. If enough time is spent, R can accurately reproduce the thought that is in T's mind by simply repeating what he thinks T has transmitted and vice versa until agreement is reached. This is two-way communication.

Feedback does not need to be verbal feedback. The receiver's facial expression will oftentimes reveal a great deal in a communication situation.

A lot of feedback can be obtained from a wink or a smile or a "get lost" look.

FEEDBACK IS VITAL

If you repeat the test described above using feedback, (with figure B), you will probably find that nearly everyone can accurately reproduce the pattern when sufficient time is taken.

Unless the communication is repetitious and highly codified, feedback should be employed to assure effective communication.

Think two-way when you communicate.

Why we sometimes don't hear what is really being said

Joe said to Sam, "You did a hell of a job." Sam responded by stomping off angrily Sam was reacting to what he thought was criticism from Joe, whereas Joe thought that he had complimented Sam by his remark. Considerable confusion and hard feelings resulted before the situation could be straightened out.

This kind of mix-up is not unusual, and I am sure that you have had similar experiences.

- If I believe a stove is hot, I will try to avoid touching it, even though in reality it is ice cold.
- Sometimes I do not hear what is really being said.
- Facts are not always viewed in the same way.

The problem is that each of us operates as if he's surrounded by a box with a filter at one end through which he communicates with the outside world. These filters are individualistic and distort (or bias) what we see and hear. This distortion is the result of such things as:

INDIVIDUALISTIC FILTERS

Anxiety	Expectations
Needs	Age
Education	Time-pressure
Ethnic background	Sex
Prejudices	Interest in subject
Values & Attitudes	Aspirations
Experiences	Environment
Moral beliefs	Cultural background

RECOGNIZE PERCEPTION

The important thing is that we behave on the basis of the world as we perceive it, not as it really is. Overlooking this fact can have significant implications such as misunderstanding of individual and organizational goals, adverse reaction to change, poor acceptance of ideas, and unnecessary conflicts. The engineering manager should try to understand the limits and biases of his own filter, and those of his subordinates and associates, and strive to compensate for them. The use of feedback is perhaps the best way to reduce filter distortion and to obtain a true understanding of a situation. Feedback should be used whenever possible.

FACE-SAVING

Face-saving is another important influence that can distort our communications because:

- We want to appear capable and strong whenever possible.
- We want to avoid situations that will make us look foolish in front of others.
- We will guard against loss of face—even if it becomes very costly for us to do so.
- We will go to elaborate extremes to avoid looking foolish.
- We will increase face-saving activities as our audience gives us derogatory feedback.
- We will employ face-saving when we feel personally incompetent, and even more so if such incompetence threatens to be made public.

Face-saving comes in two varieties:

Anticipatory—here we employ facades to protect ourselves.

Restoration—here we use retaliation to counteract any loss of face that we think we have incurred.

RECOGNIZE FACE-SAVING

Good communications require that the engineering manager be aware of his own facesaving tendencies and compensate for them. At the same time, he should try to provide an environment wherein those he is interacting with can save face when the situation calls for it.

What are the barriers to communication?

Communication should be a two-way process between the sender and the receiver. Unfortunately there are many barriers to achieving effective communication—distributed among the sender, the transmission path and the receiver. As the result of interaction with many engineers and managers from a number of organizations, I have developed the following communications barrier checklist:

Sender—Related Barriers

CHECKLIST

- has strong desire to impress
- does not understand receiver's filter bias
- fears being embarrassed
- has incomplete understanding of subject matter
- uses ambiguous words and phrases
- has strong biases
- makes incorrect and incomplete statements
- fails to listen to feedback
- fails to get and hold receiver's attention
- sets up one-way communication
- doesn't care to understand
- tries to confuse intentionally
- doesn't organize material
- lacks confidence
- speaks over head of receiver
- speaks down to receiver
- talks too long
- has adverse personality traits

Receiver—Related Barriers

- has preconception of what is being communicated
- is overly critical
- tries to save face by not asking questions
- does not understand sender's filter bias
- dislikes speaker
- has strong biases
- not tuned in to sender
- lacks interest
- does not have confidence in speaker
- is prejudiced

Transmission Path Barriers

- distractions
- physical separation
- physical noise
- inappropriate communication media

General Barriers

- difficult to distinguish between fact and opinion
- poor communication techniques
- poor timing
- failure to distinguish between fact and opinion
- fatigue
- personality conflicts
- little or no feedback
- excessive pressure for results
- situation too emotional
- win/lose attitudes
- participants have strong feelings re subject communicated
- significant rank difference between sender and receiver
- low morale
- too much time-pressure
- sender or receiver is frustrated
- no common code

REDUCE BARRIERS   You may wish periodically to refer to this checklist to evaluate whether you are creating or reducing the communication barriers in your world. I have also found that group discussion is useful for identifying the causes for these barriers and establishing plans for reducing or eliminating them. And don't forget that writing to your fellow readers through this column is another way to reduce barriers to communication.

A TYPICAL CASE   A project engineer sent a letter to a contractor claiming errors had been committed by the contractor while assembling a system for an important test. The letter further claimed that as a result of these errors, the test had not produced the anticipated data and had wasted time and money. The letter demanded that the contractor modify his entire quality control and inspection procedure to assure that similar errors would not be repeated. Upon receipt of the letter, the contractor was disturbed because the true circumstances, as he saw them, were not presented.

Communication was blocked. The contractor did not recognize the pressures upon the project engineer, such as limited time and money and the need for high reliability. In turn, the project engineer did not really want the contractor to change his entire procedure. He just wanted systems that would meet his requirements.

Eventually, through the intervention of a third party, mutual understanding was achieved and a solution acceptable to both parties was determined. Mutual understanding is required for good communication. This can be achieved when each party to the communication perceives the expressed idea and attitude from the other party's point of view, as well as from his own. It is really a matter of understanding ... not of judging.

The Johari window

A model for improving interpersonal relationships

Dr. T. F. Gautschi, P.E.

The Johari window was not imported from some far-off land, as you might suspect from its name. To the contrary, two fellows by the names of *Jo*seph Luft and *Har*ry *In*gham developed the basic concept for a program that they were running in group dynamics training.

In essence, the model can be looked upon as a communications window through which a person gives and receives information about himself.

As you are aware, people respond to and treat the world as they see (perceive) it. So, naturally, we base our management practices on how we see ourselves, how we see others and how we see our environment. The Johari window is a tool to help us analyze these perceptions.

In a two-party relationship, there is **self** (that's me) and **others** (that's you).

We can classify the information relating to me in four ways:

1. Information that **I know** about **me**.
2. Information that **I don't know** about **me**.
3. Information that **you know** about **me**.
4. Information that **you don't know** about **me**. ("**You**" can be singular, as in a two-person relationship, like husband and wife; or "**You**" can be plural, a relationship between you as a group and me.)

The four classes of information can be depicted graphically:

	INFO THAT I KNOW ABOUT ME	INFO THAT I DON'T KNOW ABOUT ME
INFO THAT YOU KNOW ABOUT ME	I ARENA	II BLIND SPOT
INFO THAT YOU DON'T KNOW ABOUT ME	III FACADE	IV UNKNOWN

This model may be thought of as being filled with a variety of pieces of information that are available for establishing a relationship..feeling data, factual information, assumptions, prejudices, task skill data, reactive tendencies and the like.

The first area (I) contains things that I know about me and things that you know about me—the **arena**. It is characterized by a free and open interchange of information between me and you.

The second area (II), the **blind spot**, contains information that I do not know about myself but of which you know. As I interact with you, I communicate information of which I am not aware, but which is being picked up (and interpreted) by you. This may be in the form of verbal cues, mannerisms, the way I say things or the style in which I relate to you.

I understand that the better base stealers in baseball study the opposing pitchers carefully so that they can learn those tiny telltale signs that the pitcher makes, but is unaware of, that will give the runner the edge he needs. The runner learns something about the pitcher that the pitcher doesn't know about himself. He works on the pitcher's **blind spot**.

The third area (III) contains those things that I know about myself, but of which you are unaware. For some reason I keep this information from you. I may not want you to know my true feelings, perceptions or opinions, perhaps for fear that you would reject me or that I wouldn't be able to control you. This area is called the facade.

The last area (IV) contains that information pertaining to me that neither you or I know about—the **unknown**.

Let's take another look at these areas:

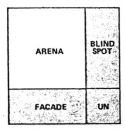

The **arena** is the dominant feature of this relationship. It is characterized by candor, openness, shared information. Things are open and above board and there is less tendency for you to interpret (or misinterpret) my actions or behavior.

This is considered to be the ideal window for establishing and maintaining any significant relationship with another person or a group.

A large **blind spot** permits me to tell you what I think of you, what I think is going on, and where I stand on issues, while at the same time being insensitive and ignoring what you are trying to tell me. I rely on one-way communication from me to you.

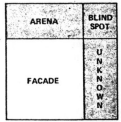

A dominant **facade** reveals a tendency to distrust others and is used to create a protective barrier between me and you. I want to ask questions but not give information or feedback to you. I want to know where you stand before I commit myself. This style may eventually evoke reactions of irritation, distrust and the withholding of information by you.

With a large **unknown**, I don't know much about you and you don't know much about me—our **arena** is very small. When I use this kind of window I might be called a turtle because I keep a tight little shell around me, which keeps me in and you out.

The question is how can I make my **arena** larger?

First, let's tackle the **blind spot**. Since this area contains information that you know about me and that I don't know about me, the only way that I can enlarge my **arena** (reduce my **blind spot**) is to encourage and accept feedback from you.

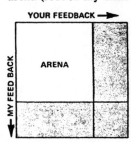

I can reduce my **facade** by giving feedback to you—by exposing myself in terms of my perceptions, feelings and opinions. If I do this, you wouldn't have to guess about, or interpret, where I stand on an issue, or perhaps what my behavior means.

In short, if I want to have a significant and meaningful relationship with you, I must establish and maintain a large **arena** by soliciting and giving feedback.

This will not be easy for those of us who have small **arenas**. It will take time and an awareness of where we are and where we want to go. But, in the long run, it will pay off in terms of better relationships in both our home and our **work** environments.

Theory X, Theory Y and the 'Lens' model

---

*Perceptions that we have of others
determine how we will treat them*

Dr. T. F. Gautschi, P.E.

The children in an elementary school were given an IQ test at the beginning of the school year. It was disguised as a test to predict "intellectual blooming". There were 18 classrooms in the school, three for each of six grade levels. One of these three rooms for each grade consisted of children with above-average ability, one for average ability and for below-average ability.

After the test, 20% of the children in each room were selected at random and labeled "intellectual bloomers". Their names were given to the teacher who was told that she could expect remarkable gains by the designated children during the coming year on the basis of their test scores.

Eight months later, all of the children were retested, and those who were identified to the teacher as "intellectual bloomers" showed an excess in overall IQ gain over the IQ gain for the other children. Moreover, it made no difference whether the child was in a high-ability or a low-ability classroom. The teacher's expectation benefited children at all levels.

At the end of the year the teachers had all sorts of good things to say about the "intellectual bloomers"; they had a better chance of being successful in the future, they were more appealing, better adjusted, more affectionate and autonomous . . . correct or not, this is the way the teachers perceived them because they were identified as "intellectual bloomers", even though they were picked at random.[1]

SELF-PERCEPTION COUNTS

This also illustrates that the way in which we respond to, and treat others, has a great deal to do with their self-perception, and how they will relate to us.

In fact, when a manager's expectations regarding a subordinate is high, the subordinate is much more likely to achieve high performance than when the manager's expectations are low. This sounds obvious, and it is; the only problem is that many of us unintentionally treat our subordinates in a way that leads to lower performance than they are capable of achieving. This may be because we give little conscious thought as to how we perceive them.

Egon Brunswick's **LENS MODEL** provides a conceptual framework to help us think about this most important process of how we perceive others. As you are aware, this is no simple task—coming to terms with what and who someone else is. Most of us don't even know ourselves!

When you think about it, most of us tend to perceive others in terms of goodness-badness, intentions (responsibleness, honesty, etc.) and relative power.

WE USE SYMBOLS

These are nice packages, but unfortunately they are not very tangible, so we must resort to discernible symbolic representatives of these characteristics—**cues**. These cues—and they vary from individual to individual—combine to form a lens through which we view (perceive) others. Thus, the accuracy with which I can perceive the real you is dependent upon the accuracy of the lens through which I view. That is, how well the cues that I use relate to reality, and the relative weight that I give to each cue. Some cues may be so important that an entire stereotype will come to mind when it is present. For example, you may feel so strongly that all boys who have long hair are dirty, lazy and untrustworthy that you completely ignore any other cues.

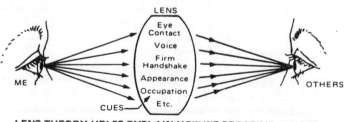

LENS THEORY HELPS EXPLAIN HOW WE PERCEIVE OTHERS

Different people use different cues, but most people include: eye contact, voice, firm handshake, appearance, occupation, age, race, sex, accent, religion, physical characteristics, education, interest, warmth, and body language, to infer who others really are in terms of goodness-badness, intentions and relative power.

For example, if you have a nice firm handshake, a good and consistent eye contact, your voice is not too loud and you seem warm and friendly, I would probably perceive you as being a sincere, honest person because experience has shown me that sincere, honest people have these characteristics. However, I could be very wrong. Some people make it a practice to understand and manipulate such cues, such as the stereotype of the used car salesmen.

In a brief encounter, the first cues that most people notice are the sex, age, race, and physical appearance, including clothes, of the other person. These may seem like superficial qualities, but they are the characteristics that determine one person's initial reaction to another.

CUES ARE IMPORTANT

Clearly, cues are important in an interpersonal relationship because they form the lens that helps us make the determination of another's goodness-badness, intentions and relative power characteristics. We can refine cues and what we can infer from them through the acceptance of feedback. However, we should be careful about generalizing cues—eg., "All well-dressed people are trustworthy."

At this point, you probably have one of two reactions to the above discussion. (1) "This is okay, but it's not applicable in the real world," or (2) "Gee, I never thought about my relationships with others in quite this way before, and I am going to try to make my LENS a little more accurate in the future by paying particular attention to the feedback that I receive . . . and give."

There is special application of the LENS model with which many of you may be familiar: McGregor's Theory X—Theory Y concept.

THEORY X

Basically, McGregor postulated that a manager can view his subordinates through a LENS that he calls **Theory X**:
- People prefer to be led, dislike responsibility
- People are basically lazy
- People lack motivation
- People work because they have to
- People are not very bright, they are gullible
- People cannot control their own affairs

This view of mankind will have direct implications on how he manages an organization—checking responsiblities, time checking, close supervision, etc. It also results in a large policy manual.

THEORY Y

Or a manager can view his subordinates through a lens that he calls Theory Y.
- People are not static—they are dynamic—need change and challenge.
- People enjoy meaningful, challenging work
- People are interested in goal accomplishments
- People are capable of managing their own affairs and, in fact, need growth opportunities
- People have many skills and potentials and these are widely distributed
- People have a potential for creativity

This view of mankind also has direct implications regarding how he manages an organization—maximizing delegation, maximizing human resources, providing people with the necessary conditions for creativity. This approach usually results in a small policy manual.

The reason that many managers use the Theory X lens is that most organizations seem to view people if they were Theory X . . . and when people are treated as Theory X, they act like Theory X. A self-fulfilling prophecy, not unlike the "intellectual bloomer" school children example discussed above.

SUMMARY

(1) **The perception that we have of others determines how we will respond to and treat them.**

(2) **Our perception of others, in terms of goodness/badness, intentions and relative power, is usually based upon an extrapolation from cues that are often superficial qualities like eye contact, appearance, handshake, warmth, etc., so we must be careful in their application and be watchful for feedback.**

(3) **The way we perceive and treat others can have a significant effect upon their performance.**

(4) **McGregor's Theory X—Theory Y concept is a special application of the lens model, in that it identifies assumptions that many managers make about people who work for them, and in turn, influences how they manage them . . . and how the subordinates respond.**

1"The Pygmalion Effect Lives", Robert Rosenthal. *Psychology Today.* Sept. '73.

4

Foundations of management leadership

*Beginning a multi-part series on the theory
and practice of 'management style' and leadership*

Dr. T. F. Gautschi, P.E.

I suspect most engineers think of management principles as something that evolved by chance. How many of us know that scientific studies were made of management principles in the earliest years of the industrial revolution?

These early studies have more than curiosity value, for they laid the foundation for more rigorous study. We owe a great deal to these investigators, as they helped us understand the oftentimes confusing world of the modern industrial organization.

FREDERICK TAYLOR'S SCIENTIFIC MANAGEMENT

When laying the foundation for modern management concepts, three pioneers come to mind: Frederick Taylor, Elton Mayo and Max Weber. Each of these men has profoundly influenced the theory and practice of management in the United States.

Taylor is credited with being the father of "scientific management". While working for Bethlehem Steel, he became interested in how ore and coal were being shoveled. He ran tests relating shovel size to daily ore output, and found that the ideal shovel size was 21-1/2 lb. The shovel size was made the standard and the yard force was cut by two-thirds for the same daily ore output. This was a startling discovery!

Taylor's concept of management was one of task management, and it stressed increasing productivity by eliminating waste motion through programs of functionalization, work simplification, motion studies, standardization and the like.

A worker was hired primarily for his brawn and not for his brain. In that era workers were part of a man/machine production system and were employed to do those tasks for which no machine was available or would be too costly.

Taylor's pioneering in these and other studies helped to bring the adolescent economy into maturity through the use of mass production techniques that enable workers to raise both their output and their wages.

Unfortunately, Taylor also created a monster. For by gearing human operations to the precision of machines, Taylor's system caused management to think of workers as little more than machines that had to eat.

A logical extension of scientific-management was to try to optimize the effect of more complex factors such as employee fatigue. It was hypothesized that fatigue and its effect on employee output could be minimized, just as an optimum shovel size could be determined for a given situation.

ELTON MAYO'S INDUSTRIAL HUMAN RELATIONS

In the spring of 1927, five girls employed as relay assemblers at the Hawthorne Works of Western Electric Co. in Chicago were invited to participate in fatigue-measuring experiments that were to last twenty-six months. The researchers, led by Elton Mayo from Harvard University, were interested in a number of questions centering upon the general problem of fatigue such as: 1) *do employees actually tire out?* 2) *are rest periods desirable?* 3) *is a shorter work day desirable?* Here the task was to identify and measure those factors that could be used to reduce the effect of fatigue and thereby increase worker output.

The theory behind the research method was simple. If you want to know how workers respond to any given set of working conditions, put them in a room by themselves where you can stabilize such factors as flow of work, shifts in personnel, and degree of experience of the operators. Then you change the working conditions in question to suit your experimental design and record the results in terms of productivity. That is, you duplicate as closely as possible the laboratory techniques of the physical scientists.

But the results of their careful experiments did not at all conform to their expectations. For this very reason these experiments have, over the years, attracted wide interest, and there has been much conjecture as to their real significance. The

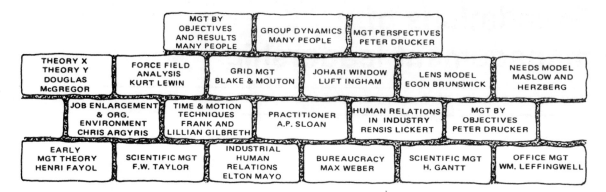

Management theory and application can be viewed as a structure always under construction . . .and yet with an overall emerging pattern.

researchers collected a vast amount of data, but were at a loss to explain what happened in the relay assembly room.

The 26 months were divided into 13 test periods. During the first nine periods, covering some 50 weeks, a number of innovations such as rest periods and shorter work days were instituted. The changes were designed to reduce worker fatigue with each successive test period and, as expected, the average output per individual increased significantly with each change. This increase in productivity outweighed the effect of working shorter hours so that total weekly output also increased substantially. Then, to verify that the greater output was directly related to the changes that were made, a period of longer hours and fewer rest periods was instituted. Surprisingly the work output continued to increase! Even after further changes, including going back to the initial test conditions, the work output remained stable or continued to increase. Clearly, the scientific management approach could not totally explain the results. Some other factors had to be involved!

Upon reviewing the data and experimental conditions several unique factors were identified:

- The girls involved in the experiment were singled out from the main production line and became a small social group or team unto themselves.
- The research coordinator acted in a consulting and coaching role, and the girls received little detailed supervision.
- The team completely understood what was going on, and each new change was discussed with them prior to its implementation.
- The team felt that what they were doing was important because management would periodically drop by to see how things were going.

It became clear to Mayo and his associates that they had stumbled upon something that would encourage workers to make a greater contribution to organizational goals than that which could be obtained by simply manipulating their physical environment in accordance with rational scientific management principles. This concept has been characterized by the term *industrial human relations.*

MAX WEBER BUREAUCRACY
Around 1900 Max Weber, a German sociologist, developed the theory of bureaucracy. Bureaucracy is a form of organization that relies exclusively on the power to influence through rules, reason and law. This concept was developed as a reaction against the personal subjugations, nepotism, cruelty, emotional reaction and capricious judgment that passed for managerial practice in the early days of the

industrial revolution. Bureaucracy is characterized by orderly organization, rules and rationality, and by an emphasis upon technical competence rather than arbitrary decision making. It has flourished with the increase in size and complexity of organizations.

In a very real sense, bureaucracy is an application of the scientific management concept to an organization as a whole.

Bureaucratic organization also has its shortcomings such as: arbitrary and zany rules, bosses with less competence than their subordinates and confusion and conflict among roles, and bureaucratic organization usually has a great deal of inertia and does not easily or quickly adapt to new situations.

Scientific management, industrial human relations and bureaucracy are not compatible concepts. Nevertheless, their application has enabled the United States to grow. And throughout the years, reconciliation of these concepts has caused a great deal of management attention . . . and frustration.

Foundations of management leadership

*Rounding out our perspective
on modern management thinking*

Dr. T. F. Gautschi, P.E.

part II

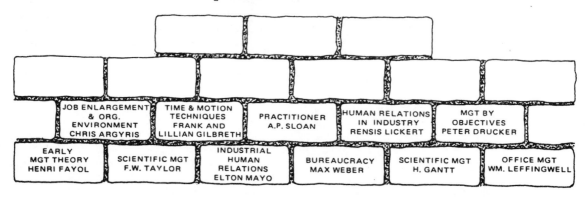

JOB ENLARGEMENT & ORG. ENVIRONMENT CHRIS ARGYRIS | TIME & MOTION TECHNIQUES FRANK AND LILLIAN GILBRETH | PRACTITIONER A.P. SLOAN | HUMAN RELATIONS IN INDUSTRY RENSIS LICKERT | MGT BY OBJECTIVES PETER DRUCKER

EARLY MGT THEORY HENRI FAYOL | SCIENTIFIC MGT F.W. TAYLOR | INDUSTRIAL HUMAN RELATIONS ELTON MAYO | BUREAUCRACY MAX WEBER | SCIENTIFIC MGT H. GANTT | OFFICE MGT WM. LEFFINGWELL

The contributions of nine other management theorists and practitioners are also important to our perspective for modern management thinking in that they tend to refine and expand the foundational work of Taylor, Mayo and Weber.

CHRIS ARGYRIS

A leading author and authority on human relations in business and industry, Argyris' major contribution has been to identify the disparity between the goals of organizations and the goals of their employees, and to stress the need for integrating them. Argyris points out that if the principles of bureaucratic organizations are used as ideally defined, employees will be required to work in environments where 1) they are provided minimal control over their work-a-day world, 2) they are expected to be passive, dependent and submissive, 3) they are encouraged to develop and use a few superficial abilities and 4) they are expected to produce under conditions leading to psychological failure, since their own sources of motivation must be either denied or postponed. He states that a basic problem for managers is one of reducing the degree of dependence, submissiveness, and frustration experienced by these employees. He believes that this can be accomplished through programs of job enlargement and employee-centered leadership.

PETER F. DRUCKER

Probably the best known of contemporary management thinkers, Drucker is an author, lecturer, teacher and management consultant. His concept of Management by Objectives is a cornerstone for modern management.

HENRI FAYOL

One of the most important European contributors to management thinking, Fayol was first recognized in the U.S. when his major work "General and Industrial Management" was published here in 1919. The work presented the universality of management, the first comprehensive theory of management and the need for teaching management in schools and colleges.

HENRY L. GANTT

A pioneer in the development of scientific management, Gantt is widely known for his Gantt Chart, which measures a work activity by the amount of time needed to perform it. Today, Gantt Charts are widely used to compare actual and planned performance.

FRANK AND LILLIAN GILBRETH

This famous husband and wife team did much to improve the understanding and practice of time and motion studies. They were the first to use motion pictures to study and improve motion sequences. After Frank Gilbreth's untimely death in 1924, his wife carried on their work until recently. A popular movie, "Cheaper by the Dozen", is based upon the life and work of the Gilbreths.

WILLIAM LEFFINGWELL Leffingwell was the first person to apply the principles of scientific management to office work. In 1917 he published "Scientific Management", which is the forerunner of all modern studies in office management.

ALFRED P. SLOAN The late Alfred P. Sloan was one of the great management practitioners of all time. In establishing General Motors as one of the largest and most profitable organizations in the world he utilized the concept of centralized policy making and decentralized operations. He also did much to encourage the development of management and the education of managers by sponsoring many individual scholarships and institutions like the Sloan School of Industrial Management at M.I.T.

RENSIS LICKERT As Director of the Institute for Research at the University of Michigan, Dr. Lickert has made outstanding contributions to the understanding and advancement of human relations in industry.

Lickert has labeled the two types of managerial supervision that have emerged from the scientific management and human relations perspectives as production-centered and employee-centerd supervision, respectively. He and his associates have conducted a number of studies to determine which orientation yields the best results in terms of morale and productivity. In carrying out this activity they found that morale and productivity are not directly related, as they had initially assumed, but that any one of four combinations as shown below can exist. However, they found that the ideal combination is high morale coupled with high productivity, and therein lies the management challenge.

DOUGLAS MCGREGOR The late Douglas McGregor was professor of industrial management at M.I.T. and a prominent author and leader in industrial human relations. His "Theory X and Theory Y" concept is an important ingredient in the development of modern management theory and practice.

McGregor's basic argument is that employers too often operate on an incorrect perception of the human nature of their employees. He has labeled this view Theory X and it assumes that employees are lazy, uncreative, and uncooperative, and that strict discipline and rewards are necessary to achieve results in the workplace. (I am sure that many of us make this assumption with our teenagers, and wonder why we are having difficulty with them.) Chris Argyris argues that employees become this way in repsonse to the environment that the employer creates.

McGregor has labeled an alternative assumption as Theory Y. Here it is assumed that employees will exercise self-direction and control in pursuing objectives to which they are committed. McGregor argues that the basis for better management should be to create an organizational environment that will encourage all employees to achieve their own goals by directing their efforts towards the goals of the organization.

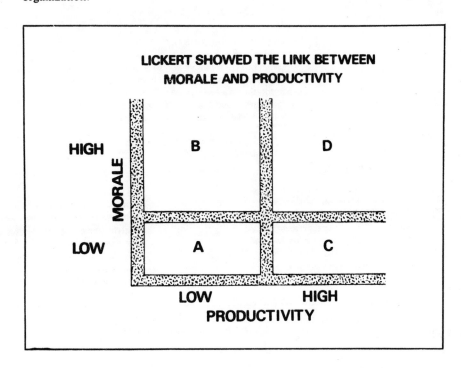

The varieties of management style

Wherein we dissect the ways
managers control their subordinates

Dr. T. F. Gautschi, P.E.

The effectiveness of an organization is greatly influenced by the style of management its leaders use. This is especially true in organizations that employ a high percentage of professionals such as engineers and scientists. The purpose of this article is to provide a framework for identifying various management syles. The next article will provide a guide for choosing the most appropriate management style.

FIG 1: CHARACTERISTIC MANAGEMENT STYLES

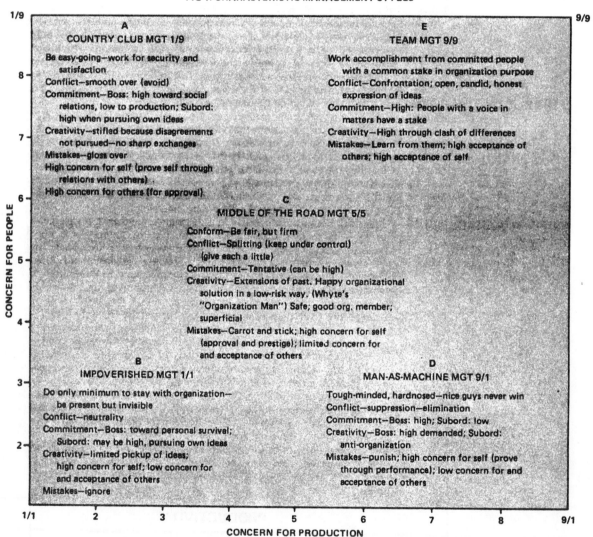

MANAGERIAL GRID

Blake and Mouton have extended the work of McGregor and Lickert into a conceptual model of management style called the **managerial grid**. This grid can be used to explore and identify various possible management styles available to the engineering manager. Its vertical dimension is **concern for people** and its horizontal dimension is **concern for production**. A management style is defined by the intersection of these two concerns.

Five basic relationships are shown in Fig. 1.

1/1 IMPOVERISHED MANAGEMENT

The 1/1 position (located in the lower left corner) is an **impoverished** management style. It depicts both a low concern for people and a low concern for production. Its basic philosophy is to do only the minimum needed to stay with the organization. Commitment is low to the organization and high to personal survival. All creativity is confined to off-the-job activities. Conflict is avoided. The 1/1 manager does not set plans or goals, he is essentially a message carrier, and he exercises little control over his subordinates. He basically adopts a laissez-faire attitude toward them.

1/9 COUNTRY CLUB MANAGEMENT

The 1/9 intersection (upper left-hand corner) indicates a low concern for production and a high concern for people. This has been labeled **Country Club** management. Its basic philosophy is to be nice and easy going—work for security and satisfaction, with a high commitment to maintaining good morale. There is a definite resistance to change, so creativity is not encouraged. Conflict is smoothed over. Planning is avoided where possible, and a definite effort is exerted to do what the boss wants. Control is exercised through gentle persuasion. Togetherness is important in the 1/9 management style. (Note the similarity between this position and the industrial human relations approach.)

9/1 MAN-AS-MACHINE MANAGEMENT

The 9/1 location (lower right-hand corner) has its roots in the scientific management approach and is a very common management style. It is called the **man-as-machine** management style. Its philosophy is one of tough-mindedness and being hardnosed. The management commitment is high, but generally the subordinate's commitment is characterized by apathy and indifference. Creativity is often anti-organizational at the worker level. Conflict is snuffed out, or suppressed, and win-lose confrontations are common. Planning activity is centralized—"planners plan and doers do". Control is exercised through authority and obedience and the offender is punished. It is based upon McGregor's Theory X wherein man is perceived to be lazy, indolent, and disinterested in his work, and must be forced to comply with organizational goals.

5/5 MIDDLE-OF-THE-ROAD MANAGEMENT

In many respects, 5/5 management (see center) is the most common management style found in organizations today. In a sense it is 9/1 management with just enough attention to human relations to make it acceptable. This style is called **middle-of-the-road**. Its philosophy is to conform and to be fair, but firm. Commitment to organizational goals is moderate. Creativity tends to be shallow. Conflict cannot be tolerated—it is generally solved by compromise. Planning and goal setting tend to be retrospective and depend upon past practice and precedence. Control is exercised through persuasion and selling.

9/9 TEAM MANAGEMENT

The fifth combination, 9/9, is termed **team management**. It assumes a McGregor Theory Y perception of man. Man is not lazy by nature, he is not resistant to organizational goals and the basic task of management is to provide an atmosphere wherein the subordinate can achieve organizational goals without being driven. The managerial philosophy is one of work accomplishment by committed people with a common stake in the organizational goals. Commitment tends to run high because the individual views his personal goals as being compatible with those of the organization. Creativity is encouraged and generally flourishes with this management style. Conflict is faced squarely and solutions are arrived at through the acceptance and integration of the information held by the various participants. This is contrasted with the win-lose philosophy of compromise. Conflict is viewed as being healthy and as stimulating creative solutions. Planning and goal setting are accomplished by the people involved in the doing. Control is exercised by understanding that the 9/9 orientation perceives of the organizational participants as being professionals in their respective fields and that the job of management is one of leadership and not one of a policeman that must push and control to enable his organization to meet its goals.

The characteristics of the various managerial styles are summarized in Fig. 1.

After discussing the management grid, the question is always asked, "Which management style is best?" The answer to this question will be explored in our next article.

How to choose a management style

A step-by-step approach to making leadership fit the situation

Dr. T. F. Gautschi, P.E.

The manner in which a leader involves his subordinates in the decision-making process has a strong influence on the effectiveness of the organization. Every manager uses some sort of model to direct his problem-solving and decision-making processes. Usually it is not a model the manager is conscious of, and it may not be the same in every circumstance, but it does fit with what the manager feels is reality. This model is used to analyze the situation and to determine the decision rules. As such, a manager's model is critical to success or failure.

Decision-making "models" fall along a continuum: bounded on one end by the scientific-management advocate who feels that the manager must make all the decisions, issue all the orders and monitor all performance. Let's call this "Model-A". The other end of the spectrum asserts that individual and group performance is directly proportional to the freedom given subordinates to make their own decisions. Let's call this extreme "Model-P".

The best managers should be able to operate anywhere along the Model-A, Model-P spectrum as the situation requires.

MANAGEMENT STYLE MODEL

The basic model is shown in Figure 1. The factors that should influence the leader's management style are listed in four categories: attributes of the manager, attributes of the subordinate(s), attributes of the situation and the character of the problem. Each of these factors should be further divided into elements providing answers depending upon the total situation. Then, once a set of selection rules has been established, the manager should be able to identify the most appropriate management style for any given set of factors.

A range of delegation possibilities (leadership styles)[1] along the Model-A Model-P spectrum can be defined as follows:

A-1 (Autocratic): The manager solves the problem or makes the decision, using available information, but without participation by subordinates. (Grid style 9.1)

A-2 (Autocratic): The manager obtains whatever information is required from subordinates, and then makes the decision. (Grid style 9.1)

P-1 (Consultative): The manager shares the problem on an individual basis with each subordinate, gets their ideas and suggestions, then makes the decision. (Grid style 5.5)

P-2 (Consultative): The manager shares the problem with his subordinates as a group, obtains collective ideas and suggestions, then makes the decision. (Grid style 5.5)

P-3 (Consensus): The manager shares the problem with subordinates and together they reach consensus agreement on a solution. (Grid style 9.9)

P-4 (Delegated): The manager delegates the problem to a subordinate, provides relevant information, and the subordinate makes the decision. (Grid style 1.9)

RANGE OF VARIABLES

The range of situational variables can be divided into four major classes: attributes of the manager, attributes of the subordinate, attributes of the situation and the character of the problem itself.

Attributes of the Manager:

● Value system as it relates to organizational efficiency, personal growth, and company profits.

● Confidence in subordinates

● Leadership inclinations

● Tolerance for ambiguity—feelings of security in uncertain situations, and the

1. Some of these elements are based upon V. H. Vroom's work that is reported in, *Leadership & Decision Making* by V. H. Vroom, P. W. Yetton, University of Pittsburgh Press, 1973.

need for predictability and stability.
- Aspirations and personal goals
- Real and perceived capabilities, knowledge and experience

Attributes of the subordinates:
- Personal characteristics such as: need for freedom and independence, concern for rationality, competence, perfectionist and achievement desires
- Readiness to assume responsibility for decision making
- Tolerance for ambiguity—some prefer detailed directions and specifically stated constraints, others prefer broad general directions
- Interest in the problem or task at hand, and perception of its importance
- Prerequisite knowledge and background

Attributes of the situation:
- Changing competitive conditions (e.g., rate of change demanded by the marketplace)
- Government regulations
- Union relationships

MATCHING A STYLE

Each organization has certain ways of doing things. Certain kinds of behavior are approved and others are not. For example, the desirable executive might be viewed as one that is forceful, dynamic and knows all the details. On the other hand, emphasis might be on the manager that thoughtfully and quietly works behind the scenes accomplishing the organizational goal through others.

The size of organization also makes a difference. The larger organizations tend to be more formal and less flexible.

The appropriate management style also depends upon the geographical dispersion of the organizations. For example, a style near the Model-A end of the spectrum is likely to be more appropriate to an organization whose participants are separated by great distances, than to one whose members are in one location, especially if the organization has grown through acquisition or if it is located in more than one country.

The effectiveness of a group operating under various management styles depends upon the confidence the members have in one another, its past history of successes, its duration, and how well it works together.

Time, along with resource pressures, is perhaps the force that a manager feels the most. Too often an organization, especially those in highly dynamic fields, works from crisis to crisis. In these cases the manager feels that he/she must use the Model-A approach—there just doesn't seem to be enough time for any other style.

There is also resource pressure. The manager is continually faced with making tradeoffs among various alternative actions in order to not exceed the resource allotment.

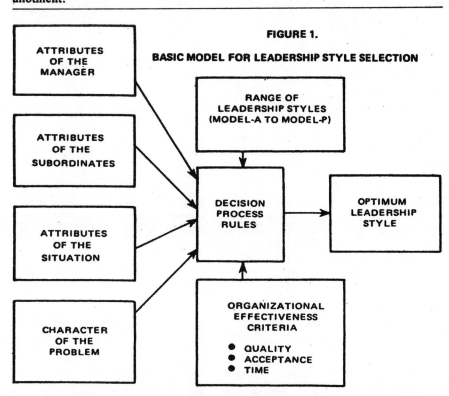

FIGURE 1.

BASIC MODEL FOR LEADERSHIP STYLE SELECTION

ANOTHER CRITERION

The character of the problem[1] determines the management style:

- Is there a quality requirement where the solution will help the system attain its goals?
- Does the manager have sufficient information to make a quality decision?
- Is the problem structured? i.e., Do procedures exist for handling the problem?
- Is acceptance of the decision by subordinates critical to its effective implementation?

In theory the suggested model should list all of the above situational factors (and perhaps others) to assure that the optimum decision is made. However, in practice, this would be very cumbersome, so the manager should reduce the list by combining some factors, and eliminating others that would not be involved. In a word, the manager should tailor the model to fit his or her specific situation.

SUMMARY

It is clear that no one management style is best, but that the appropriate choice should be determined by the attributes of the manager, the subordinate, the situation and the characteristics of the problem. Once these factors are identified, the manager should develop a decision rule to determine which management style is optimum for the given set of factors.

In practice most managers perform this process without specifically identifying the factors or the related decision rules. The model suggested in this paper should help these managers become more aware of the process they should use when trying to decide on a leadership style.

Using this model to work through a number of actual problems should help the manager make more optimum decisions. Generally, as the manager operates on a day to day basis, the choice of management style is limited. About the best one can do is to take into account the various factors as they are perceived and then operate accordingly. However, the manager can affect change in these factors in the longer term and thereby broaden the choice of alternatives. This can be accomplished through advanced planning, and analysis of the delegation and decision-making process.

Leadership style of the ideal engineering manager

An "impossible dream" described; plus the start of "Critical Incidents"—real management problems that call for your solutions

Dr. T. F. Gautschi, P. E.

Did you ever think about what the "ideal" engineering manager would be like? In a recent seminar I posed this question to 25 middle-management engineers. Their responses were so interesting that I thought I would share them with you.

The ideal engineering manager:

- **is an excellent communicator**
    aware of new technological developments; aware of trends in markets
    holds periodic meetings to discuss policies, plans and goals
    provides reliable feedback to subordinates
    sensitive to feedback—observes and listens
- **is a planner who works constantly for improvement and can operate in a complex dynamic environment**
    concerned with both short and long-range plans
- **has the ability to motivate people**
    enthusiastic; sets a good example
    gives recognition when warranted
    encourages subordinates to adopt company and department goals as their own
- **recognizes the individualities of subordinates**
    their aspirations, strengths, weaknesses, needs, goals and fears
- **need not be an expert in all fields,** but should have a solid base to understand the explanations of experts and be able to view the system as a totality
- **has a working knowledge of the allied fields** of marketing, manufacturing, finance, personnel management, and customer requirements

DELEGATES
- **has the ability to delegate**
    confidence in subordinates; listens to the ideas of others
    not afraid to make a mistake; has tolerance for ambiguity
    uses management by objectives—joint goal-setting, honest, timely feedback, sets clear, well-understood project goals and objectives
    gives subordinates freedom to make decisions within constraints
- **is ambitious to make the company the best in the industry**
- **sets high priority on training** and personal improvement of subordinates
- **makes good and outstanding people available** for promotion
- **is thoroughly familiar with the company,** its customers, its history, organization, its products and personnel
- **is a stabilizing influence in the time of crisis**
    calm, composed, realistic; maintains an overview perspective
    able to cope with stress; sets overall tone; sets work priorities
    tries to develop a certain level of detachment
- **is aware of organizational politics,** but does not get involved
- **has a good understanding of the job,** as well as that of subordinates
- **maintains good rapport** with outside organizations
- **is ethical and is fair and objective** in dealing with others

COURAGE
- **has the courage of convictions**
    doesn't back down under pressure
    looks at both sides of an issue
    has a 'tough hide' to criticism; can make hard decisions
    can stick to important principles or convictions
    confidence in self and organization
- **keeps in good health—mentally and physically**
    can work long hours when necessary, even under considerable stress
- **provides the proper physical and psychological environment** for subordinates to be most productive
- **is highly perceptive—**doesn't require everything to be spelled out

can read people's faces; can read between the lines
has good timing
- **makes timely and realistic decisions**
    open to all inputs
    takes responsibility—even when things go badly
- **is cost conscious**
    maintains perspective between resource use, technical performance and schedule
- **tends towards the participative end** of the leadership spectrum
    arouses the will to achieve
    objective; creative
    constantly challenging
    flexible
- **correctly appraises each subordinate's performance**
- **is a team player**
    able to admit when wrong and willing to change direction
    has humility

TEAM PLAYER

We all recognize that becoming the "ideal" engineering manager as described above is an impossible goal to attain, but it can serve as guide and a reminder to those of use who would like to be better managers than we are.

Critical Incidents

Now that we have discussed the qualities that go into making an effective engineering manager, it's time to put your management skills to the test. Beginning with this issue's Management Forum, we will present, as space allows, a series of "critical incidents", real-life situations calling for management leadership. These case histories present a unique opportunity for you to analyze your own management style, and to see how you would respond to the situation.

WRITE TO ME

Please write to me with your solutions to these management problems; replies should be sent to Ted Gautschi, 221 Columbus Ave., Boston, MA 02116.

Critical Incident #1
"Program Conflict"

On a major machine design program, made up of three separate design projects requiring close interfacing, the program manager assumed a second role as project engineer of one of the three projects. In the initial stages of the program the team worked well, spirit was high, and technical discussions and trade-offs were open and well received.

Well into the program one of the project's engineers began increasingly to dispute the judgements of the program manager. This was not on the basis of technical argument, but on the observation that the program manager was effectively favoring his own project, by shifting the tougher decisions to the other projects. The dispute took the form of behind-the-back comments and began to strain what had been a very effective team.

Both men were critical to this program and strong contributors to the growth possibilities of the division as a whole.

How should this problem be resolved for the short and the longer term?

Critical Incident #2
"Transfer Requested"

Two days after taking over the job of supervisor for one senior engineer and five high-level technicians, I was informed by the senior engineer that he abhorred the idea of working with me—for the sole reason that I was a woman. He requested a transfer. This person was extremely valuable to the department because of his vast background in the work we were doing, and I, being new in the job, had planned on relying on him heavily. In addition, because of the very specialized nature of the job, the chances of finding an adequate replacement were extremely remote. Prior to my taking the new position, the department had two senior engineers and one supervisor, besides the technicians, so that all indications were that the department needed at least two engineers.

What should be done in this situation?

A primer on group dynamics

A modest knowledge of group psychology can greatly improve the performance of organizations

Dr. T. F. Gautschi, P.E.

We hear a lot about group dynamics these days, so I thought that it might be worthwhile devoting an article to it.

Group dynamics is used to describe what happens in groups as a result of the complex forces that are at work in them—in other words, what causes a group to behave the way it does.

The initial impetus to serious interest in this field resulted from some research on group interaction started in the late 1940's. In these studies it was found that when a group of strangers met with a non-directive trainer and had no agenda, no announced purpose and no assignment, two interesting things would happen.

PREDICTABLE PATTERN

1. The group behavior would follow a predictable pattern. Initially the participants were quite self-centered: "I wonder what is going to happen that will affect me?" "Should I attempt to lead toward something or should I wait and follow?" "How much should I tell them about myself?" "Should I withdraw or proceed, listen or talk, joke or swear, comfort or punish, complain or suggest?" Then a sense of frustration and conflict would set in. "Why am I here?" "We are just wasting our time."

   Next, the group would make some attempts toward achieving group unity, often at the expense of "old stoneface", the non-directive trainer. Once the ice was broken, the group usually took on the task of trying to define its goals. This involved conflict and lively interchanges and eventually established an environment for dynamic human interaction. Finally the group would engage in a series of individual assessments with an emphasis upon group productivity and problem solving. This entire process would cover perhaps a two-week period. It gave each member a better understanding of what goes on in a group, and it provided him with a mirror in which he could observe himself—a chance to get feedback from the others about how his behavior came through.

2. Most of the people involved would find the experience to be very rewarding, often reporting that it had significantly changed their lives.

These early sensitivity experiments opened a whole new area of thought—and expectations—because in the laboratory environment they enhanced candid communication within the group and produced desirable behavior changes on the part of the participants. Some tried to duplicate these laboratory experimental results in industrial situations without understanding the true nature of group dynamics or what goes on in the business world. As a consequence, the results were not always as intended and sensitivity training became the subject of much controversy.

WIDESPREAD TOOL

Today, nearly 30 years later, many universities, corporations, hospitals, government agencies and consulting firms are engaged in research and application in the field of group dynamics. Along with this proliferation of activity, the volume of technical literature has grown from the merest trickle to a veritable flood. In 1950, around 100 items were published in this field; today the annual publishing rate numbers in the thousands! The mass media is also paying more attention to group dynamics—in books, newspapers, TV, magazines and films.

A good example of the relevance and importance of these efforts is the current interest in Transactional Analysis—a technique that was originally developed in association with psychotherapy. TA uses the group as a setting and helps its participants to become more aware of themselves, the structure of their individual personalities, how they communicate (transact) with others, the games they play and the scripts they act out. In so doing, TA provides a perspective on human behavior that most people can understand and put to use.

TEAM BUILDING

Perhaps the most significant application of group dynamics is in management and leadership in industry—especially as it relates to team building and interpersonal activities. An understanding of what is happening in a group will tend to remove communication barriers and encourage candor and true interaction; which, in turn, generates commitment through involvement with effective performance being the end result. These applications make use of research findings such as:

- Individuals will be attracted to a group when it satisfies their needs, helps them to achieve goals that they feel are important, is congenial, and when such group membership is highly valued by outsiders.
- Participants will be committed to a group decision or goal in proportion to their participation in determining such decisions or goals.

  Group effectiveness is directly related to:
  - the amount of agreement to a clear goal
  - the amount of agreement or conflict concerning the means that the group will use to reach its goal
  - the availability to the group of needed resources
  - the degree to which the group is organized appropriately for its task and how it uses its human resources
  - the extent to which the group is concerned with its process of decision making

The development of the science and application of group dynamics is continuing to receive wide attention. A working knowledge of Group Dynamics is essential to management, which is placing increasing emphasis upon understanding the forces at work in groups, the development of sensitivity to the needs of individuals and groups, and the development of skill in diagnosing human relation problems. This results in more effective organizational performance because its various members are encouraged to be totally involved in achieving goals that they understand.

BIBLIOGRAPHY

The brief bibliography below lists some useful introductory books in the field of Group Dynamics.

Berne, Eric, *Games People Play,* New York, Grove Press, 1964.

Berne, Eric, *What Do You Say After You Say Hello?,* New York, Grove Press, 1972.

Burger, Robert E., and Addeo, Edmond G., *Ego Speak,* Radnor, PA, Chilton Book Co., 1973.

Harris, Thomas A., *I'm OK, You're OK,* New York, Harper & Row, 1969.

James, Muriel, and Jongeward, Dorothy, *Born to Win,* Reading, MA, Addison-Wesley Publishing Co., 1971.

Knowles, Malcolm and Hulda, *Introduction to Group Dynamics,* Revised, New York, Associated Press, 1972.

Critical Incident #3
"The Frustrated Project Engineer"

The company is set up as a matrix organization and as project engineer I have technical and management responsibility for the engineering activities of a development program. The functional department (electrical design) required for one of the tasks on my program has appointed a person as lead engineer who is more senior in authority than me. This person has other responsibilities and seems to have a basic disinterest in my program. He is unsatisfactorily supervising his department's work and is, in addition, conducting some activities in what I consider the wrong direction. In an effort to correct the situation, I tried to establish better communications with the lead engineer and find ways to improve his contributions. However, I soon learned that he had little time to even discuss his operations with me. So I contacted his subordinates. They seem to be in agreement with my way of thinking and pointed out that their leader's management (or lack of it) has been holding them back. For a while things improved. But eventually the lead engineer became aware of my bypassing him and complained to higher management who insist that I work through the lead engineer.

What should be done to correct this situation?

Dr. T.F. Gautschi, P.E.

AUTHORITY, power, politics and leadership

The briar patch of organizational life

These survival factors are the stuff out of which the manager must fashion his strategy, based on timing, influence, and the right use of power. The manager does not operate in a self-contained vacuum. His work is part of the flow of social forces. He is placed in a managerial position for a purpose, but it is not self-perpetuating. It is more than mere housekeeping. It is more than the application of textbook theories, important as these are. The manager is a tactician and a philosopher. He must live by his wits, his competitive instincts, his understanding of social forces, and his ability as a leader. He does not operate in a fixed environment. He must change his environment or adapt to it where necessary, and then try to influence it in any ways which seem indicated in the accomplishment of the ultimate purposes of the program.

Marshall E. Dimock

FOUR KEY TERMS

Four terms—authority, power, politics and leadership—represent important concepts in today's organizational world. Yet, for most of us, they bring forward feelings of confusion, frustration, anxiety and perhaps even indifference.

Since these are such important concepts, we will devote this, and several subsequent articles, to their exploration and to the development of appropriate guidelines for our venture through the briar patch of organizational life.

Part of the confusion surrounding these concepts is created by the lack of commonly accepted definitions. After considerable thought and research, I believe that the following are the most useful.

DEFINITIONS

AUTHORITY is the *right* to command as bestowed by the formal organization.
POWER is the *capacity* to secure dominance of one's values or goals.
POLITICS is the *process* by which power is acquired and exercised.
LEADERSHIP is the conscious *utilization* of power to meet organizational goals.

AUTHORITY

The traditional concept of organization is built upon the principle that someone has the *right* to command "someone else", and that "someone else" has the duty to obey the command.

It is important to note that the right to command does not necessarily connote the capacity to command. This point is sometimes obscured by the fact that "right" provides certain sources of power to the person in the position of authority. In fact, at the extreme, right and capacity could be as one. This was probably the situation in the Henry Ford empire in its early days. However, most of us would be making a mistake if we were to equate right and capacity.

GUIDELINE #1

Employees will only continue to cooperate, or perhaps even remain, with an organization, as long as they feel that the satisfaction of their needs outweighs the burdens and sacrifices that they must make. (See "Human Needs & Motivations", *Design News* 1-6-75.) In reality, we only have the amount of authority that our subordinates are willing to give us. This is especially true in a professional environment. We must be especially careful to undergird our right to command with the appropriate capacity (power) if we want to develop a highly effective organization.

Two interesting illustrations come to mind:

THE NEW VP

A new V.P. for engineering and manufacturing was assigned from the corporate staff to a division of a large corporation. For the first year or so, this new man kept a very low profile while getting to know the people and products of the organization which reported to him. But as time went on, and he gained power in the organization, he made his presence felt more strongly, and he was able to shape the organization into a very effective contributer to the corporation goals. If he had tried to make the changes quickly and based solely upon the authority that he was given by the corporation, and without establishing an appropriate power base, he would have had great difficulty in turning the organization around. At one extreme, he would not have received the cooperation that was required. And at the other extreme, the key people would probably have left the organization.

TRICK OR TREAT?

Dave was an excellent department manager in addition to being a skilled engineer. His supervisor was responsible for a laboratory consisting of several departments, and was doing an inadequate job. Finally, the corporate management removed the lab manager, and Dave saw his way open to a promotion. After a brief interval, a new lab manager was appointed from another division of the company, who promptly began reorganizing the laboratory. One of his moves was to shift Dave from a department manager to a staff position, ostensibly to take full advantage of Dave's experience and counsel, but perceived by Dave as removing him from a position of influence.

A major program was started by a customer, and Dave was asked to manage the proposal which could lead to a multi-million dollar contract. Dave immediately accepted the challenge, and gathered a team of experts from his old department, including some specialized talents unique in the company. The team worked out a technical proposal promising some fairly substantial state-of-the-art development work, at a cost that seemed very low. The lab manager was uneasy, but was assured that the team's technical expertise would handle the job.

The customer was delighted with the proposal, and negotiations were concluded quickly. The lab manager called Dave in to ask him to manage the program. Dave showed up with the key technical personnel from the proposal team, and announced that he and the team were resigning to start their own company.

The first illustration is a good example of a person with considerable formal authority taking time to establish a power base before attempting any significant organizational change. The second is an indication of what can happen when an adequate power base is not established before taking action.

GUIDELINE #2

Be sure to undergird your right to command (authority) with the appropriate capacity (power) if you want to develop a highly effective organization. The alternative to this guideline is for the manager to rely upon raw power (physical, economic and formal authority) and accept its consequences.

In our next article we will discuss the concept of power.

...My experience tells me that there is no simple formula in this matter of organization. The role of personality can be so important that sometimes it is necessary to build an organization, or rather perhaps a section of it, around one or more individuals rather than to fit individuals into the organization.... Great constraint, however, is required when any part of a corporation has to be adapted to an individual, because there are limits to this process as well as to the other. And as I have said...it is imperative for the health of the organization that it always tends to rise above subjectivity.

Alfred P. Sloan, Jr., My Years With General Motors

Authority, POWER, politics and leadership

Power factors are involved in every organizational decision

> *No word is used more carelessly by us than the word power.*
> *I know no conception which needs today more careful analysis.*
> *We have not even decided whether power is a <u>good</u> word or a*
> *<u>bad</u> word. Is the wish for power the desire of grasping*
> *and unscrupulous men, is it the instinctive urge of our lower*
> *natures; or is power a noble, the noblest, aim? Or is*
> *it neither of these? What is power? Is it influence, is*
> *it leadership, is it force? Why do we all like power?*
> *Because we wish to use it to satisfy our desires, or do we*
> *just like the feeling itself?*
>
> Henry C. Metcalf & L. Urwick

GUIDELINE #2

In the previous issue of Management Forum (8-23-76) we defined the concepts of authority, power, politics and leadership. Our second guideline states: *Be sure to undergird your right to command (authority) with the appropriate capacity (power) if you want to develop a highly effective organization.*

As this statement implies, authority and power are not the same things. The formal organization assigns authority, that is, the *right* to command—to make decisions and supervise others. This does not necessarily mean that the individual recipients of authority possess the *capacity* (power) to assure dominance of their values and goals.

For some reason many people resist the power concept, perhaps because they link it with "Machiavellian behavior"—that is, the strategy of acting dispassionately in one's own self interest.

THE PRINCE

Nicolo Machiavelli was the 15th century Florentine civil servant and social scientist who wrote <u>The Prince</u>, a handbook prescribing how to acquire and keep power. Because it contains a great deal of practical truth, it has been used through the ages to guide nations and rulers in their relationships with each other and their neighbors.

A few years ago, after some discussion of The Prince with me, the executive vice president of a large organization ordered copies for all his top executives. He wanted them to be able to recognize Machiavellian behavior in others, and to practice appropriate techniques themselves!

Since we concluded in our ethics survey (*Design News* 11-5-73), that "we all want to be ethical—as long as it doesn't cost too much,", I believe that it follows that most people will act dispassionately in their own self interest when the stakes are high.

GUIDELINE #3

Even though it may be socially unacceptable to admit that one aspires to power, or is concerned about power relationships, we must face the fact that power factors enter into every organizational decision. Any other view is naive and foolish.

However, concern about power does not necessarily mean that a person is committed to Machiavellian tactics. Power has a positive side as well. After all, organizations could not function without some kind of power relationships. The positive side seems to be characterized by a concern for group goals and their achievement. In fact, a leader will have the greatest overall influence when he makes his followers feel powerful and able to accomplish great things on their own.

We must also keep in mind that the ultimate source of power is not the superior, but the subordinate. (See Guideline #1).

The kinds of power used in organizations can be characterized as physical, economic, expertise, performance, charismatic and authority.

Physical power is more obvious in primitive societies. However, I can still remember when the boss was the biggest and strongest person on the team, and when striking workers and management committed acts of violence against each other. Today, physical power is more subtle; however, the potential for its use still exists, and more than likely, some decisions are based upon this factor.

Economic power requires the ownership or control of money or other resources. It is manifested by giving, promising to give, withholding, or threatening to withhold financial or other forms of goods. Many organizations are controlled in this manner—especially those dependent upon the generosity of others.

Expertise is a common basis for power. Staff and certain technical personnel oftentimes have special knowledge, or the control of information channels, that provide a focus for power. (One can even gain power by being knowledgable about the nature and dynamics of power!)

Specialization, as practiced by most organizations, creates an automatic pattern of dependence. The organization can only meet its goals when the various specialists are working together. This provides each specialist with a measure of power. It also limits the possibility of absolute power being exercised by any person or group.

GUIDELINE #4

The amount of expertise—power available to each person—is determined by the importance and uniqueness of his specialty.

- A consistent .350 hitter in baseball can write his own ticket, whereas a .250 hitter is just another player
- A few years ago when software programs **were** developed uniquely for each application, the knowledgeable programmer was accorded quite a bit of organizational power. Today, with program standardization, this power has been reduced significantly.

Performance that is perceived as being successful is an important basis for power. Nearly everyone likes to be associated with a successful performer—whether it be an organization or an individual. This requires that a person know what needs to be done and then do it. The U.C.L.A. basketball teams of the past decade are a good example of this.

Charismatic power results when a person has great personal magnetism. Such a person can dominate decision-making regardless of the logic of his position because his manner simply demands respect and admiration. It is not so much a matter of force as it is one of inspiration.

GUIDELINE #5

Charismatic power seems to be derived from an ability to vividly express the goals and aims that the followers desire, along with creating a feeling of confidence that they can achieve them.

To be most effective, this requires a great deal of personalized direct interaction with many people throughout the organization and the ability to inspire confidence and enthusiasm.

Authority comes from one's position in an organization.

GUIDELINE #6

A certain amount of power goes with every office, regardless of the qualities of the office holder. As discussed in the previous issue, authority is the right to command. In a sense it is a relationship between persons—thus the supervisor has the right to assign work, to evaluate performance, provide rewards, and to hire and fire.

MORE POWER

Power begets power. Power holders can increase their power in proportion to the amount of power that they already have.

Most power holders do not resort to raw power unless it is absolutely necessary. They prefer to conduct the majority of their dealings based upon the power that others perceive them to have.

> *I believe also that he will be successful who directs his actions according to the spirit of the times, and that he whose actions do not accord with the times will not be successful.*
>
> *Nicolo Machiavelli*

In our next issue we will take a closer look at some of the concepts that Machiavelli prescribes in *The Prince* that have relevance for today's manager.

Dr. T.F. Gautschi, P.E.

Authority, POWER, politics & leadership

A closer look at Machiavelli

> *A Machiavellian is clear-minded and carefully weighs the risks and benefits of every move. And he won't automatically accept any rules or constraints but examines each before deciding to obey or flout them.*
>
> *Business Week Oct. 13, 1975*

According to this quote, a Machiavellian is one who tries to take the rational approach to situations. He seldom threatens or attacks others—he is too clever. Instead, he identifies and analyzes rivals and tries to exploit any weakness he finds in them or in the system.

In a sense, the Machiavellian follows the creed to "do unto others before they do unto you."

Nicolo Machiavelli was the 15th century Florentine civil servant and social scientist who wrote *The Prince*, a contemporary handbook prescribing how to acquire and keep power.

Although many of us might quarrel with Machiavelli's ethics, *The Prince* does contain many intriguing concepts. Today's manager should be familiar with these concepts to help him participate more successfully in his organization's inevitable political environment—either to "do unto others" or to protect himself as he chooses. The purpose of this article is to present relevant passages from *The Prince* [1].

Decentralization and Acquisition
"Whenever those states which have been acquired have been accustomed to live under their own laws and in freedom, there are three courses for those who wish to hold them: the first is to ruin them, the next is to reside there in person, the third is to permit them to live under their own laws, drawing a tribute, and establishing within it an oligarchy which will keep it friendly to you."

Introduction of Change
"And it ought to be remembered that there is nothing more difficult to take in hand, more perilous to conduct, or more uncertain in its success than to take the lead in the introduction of a new order of things."

A Person Rarely Forgets Insults
"He who believes that new benefits will cause great personages to forget old injuries is deceived."

Dispensing Good News and Bad News
"From this one can draw another important conclusion, that princes ought to leave affairs of reproach to the management of others, and keep those of grace in their own hands."

[1] *The Prince* by Nicolo Machiavelli, J. M. Dent & Sons, Ltd., London, 1st edition 1908, last reprint 1952.

Reduction in Workforce
"Injuries (which are necessary to inflict) ought to be done all at one time...so as not to have to repeat them daily...to do otherwise one is always compelled to keep the knife in his hand...in this manner being tasted less, they offend less. Benefits ought to be given little by little, so that the flavor of them may last longer."

How to Keep Them Faithful
"Therefore a wise prince ought to adopt such a course that his citizens will always in every sort and kind of circumstance have need of the state and of him, and then he will always find them faithful."

Prepare for Adversity When Things Are Going Well
"A wise prince ought to observe some such rules, and never in peaceful times stand idle, but increase his resources with industry in such a way that they may be available to him in adversity, so that if fortune changes it may find him prepared to resist her blows."

Is It Better to be Loved Than Feared, or Feared Than Loved?
"Upon this a question arises: whether it be better to be loved than feared or feared than loved? It may be answered that one should wish to be both, but, because it is difficult to unite them in one person, it is much safer to

be feared than loved, when, of the two, either must be dispensed with. Because this is to be asserted in general of men, that they are ungrateful, fickle, false, cowardly, covetous, and as long as you succeed they are yours entirely; they will offer you their blood, property, life, and children, as is said above, when the need is far distant; but when it approaches they turn against you. And that prince who, relying entirely on their promises, has neglected other precautions, is ruined; because friendships that are obtained by payments, and not by greatness or nobility of mind, may indeed be earned, but they are not secured, and in time of need cannot be relied upon; and men have less scruple in offending one who is beloved than one who is feared, for love is preserved by the link of obligation which, owing to the baseness of men, is broken at every opportunity for their advantage; but fear preserves you by a dread of punishment which never fails."

Counsel
"A prince, therefore, ought always to take counsel, but only when he wishes and not when others wish; he ought rather to discourage every one from offering advice unless he asks it; but, however, he ought to be a constant inquirer, and afterwards a patient listener concerning the things of which he inquired; also, on learning that any one, on any considerations, has not told him the truth, he should let his anger be felt."

Some Only Consider the Ends and Ignore the Means
"Everyone sees what you appear to be, few really know what you are, and those few dare not oppose themselves to the opinion of the many, who have the majesty of the state to defend them; and in the actions of all men, and especially of princes, which it is not prudent to challenge, one judges by the result."

Gaining Respect
"Nothing makes a prince so much esteemed as great enterprises and setting a fine example."
"A prince is also respected when he is either a true friend or a downright enemy, that is to say, when, without any reservation, he declares himself in favour of one party against the other; which course will always be more advantageous than standing neutral."

Watch Out for the Yes-Men
"Princes, especially new ones, have found more fidelity and assistance in those men who in the beginning of their rule were distrusted than among those who in the beginning were trusted."

Selection of Subordinates
"The choice of servants is of no little importance to a prince, and they are good or not according to the discrimination of the prince. And the first opinion which one forms of a prince, and of his understanding, is by observing the men he has around him; and when they are capable and faithful he may always be considered wise, because he has known how to recognize the capable and to keep them faithful. But when they are otherwise one cannot form a good opinion of him, for the prime error which he made was in choosing them."

Decision-Making
"Therefore a wise prince ought to hold a third course by choosing the wise men in his state, and giving to them only the liberty of speaking the truth to him and then only of those things of which he inquires, and of none others; but he ought to question them upon everything, and listen to their opinions, and afterwards form his own conclusions. With these councillors, separately and collectively, he ought to carry himself in such a way that each of them should know that, the more freely he shall speak, the more he shall be preferred; outside of these, he should listen to no one, pursue the thing resolved on, and be steadfast in his resolutions. He who does otherwise is either overthrown by flatterers, or is so often changed by varying opinions that he falls into contempt."

Only Be Ethical Until the Costs are Too High
"Therefore it is unnecessary for a prince to have all the good qualities I have enumerated, but it is very necessary to appear to have them. And I shall dare to say this also, that to have them and always to observe them is injurious, and that to appear to have them is useful; to appear merciful, faithful, humane, religious, upright, and to be so, but with a mind so framed that should you require not to be so, you may be able and know how to change to the opposite."

Dr. T.F. Gautschi, P.E.

Authority, power, POLITICS and leadership

Politics, the process by which power is acquired and exercised, is like a poker game

> *Executives—whether in business, government, education or the church—have power and use it. They maneuver and manipulate in order to get a job done, and in many cases, to strengthen and enhance their own position. Although they would hate the thought and deny the allegation, the fact is that they are politicians...everyone who exercises power must be a politician.*
>
> *Norman H. Martin and John H. Sims*

POWER THROUGH POLITICS

Politics is the process by which power is acquired and exercised within an organization. It is the process by which contesting forces compete for favorable outcomes on decisions involving who gets what, when and how. Political activity is encouraged by those situations where there are no prescribed routine answers—where there is no stated policy. It also centers around the interpretation of existing policies, and those situations involving value judgments. Since any organization that would attempt to totally reduce these arenas of political activity by instituting rules, regulations and policies from the top would quickly die of strangulation in its own red tape, politics becomes the dynamic that enables the formal organization to function. Thus, all organizations are political structures. They all operate by distributing authority and providing a framework for the exercise of power.

GUIDELINE #7

The direction of communications, their frequency, and their content reveals a great deal about the power relationships within an organization. It is as simple as who talks and listens to whom about what.

With regard to communication content, it is usually found that those points in an organization where judgments and conclusions are transmitted, as contrasted with raw facts, are centers of power. A lower echelon in an organization can maintain a strong power base by communicating upward as many judgments, and as few facts, as possible.

GUIDELINE #8

People who decide what information to transmit and with what interpretation, have considerable power in an organization.

GUIDELINE #9

The assignment of functions within an organization has a significant effect upon the formulation of its power structure. As we stated in Guideline #4 (*Design News* 9-6-76): "The amount of expertise (power) available to each person is determined by the importance and uniqueness of his specialty." This importance can be measured by the impact of the function on the achievement of the organizational goals. The uniqueness is influenced by how many people perform the same function, and how easy it would be to find and train a replacement.

> *Consider the case of the Vice President for Product Integrity for Gillette Company. He is directly responsible for the safety and quality of all 850 Gillette products. He can yank any of them off the market at any time they fail to meet the standards he sets. He can also stop new-product introductions, order packaging changes, and veto proposed acquisitions, all of which can upset plans of executives far senior to him. This power base is supported by the chairman requiring that "everything must clear through Product Integrity before it goes out." This vice president has significant power based upon the uniqueness of his responsibility.*

GUIDELINE #10

Power is closely related to dependence. *Within organizations one can generate a power base (cause others to be dependent upon him) by controlling access to information, persons and resources.*

Such information can include knowledge about the organization, its procedures, its history, its environment, and knowledge about the people who comprise the organization.

A vice president in an organization with which I am familiar had seven managers reporting directly to him. Three of them had considerable power and the other four did not. Upon investigation, it was found that the vice president met frequently with the three high-power managers, and he hardly ever met with the other four! They just weren't in on what was happening.

Often, as a person's length of time in an organization increases, his power increases because he has increased access to information, people and resources.

When I was a member of a large laboratory that was associated with the space program, my secretary was a valuable source of power. She had been with the laboratory about 10 years. During that time she had worked in security, personnel, procurement and as a receptionist. She knew the "ins and outs" of each organization as well as all the important rules, and she could get things done informally that would have taken a great deal of my time and energy to accomplish on a formal basis. Usually it was just a matter of a telephone call to the right person.

GUIDELINE #11

There is a direct relationship between the amount of time and effort a person is willing to put into an area and the power he can command.

In the above illustration my secretary was able to exercise considerable power because she put time and effort into establishing and maintaining useful contacts throughout the organization, and I liked being able to leave the "details" to her.

GUIDELINE #12

Power is directly related to a person's geographical and organizational centrality.

A few years ago the young chief executive of a large aerospace corporation told me that he got to his position through the secretarial route. After some investigation, he had decided that the fastest way up would be by becoming an executive secretary—it certainly worked for him!

As we all have experienced, executive secretaries do have considerable power—in terms of the executive's appointments and schedules—and they usually know what's going on before most other people in the organization. Large organizations are made up of suborganizations, each of which is bound together by power factors like those of the total organization.

GUIDELINE #13

Each suborganization has its internal power structure, which is headed by a leader who is supreme within the subsystem, but who is a non-leader when viewed from the perspective of the total system.

In the U.S. Navy, the captain of a ship is in supreme command, whether he be a lieutenant or a "four-striper". However, when he is in the presence of the flotilla commander, he is just "another one of the boys". This contrast is especially vivid when one leaves a sea command for a staff position in the pentagon.

RISKING POWER FOR POWER

Each time a manager uses his power wisely, it is increased; each time he makes a mistake or abuses or misuses his power, it is decreased. Thus, in every decision, and other public action, the manager is risking a certain amount of power in order to gain a greater amount of power.

For some, the more power they gain the more power they desire; and the greater the risks they are willing to take. In any case, it is necessary for the manager to develop and maintain sufficient power to do his organization's work in the total environment in which it must operate. One of management's persistent challenges is to use this power wisely and constructively so that it will be increased and not decreased.

GUIDELINE #14

Every manager is allotted a certain measure of power when he is assigned to a position. Then, as he performs his function, the level of this power will vary upward and sometimes downward, depending upon how he uses his power and employs the power factors available to him.

It is like a poker game. Each participant has a certain amount of resources when he enters the game. (For the manager these are an integration of his physical power, economic power, formal authority, expertise power, performance power, charisma and political acumen). He must risk portions of these resources to gain more or even to stay in the game—and at times he will win, and at times he will lose. At the end some will have lost much or all of their resources and others will have made significant gains. The losers will leave, and the winners will stay or go on to bigger games. The winners must face risks and get results.

The fifth, and last, article in this series on authority, power, politics and leadership will focus on leadership—the conscious utilization of power to meet organizational goals.

Dr. T.F. Gautschi, P.E.

Authority, power, politics and LEADERSHIP

Leadership paths through the wilderness

Stogdill prefaced his recent extensive survey of research on leadership with the following statement:

> *Four decades of research on leadership have produced a bewildering mass of findings. Numerous surveys of special problems have been published, but they seldom include all the studies available on a topic. It is difficult to know what, if anything, has been convincingly demonstrated by replicated research. The endless accumulation of empirical data has not produced an integrated understanding of leadership.*[1]

LEADERSHIP IS COMPLEX

He then proceeds to support his statement by reviewing the research accomplished to date. It is a massive task—his bibliography alone occupies some 150 pages.

No wonder we have feelings of confusion, frustration, anxiety and perhaps indifference regarding this important, but little understood, concept. In a sense, everyone is an expert, because we practice leadership in some form or other; and in another sense, no one is an expert, because we really do not have an integrated understanding of this subject.

The purpose of this article is to identify a few of the more useful paths, relating to the concepts of authority, power and politics, through the wilderness of information that is available.

HOW IT ALL FITS TOGETHER

Leadership is *not* the same as management, power, authority or politics. Yet these concepts are closely inter-related. As we have discussed before, management is the performance of the following functions—planning, organization, staffing, directing, communicating, controlling, reviewing and budgeting. Power is the *capacity* to secure dominance of one's values and goals. Authority is the *right* to command as bestowed by the formal organization. Politics is the *process* by which power is acquired and exercised. And leadership is the conscious *utilization* of power to meet organizational goals.

Every productive organization has an INPUT, a TRANSFORMATION PROCESS and an OUTPUT and interacts with an overall environment.

- **Management** defines and establishes the total organizational form including goals and constraints.
- **Authority** is used to define the formal relationship between the various parts.
- **Power** is used to define the non-formal relationships.
- **Politics** is used to determine how the power is allocated.
- **Leadership** is the dynamic that operates in the organization so that it will meet the constraints and goals as established by management.

If we liken the organization to an automobile: *management* decides where it should go, when it should go, who are the passengers and assures that all of its parts are in satisfactory working order. *Authority* would prescribe the relationships between the various parts (e.g. the battery energizes the starter motor). *Power* is like the fuel from which the engine derives its energy. *Politics* is the process by which the fuel is allocated. Finally, *leadership* is the dynamic function that is performed by the driver when he operates the automobile to assure that the goals and constraints, as established by management, are met.

[1]Stogdill, Ralph M., *Handbook of Leadership*, A survey of Theory and Research, New York, Free Press. 1974.

GUIDELINE #15 *The real measure of leadership is determined by the performance of the group that is being led.*

GUIDELINE #16 *The primary requirement for leadership is to know what is to be accomplished and to be able to communicate it effectively.* It is both surprising, and distressing, to discover how many people in important positions cannot specify what they are trying to accomplish.

Many leaders employ raw power (physical, economic and form authority) to accomplish their goals. In the short term this can be very effective, but it will usually have adverse long-term consequences in terms of high employee turnover, minimum commitment, low morale, counterproductive activities and the like.

GUIDELINE #17 In a very real sense, *the leader can only continue to exercise the amount of power (influence) that he is allowed to by his subordinates—even though his position is reinforced by economic, legal and other sanctions.*

Raw power is particularly inappropriate in a professional environment where innovation, flexibility, commitment and involvement are important.

GUIDELINE #18

THE WISE LEADER *There is a valid alternative to raw power.* It is exemplified by the following characteristics:

—The leader has a view of people, which is closer to the theory Y end of the spectrum (see *Design News* 2-3-75).

—The leader is both self-confident and interpersonally competent. His decisions and behavior are based upon an awareness of or a sensitivity to his own needs and desires, as well as those of his associates.

—The leader provides social and emotional support for other group members by helping them to define what they should be doing, how they should be doing it and how they should feel about doing it.

—The leader uses the management style most appropriate to the situation, the problem, and the forces within him and his subordinates (*Design News* 2-17-75 and 3-3-75).

—The group tends to select as leader a member who can maintain the group role structure and can help clarify and establish task direction.

—Followers are more satisfied when their leaders are able to predict the superior's reactions, and when their leader has significant influence upon the superior.

—The leader is careful about how he seeks and receives counsel. He may take the views of others into account, but he knows the decisions must be his.

—The leader establishes alliances with those above and below him, as well as with his peers.

—The leader communicates wisely. He recognizes that timing is important—especially when future plans are involved. He should be concerned with who gets to know what and when and be sure to establish accurate upward and downward channels of communication.

—The leader should know how to settle differences through the integration of the various valid inputs. He must be aware of which issues are core and which ones are negotiable. (*Design News* 10-6-75.)

—The leader recognizes, encourages and rewards informal arrangements that facilitate the accomplishment of organizational goals.

—The leader knows that the values guiding the making of a decision are not always given in advance, but often emerge during the decision-making process. He tries to maintain flexibility and avoid premature commitment to a particular position. When conditions change, he can change his course without loss of face.

—The leader takes great care to find subordinates who combine technical competence with reliability, dependability and loyalty.

—The leader never places too much dependence on a subordinate, or anyone else, unless it is clearly to the latter's advantage to be cooperative.

—The leader is open-minded and receptive to opinions that differ from his. He wants to hear the "bad news" as well as the "good news".

In conclusion, the above, along with the previous four articles (8-23-76, 9-6-76, 9-20-76 and 10-11-76), should provide us with some food for thought, and some guidelines (recapped below) for our venture through the briar patch of organizational life.

18 guidelines to organizational life

1. Employees will only continue to cooperate, or perhaps even remain, with an organization, as long as they feel that the satisfaction of their needs outweighs the burdens and sacrifices that they must make.
2. Be sure to undergird your right to command (authority) with the appropriate capacity (power) if you want to develop a highly effective organization.
3. Even though it may be socially unacceptable to admit that one aspires to power, or is concerned about power relationships, we must face the fact that power factors enter into every organizational decision.
4. The amount of expertise—power available to each person—is determined by the importance and uniqueness of his specialty.
5. Charismatic power seems to be derived from an ability to vividly express the goals and aims that the followers desire, along with creating a feeling of confidence that they can achieve them.
6. A certain amount of power goes with every office, regardless of the qualities of the office holder.
7. The direction of communications, their frequency, and their content reveals a great deal about the power relationship within an organization. It is as simple as who talks and listens to whom about what.
8. People who decide what information to transmit and with what interpretation, have considerable power in an organization.
9. The assignment of functions within an organization has a significant effect upon the formulation of its power structure.
10. Within organizations one can generate a power base (cause others to be dependent upon him) by controlling access to information, persons and resources.
11. There is a direct relationship between the amount of time and effort a person is willing to put into an area and the power he can command.
12. Power is directly related to a person's geographical and organizational centrality.
13. Each suborganization has its internal power structure, which is headed by a leader who is supreme within the subsystem, but who is a non-leader when viewed from the perspective of the total system.
14. Every manager is allotted a certain measure of power when he is assigned to a position. Then, as he performs his function, the level of this power will vary upward and sometimes downward, depending upon how he uses his power and employs the power factors available to him.
15. The real measure of leadership is determined by the performance of the group that is being led.
16. The primary requirement for leadership is to know what is to be accomplished and to be able to communicate it effectively.
17. The leader can only continue to exercise the amount of power (influence) that he is allowed to by his subordinates—even though his position is reinforced by economic, legal and other sanctions.
18. There is a valid alternative to raw power.

Understanding an engineer's personality

Dr. T.F. Gautschi, P.E.

A few years ago when I was associated with the development of a new anti-submarine torpedo, eight key engineers responsible for development of various subsystems went out to witness the first live test run. Each was proud of his contribution; together we had an esprit de corps like that of a good football team. We didn't get the first run off until late in the day. The torpedo ran perfectly, but just as it was surfacing at the end of its run it hit a steel buoy and sank. Within one hour and without prompting from supervisors, each man had his subsystem out of the torpedo and had made arrangements to stay late to assess and repair the damage caused by water and impact.

These men showed one of the typical characteristics of the engineering personality: pride in his work. In a sense, an engineer lives to work, more than he works to live. Work is a vital part of his life, not just a way to pass time or earn money. He has strong achievement desires and tends to get emotionally involved in his creations.

But pride in his work is only one of many personality traits engineers share—there are many others. It's important for a manager to understand these traits, for they will determine how well he relates to his engineer associates. Let's take a closer look.

**ENGINEERS
WANT FREEDOM**

With rare exceptions, the engineer wants and needs considerable freedom, especially if he is near the research end of the engineering spectrum. He desires freedom from strict supervision, freedom to plan the details of his work, freedom from rules and regulations, freedom from interruptions, freedom to discuss his work with his colleagues and superiors, freedom to publish technical papers, and especially freedom to spend part of his time working on ideas that are completely his own and unrelated to his assigned work.

**ENGINEERS
ARE LOGICAL**

The engineer lives in a logical world. By training and inclination he is unwilling to accept forms, rules, techniques, or schedules unless he sees some logical reason for their existence. Because he does tend to look at things logically, he often overestimates the importance of reason and underestimates the importance of emotions in human situations. He expects that people will be as predictable as physical laws. For these reasons, an excellent engineer may be a poor administrator.

**THE ENGINEERING
PERSONALITY**

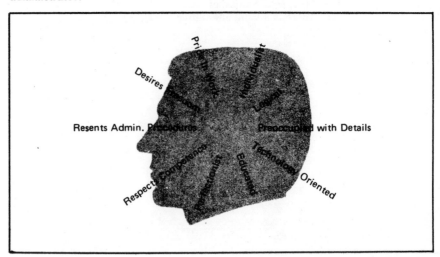

**ENGINEERS
ARE PERFECTIONISTS**

The engineer tends to be a perfectionist, paying a great deal of attention to detail and accuracy. This often expresses itself in critical, unappreciative attitudes toward other people, especially those who work for him. As a perfectionist, the engineer is not satisfied until his work achieves its maximum performance potential. He tends to make cannon balls as round and smooth as possible, not just round and smooth enough to do the job.

**ENGINEERS
ARE INTELLIGENT**

The engineer usually has one or more college degrees, and tends to be very intelligent. However, his education and intelligence are often very specialized—"a mile deep but only a yard wide". The typical manager is usually the reverse—he knows something about everything, but not much about any specific subject.

**ENGINEERS
ARE LONERS**

The typical engineer prefers to work by himself as much as is consistent with the program he is working on. He has his own personal curiosities, plans for work, and methods for carrying out his plans.

The engineer typically does not understand or care much about the problems that confront management. He expects prompt support services exactly as he specifies—and with no red tape. He especially resents pressure from the outside to hurry his results or change his approach for other than what he feels are logical reasons.

The engineer respects the person of proven competence, measured in terms of his current contributions rather than his degrees or honors.

Many engineers tend to be technology- rather than institution-oriented. As such, they look to success through their profession; their interest in the company is limited to its adequacy as a provider of facilities and opportunities for them to pursue their work. Some describe the technology-oriented person as a "cosmopolitan", and the institutionally-oriented person as a "local".

Although the above characteristics and attitudes involve a certain degree of oversimplification, we can certainly agree that they are at least tendencies, and must be taken into account by the engineering manager who wants to develop an efficient, dedicated engineering organization.

After typing this article, my wife says she understands me better.

Readers comment on my conclusions

I read with great interest your article [on the engineer's personality] in the Design Management Forum. I found it to be the most personally insulting item I have ever seen in print. Furthermore, you did a great disservice to your profession in writing it. The stereotype you describe may well suit yourself, or perhaps design engineers in general, (I say this not because I believe it, but because the article did appear in a design engineering magazine) but I hardly think it describes most successful engineers, or as you say, "the engineering personality".

● ● ●

If an engineer is a logical, reasoning person, why does he have so much trouble organizing his thoughts when it comes to writing memos and reports? Again, his logical and reasoning mind should make him not only capable but desirous of doing a good planning job. In my experience, engineers who are planners soon become managers and the other 90% flaunt the practice of planning as a troublesome exercise made necessary by management . . . . Just as "surveying" was once a required part of every engineer's training perhaps communication, human relations and management ought to be requirements for every engineer today.

● ● ●

Your article on an engineer's personality was well done. Now, please explain why a "manager" should have trouble with someone who is logical, educated and a perfectionist*, works well alone, and judges a man by his contributions and not his degrees.
*Who in hell would want to fly in an airplane designed by a non-perfectionist?

● ● ●

It is the top management, archaic in many cases, with their "yard deep and a mile wide" knowledge who should know the engineers' personalities and treat them accordingly in order to maintain the engineer's esprit de corps at peak levels at all times.

● ● ●

. . . if you would like to further explore the subject, you might also find that engineers are very conservative in both their political and moral standards . . . One can verify this by asking how they voted in any election involving two candidates with the same general attributes, but one more conservative than the other. Their standards of morality are pure 18th century . . . have you ever heard engineers discuss sex? Cars, housing, transistors, yes, but sex, never . . . Their incidence of divorce and extramarital affairs is very low.
Perhaps the explanation lies in the fact that engineers become involved in their work to the point of excluding the changing society and morality around them.

5

Dr. T.F. Gautschi, P.E.

Motivation in perspective

There are a number of tools that a manager can use to motivate people

The ability to motivate others towards the achievement of organizational goals is an important capability that every manager should have. In this context, motivation is defined as relating to all aspects of a person's behavior when a conscious attempt is made on the part of the manager to influence the direction and rate of such behavior. As managers, we motivate in accordance with our mental model of the motivational process.

MENTAL MODELS ARE IMPORTANT

We use mental models, whether we realize it or not, to deal with every situation that we face. These models enable us to cope by relating the various inputs that we receive, and then providing a framework for decision making when required. They cover all aspects of our lives. We use them to picture how the stock market works, how our business operates, and even for picturing how we appear and interact with others. Clearly, the quality of any decision is determined by the accuracy of our mental model relating the factors pertaining to that decision. In a sense it could be argued that the whole point of education is to help a person develop more realistic mental models—the same could be said for the utilization of such modern techniques as simulation and operations research.

HABITS HELP US COPE

Every manager, whether he realizes it or not, has a mental model regarding the subject of motivation. The purpose of this article is to help develop more realistic mental models pertaining to this important subject.

There are two basic categories of motivational approaches: external to (outside) the employee, and internal to (inside) the employee.

External

HABIT—The desired response is insisted upon, and rewarded, each time the stimulus is presented. Habit helps us to cope with our complex life without having to think about every little detail of everything we do. So if a manager can change a person's habit pattern it will result in a change in that person's behavior. Examples:

- Drill and the manual of arms in the military. Here the soldier is programmed to the point where the appropriate response is automatic without thinking.
- The workers on a production line can be so programmed that they can perform a fairly complex operation while thinking about something else entirely.
- An experienced driver will push in the clutch and move the gear lever to the appropriate position with little or no thought.
- Experienced tennis players do not need to think through each element of a particular stroke—they just think about where they should hit the ball.

**GROUPS FORM
HABIT PATTERNS**

Any time a group begins to work together for the first time, they will quickly establish work, behavior and interaction habit patterns that may continue for the life of the group. For instance, have you ever noticed that nearly everyone takes the same seat at a conference or seminar, even when there are no assigned seats—and even when the affair lasts over several days? In such situations, I have even had someone ask me to move because I was in his seat!

Be especially aware of this when setting up a new organization, or moving or changing an existing organization. New habits will be established, so particular attention should be paid to the desired behavior, interaction and work patterns.

To affect behavior, the performance target should be made clear, immediate feedback should be provided, and behavior in the desired direction rewarded.

A number of years ago when I was an undergraduate I was assigned a new roommate who was senior to me. He was an astronomy major, so he often came in late at night. He was deaf, and the first evening he came in he made a lot of noise and woke me up. (I learned later that he did this with all of his previous roommates every night for three years!) So I got up and turned on every light in the room, and started studying. After a few minutes he got up and turned the overhead light off. When he was comfortably settled in bed, I turned the overhead light on again. We went through this cycle several times. He never woke me again by being noisy! The goal was no noise. The feedback was immediate, and the reward was not shining light in his eyes.

External

**SUBTLE
MANIPULATION**

HUMAN ENGINEERING—Here the manager manipulates the environment so that it stimulates the appropriate behavior. Sometimes the new behavior also becomes a habit.

- A short meeting can almost be assured if it is called 20 minutes before lunch or 20 minutes before quitting time.
- Bright and vivid wall coloring or music will generally encourage activity; subdued and quiet colors or music are better related to contemplation.
- The location and layout of office areas often determine interaction and work patterns.
- A central cafeteria will encourage informal meetings—especially when the employees are located in a number of different buildings—and will discourage going out to lunch.
- When the research activity is located near the production activity more interaction takes place than when it is not.
- Employees tend to take better care of a facility when it is kept clean and uncluttered.
- Instead of preaching participative management, a more effective strategy might be to set up a structure that encourages the employees to work together—for example through the use of a matrix type organization and appropriate office layouts.

External

**FINANCIAL REWARDS
ARE IMPORTANT
MOTIVATORS**

ECONOMIC MAN—This has been, and continues to be, the major approach to motivation. The process is easily understood—reward behavior in the desired direction with financial factors (in-grade pay increases, promotion, and bonuses.)

Our recent Management Forum survey on Employee Loyalty certainly supports the assumption that most people will respond to financial incentives. There is no question that it works, at least for a time. However, if you were to get a 10% increase in pay would you work 10% harder? How about a 25% increase?

Some claim that "Most workers do not come to work for fulfillment from the work itself. They come to work to eat, to exchange their time, effort and skills for what they can buy outside of the workplace. They want more of the good things in life that they see paraded in front of them 'in living color on TV'. They want to satisfy their material aspirations." (Mitchell Flin, "Job Enrichment Does Not Work", *Atlanta Economic Review*, Nov.-Dec. 1975)

Internal

**ACHIEVEMENT NEEDS
MAY BE HIGH**

ACHIEVEMENT MOTIVATION—is based upon the concept that for some, job motivation is dependent upon the amount of satisfaction that is anticipated from achievement, the difficulty of the task, and the probability as to what level of achievement may be attained. Persons who have a high need to achieve require only to know the goals and to receive feedback on how they are doing. Most managers and professionals have a fairly high need to achieve. This is the primary basis for the Management by Objectives program concept. There is also the possibility that the "need to achieve level" can be increased through appropriate training.

CONCLUSION

Internal

JOB ENRICHMENT AND SELF-MOTIVATION—This approach is based upon the Maslow/Herzberg concepts, which postulate that the key to motivation is to make task performance a path to need satisfaction. This tool is discussed in several recent Management Forum articles: 1-6-75, 7-21-75, and 8-8-75.

Because people are different there is no one best approach to motivation, and everyone "motivates" in accordance with his own mental model, whether he realizes it or not. However, there are a few useful guidelines to motivation:

- Be flexible—don't rely on one approach alone.
- Motivation is highly individualistic—what turns one person on may turn another person off.
- Be alert—motivational opportunities and needs change with time and circumstances.
- Some, but not all employees have a high achievement motivation.
- All employees will *not* respond to the higher levels needs. Some like repetitive work and do not want responsibility. Some like the idea of more or less turning their brain off at the door. Others can be strongly motivated by work tasks that provide them the opportunity of fulfilling their higher level perceived needs (most engineering professionals fall into this category).

Human needs and motivation

*The ability to motivate is
an important management tool*

Dr. T. F. Gautschi, P.E.

The ability to motivate others towards the achievement of organizational goals is an important capability that every manager should have. Fortunately we don't have to rely upon intuition in this area, because there is a proven set of concepts that we can use to guide us.

The concepts are based upon the work of two men—**Abraham Maslow** and **Frederick Herzberg**.

Maslow demonstrated that much of our behavior is explained by the needs that we perceive. When we experience a particular need it acts as a goad to action, and as a director of our activities; it determines what is important to us and shapes our behavior. Our perceived need creates a tension within us that persists until it is satisfied. Once satisfaction is experienced, the tension subsides and the need that caused it ceases to be an influence on our behavior.

Maslow categorized our needs into a five-level hierarchy that we ascend as each successive need level is satisfied. That is, we are initially concerned with our **Basic** (physiological) needs, but once they are reasonably well satisfied (and this degree of satisfaction is culturally defined) our **Safety** needs become our consuming interest, and so on up the hierarchy through **Belongingness**, **Ego-Status** and **Self-Actualization**.

These five fundamental need levels account for most of our behavior. Progression through this hierarchy can be likened to climbing a range of mountains, where we do not become aware of the next peak until we have successfully negotiated the previous peak. Thus, if for some reason our satisfaction of a particular need is blocked, we may not ever develop an awareness of any higher need.

MASLOW'S HIERARCHY OF NEEDS

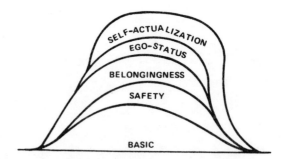

MOTIVATORS

For example, if a person goes without food long enough he becomes a sort of human Piranha—thinking, dreaming, and seeking food without any other concern. He doesn't think about building monuments, status symbols, power or even the opposite sex! His only concern is food, food, food.

This was tragically demonstrated by the Donner party in the early 1880's when they became marooned in the mountains by enormous snow drifts and freezing cold. As they exhausted their food supply, the party gradually deteriorated and eventually they turned to eating each other.

Our needs have certain general characteristics, which, in turn, are translated into job-related factors. These relationships are shown in the attached table.

WORK SITUATION

Herzberg improved the application of the Maslow concept to the work situation by establishing that some of our needs are motivators while others are potential dissatisfiers. These are shown in the table as "motivational factors" and "maintenance of hygiene factors", respectively. The lower-level needs that relate to **Basics**, **Safety** and **Belongingness** are the potential dissatisfiers. That is, improving or increasing them cannot be used to motivate behavior, but their absence can become a source of dissatisfaction.

A firm cannot motivate a person toward more effective achievement of organizational goals by increasing his fringe benefits or improving his retirement and pension plan; but if these factors are inferior to those provided by other companies in the local area or in the same industry, they will be a source of dissatisfaction; and when the disparity is serious enough, they will divert attention from any higher-level needs.

Unfortunately, the job-related maintenance or hygiene factors have been traditionally perceived by management as being the only important motivators, and great amounts of time and resources have been expended in them without proportional improvements in the attainment of organizational goals.

FULFILLING NEEDS

Effective job performance really depends upon the fulfillment of both maintenance and motivational needs. An employee cannot be motivated by **Ego-Status** needs if he is preoccupied with his **Basic** or **Safety** needs. This was amply demonstrated in recent years when highly qualified aerospace engineers accepted almost any kind of work as long as it would enable them to feed and house their families.

Maintenance needs are ususally satisfied on a group basis, and although their fulfillment has little motivational value in terms of achieving organizational goals, their fulfillment is essential to the avoidance of dissatisfaction and to the maintenance of a work force that is prepared to respond to the higher level motivational factors.

In turn, the motivational factors, as shown in the table, focus on the individual and his achievement of company and personal goals. They are task-centered, and are most effective in an organizational environment that stresses:

- The encouragement of individual goal-setting
- The maintenance of high performance expectations
- The exercise of independent judgment
- The recognition and provision of rewards commensurate with achievement
- The maintenance of an atmosphere in which conflict and failure are a basis for growth and not for criticism or punishment

The key to motivation is to make task performance a path to need satisfaction. As managers we can raise the probability that each of our subordinate's efforts will be committed to organizational goals if he believes that his needs will be met by so doing. So it is important that we become sensitive to the particular pattern of needs possessed by each of our subordinates and then provide paths to their satisfaction through goal-oriented task performance.

NEEDS CHANGE

In carrying out this activity we must remember that a person's needs change with time and circumstances.

The young person just out of college may be most concerned with ego-status and self-actualization needs. Then one day he gets married, has a child, and acquires a house with a mortgage. And all of a sudden his perspective changes. He becomes so preoccupied with his **Basic** and **Safety** needs that he almost completely forgets about those higher-level needs that seemed so important before.

Later, after he somehow adjusts his standard of living expectations to his realistic income possibilities, and he gets used to living with family responsibility and mortgages, his higher level needs will again become important to him. As he approaches middle age, this becomes increasingly important for him and his wife, especially when they are no longer preoccupied with the **Basic** and **Safety** needs, and they start asking questions like, "What have I accomplished with my life so far, and what am I likely to accomplish in the future?" There are many variations on this theme, and my only purpose here is to remind us that everyone has a different need pattern and that this can change.

Summary:

- Managers should be sensitive to the particular pattern of needs perceived by each subordinate, because perceived needs act as goads and directors of a person's activities.
- Managers should make a conscious effort to create an environment that will enable their subordinates to fulfill both their maintenance and their motivational needs.
- Reasonable satisfaction of the lower-level (maintenance) needs is required to provide a foundation for the application of higher-level (motivational) needs.
- The way to motivation is to make job-related task performance a path to the satisfaction of the higher-level needs of **Ego-Status** and **Self-Actualization**.

* GENERAL CHARACTERISTICS
● JOB RELATED FACTORS

Basic Need

* Food
* Shelter
* Clothing
* Creature comforts
● Concern for pleasant working conditions
● More leisure time
● More luxurious personal property
● Increased salary
● Reduced strain and discomfort

Safety Need

* Security
* Orderliness
* Harm avoidance
* Predictability
* Protection
* Avoiding risk
● Fringe Benefits
● Retirement and pension plan
● Seniority protection
● Behavior of supervision
● Clear and consistent performance standards
● Company policy and administration
● Established career paths

Belongingness Need

* Group membership
* Affiliation
* Acceptance
● Friendly collegues
● Opportunities for interaction with others
● Harmonious interpersonal relations
● Team membership

Ego-Status Need

* Displaying competance
* Desire to excell, to stand out,
    to be recognized
* Prestige
● Opportunities for advancement & growth
● Recognition on the basis of merit
● Job assignment allowing display of skills
● Status symbols
● Inclusion in planning activities
● Responsibility

Self-Actualization Need

* Considerations of one's potential
* Autonomy
* Creativity
* Proving oneself to oneself
● Involvement in creative activity
● Greater ego involvement
● Increased investment of oneself in work
● Freedom to make own decisions

Dr. T.F. Gautschi, P.E.

Turning workers on:
the strategy of job enrichment

This powerful management tool
increases a worker's motivation and satisfaction
which, in turn, increases productivity

Prior to the Industrial Reveolution a strategy such as job enrichment would have been meaningless, because the individual worker—such as the blacksmith, cobbler or farmer—was responsible for the entire job. But as the economy became more industrialized, individual tasks were made more specialized in order to fit them into the production line methods of manufacture. In fact, the major thrust of the early scientific management movement, which was fathered by Frederick Taylor, was to consider man as a human machine to be employed in an optimal fashion whenever it was not economically feasible to use a mechanical or electrical machine. Carried to the extreme, this strategy reduces man to no more than a programmable robot.

NEEDS, EMOTIONS ARE IMPORTANT

The Hawthorne experiments that were conducted fifty years ago were originally intended to provide data on how the human being reacts to various physical environmental conditions (such as lighting intensity) so that the conditions could be adjusted in order that he would work at his optimum level. The outstanding feature of this experiment was the discovery that a person could not be programmed like a machine without regard to his needs, feelings, emotions and perceptions of what was going on because these human factors do have a significant effect upon a person's job performance (see DN 1-6-75).

THE HUMAN DIMENSION

Strategies such as job enrichment, participative management, collaborative management, job enlargement and most of the human relations movement are all intended to restore the human dimension that is lost when a person's tasks are designed without regard to his/her human personality. This restoration is especially important for today's workforce, which expects more than just financial reward for leasing their bodies out for a period of time.

I believe that the results of our recent Employee Loyalty Survey (see DN 4-7-75) indicate that if professional people received more from their jobs they would be more highly motivated to do their jobs better and as a result receive more satisfaction and be more productive.

WHAT TURNS WORKERS ON?

In a word, job enrichment is based upon the assumption that people can be personally "turned on" to their work. The question then is, "what turns them on?" Three key job characteristics have been identified that will turn the individual worker on to the degree that they exist in the work situation (see figure).

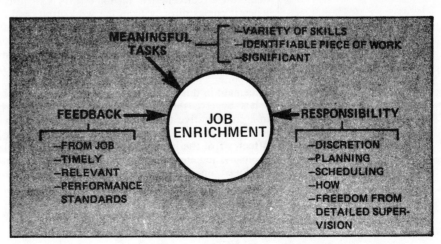

KEYS

1. *Meaningfulness.* The individual must perceive his work as worthwhile or important by some system of values that he accepts—it must be meaningful to him. He must be able to explain to himself, and to others, what is important about what he is doing.

To be meaningful the task should involve:

(a) A variety of skills that challenge his abilities.

(b) An identifiable piece of work; ideally, a whole job from beginning to end with a measurable outcome. For example, the engineer who gets the opportunity to test the product that he has developed under actual operating conditions, and perhaps interface with the customer regarding the results, is much more likely to be turned on than the engineer who designs a subsystem and passes it on to someone else who then puts the total system together without his involvement. Sometimes it might be advisable to combine several smaller subtasks into one large meaningful task and assign the total task to a team of workers.

> *A few years ago when I was the member of a Navy Laboratory, we had the challenge of developing a new gas-powered engine for propelling an anti-submarine torpedo. Due to a peculiar set of circumstances we had only three months to design, fabricate, document and test the first prototype model. Normally, this task would have taken 12 to 18 months! It was successfully accomplished by assigning the entire program to a small team and executing it on a parallel task basis. That is, a team, which was made up of specialists in thermodynamics, stress, mechanical engineering, material procurement, as well as the lead machinist and draftsman, was assembled. The problem was discussed in detail and the team developed a plan of action whereby as much as possible would proceed in parallel, i.e. the procurement of the long lead materials was initiated before the design was completed. Then each morning the team met to discuss progress and make changes as necessary. The task ended with the team testing the final prototype engine in a test cell. As you might expect, motivation and committment to the total task was high.*

(c) *Significance.* The impact that the job is perceived to have on the lives of others is important. For example, if I felt that "Management Forum" was only an intellectual exercise and had no positive impact on some of you readers, it wouldn't be nearly as important to me.

2. *Responsibility.* The amount of responsibility that the job environment provides has a significant influence on how strongly the worker is turned on. This responsibility involves discretion in planning and scheduling work, and how it should be accomplished, and a certain amount of freedom and independence from close review and detailed direction. Management by Objectives (see DN Jan 12 & 26, Feb 9 & 23), when properly administered, meets these criteria. Under the MBO strategy the worker is endeavoring to achieve jointly specified results, and is not trying to accomplish something which he has not planned and in accordance with a set of detailed directions that he had no part in developing.

3. *Feedback.* The degree, and manner, in which the worker gets information about the effectiveness of his job efforts is significant. Feedback is most powerful when it comes directly from the work itself, and not through some management hierarchy. Careful design of the computer-driven management information system can often provide timely and meaningful feedback to the individual worker or team—perhaps through a CRT or some sort of printout.

Along with information feedback the worker needs standards or criteria to determine what successful performance is. Too often there is no common agreement in this area.

TOUCH ALL BASES

It is suggested that job enrichment is most likely to be successful when approached in a collaborative manner by management along with the employees whose jobs will be affected. It must also be remembered that job enrichment activities must affect all of the interfacing activities in the organization to be most effective.

Finally, job enrichment can be a very powerful management tool for turning the employee on—especially in the professional environment. The assurance of meaningful, responsible jobs along with the necessary feedback can result in higher productivity as well as meeting the needs of the comtemporary professional employee for a more significant work experience.

Flexible working hours:
a form of job enrichment

Dr. T.F. Gautschi, P.E.

Over the past 10 to 15 years, flexible working hour (FWH) schemes have become a way of life for many U.S. and European companies. On the surface, the concept seems too simple to have created such a stir, or to provide the advantages that its advocates claim for it. Nevertheless, it does provide positive benefits for many, and therefore is worth some discussion.

Briefly, FWH is an arrangement that gives the employee (or a small work group) some freedom or discretion in choosing the hours he will work each day. Generally, for a one-shift operation two core periods are specified—one before noon and one after noon. For example, the forenoon core could be specified as being from 9 to 12 noon and the afternoon core as 2 to 4 p.m. The possible work period is shown to be 7 a.m. to 6 p.m. Everyone would be required to be present during the two core periods, but each employee (or group) would be free to choose how they would work the other required time during the week, or specified pay period. For a five-day week (in the above example) there are 25 core hours per week, the time periods for working the remaining 15 hours (assuming a 40-hour week) would be up to the employee's discretion.

Thus, each employee gains a certain measure of control over his working time. He is allowed to use his judgment regarding arrival time, lunch period and departure time. Although this doesn't sound like a lot, it is a big step for many firms to take, and it can provide significant benefits to the employee and to the firm when it is properly implemented. It is a form of job enrichment because it does give the employee some discretion regarding his job. It is a step towards participative management.

The FWH concept does *not* require supervision to be present during the total possible working period. This, in turn, encourages supervisors to delegate more and to spend more time on its basic management tasks of planning, organizing, staffing, etc. This aspect also has a job enrichment dimension, and could prove to be one of the major contributions of FWH.

Often those firms utilizing FWH enjoy an increase in productivity through a reduction in sick time, absenteeism, turnover and overtime. In addition, organizational morale and employee attitudes towards management and the firm and coordination activities usually experience a marked increase.

FWH permits employees to better balance the demands of their personal lives with the demands of the organization e.g., an employee may want to adjust his working hours so that he can take his children to school before coming to work. FWH also makes it easier to accommodate outside sports or other activities.

People seem to have different personal rhythms. That is, we tend to have different energy levels at different times. Some people seem to be most alert and active early in the day; others may be very sluggish in the morning and do much better as the day progresses. FWH allows the employee to tailor his working hours to better fit his natural rhythm. This should increase productivity and morale. Also, some employees need more rest periods to reduce fatigue. FWH again enables a person to better fit his rest needs with the work requirements.

Work loads tend to vary over a period of time—as determined by schedule requirements, interface activities, equipment breakdowns, etc. Again, FWH can help the employee better match his working hours with the job demands. FWH can also make it easier for employees to avoid peak demand times for transportation, power and recreation. This can also result in a positive impact upon the employee's family and community.

Unlike most participative (or job enrichment) systems, which tend to be effective only in the longer run, FWH produces immediate short-term benefits as well as longer run benefits. An interesting feature of FWH is that it is not thrust upon the employee. It is simply available, and the employee can use it as he sees fit. He can test it on a trial basis with little personal risk. It doesn't involve any sort of commitment on the part of the employee.

Many organizations—especially marketing and engineering—follow an informal version of FWH. That is, the employees adjust their working hours to some extent to meet their personal and job needs. But since it is informal, not everyone understands what is going on, and abuses by or to the employees often occur. For example, I can remember more than one instance of working late to get something out, and then when I arrived a little late the next morning hearing someone say, "Boy, I wish I had banker's hours." Most organizations have a few people who arrive on time, leave on time, but take extra-long lunch hours. And there are always one or two who arrive late and leave early to "make up" for it! With a formal FWH everyone understands the rules and there is probably better compliance.

If your organization is not now using some form of FWH, I would like to suggest that it be given consideration. It certainly is *not* a system that will overcome an existing bad environment, but it has the potential of helping a good environment become even better.

Delegation—entrusting work to others

Dr. T. F. Gautschi, P. E.

And it shall be that every great matter they shall bring unto thee, but every small matter they shall judge themselves. So shall it be easier for thyself, and they shall bear the burden with thee.

Exodus 18:13-22, The Bible

Just as Moses could not solve all problems all the time, today what we as managers can accomplish is limited by the amount that we are willing and able to delegate. *There just isn't enough time for us to do everything ourselves.* The problem is that at times some of us feel that we are indispensable to the organization—that no one else can really do a good enough job.

One of my friends felt that way. He managed a very large organization. In order to keep up with all of the details and make all of the decisions that he felt that he had to make, he worked long hours at the plant 6 or 7 days a week and he always carried a couple of briefcases of material home to read in his "spare" time. Within a month of the time that he died at the age of 49, the organization had completely assimilated his loss, and I don't think that it faltered very much during the interim period either. *No person is indispensable.*

Delegation is simply entrusting part of the work or its management to others. Successful delegation has three requirements:

- You must identify and assign the duties or objectives to be accomplished
- You must assign authority to carry out the assigned duties
- The subordinate must accept the obligation or commitment to accomplish the assigned duties. Delegation is like a three-legged stool—it must have three legs to be stable.

Most of us fail to delegate for one or more of the following reasons:

ANXIETY:
We are so anxious to prove ourselves to others that we are unable to delegate parts of our job.

INSECURITY:
After a promotion we may not feel comfortable in our new job, so we give in to that irresistable urge to continue to tell our replacement how to do it.

INADEQUACY:
Sometimes we are simply afraid of being shown up by our subordinates.

IMPATIENCE:
Often, we use the excuse that it would take longer to explain than to do it ourselves.

HABIT:
Our failure to delegate can be an unthinking habit.

CONFIDENCE:
We may lack confidence in our subordinates. We just may not feel that they can do the job as well as we can.

AMBIGUITY:
Some of us have a low tolerance for ambiguity—we must know what is going on all of the time.

NOT WELL ORGANIZED:
Our planning may be such that we haven't identified tasks or the priorities for delegation.

Depending upon the circumstances, delegation can mean different things to different people. It is convenient to visualize the delegation concept as a continuum with "the subordinate takes action and no further contact with his manager is required" at one end and "the subordinate looks into the problem and gives the manager all of the facts and the manager will decide the course of action" at the other end. Let's call the former type 1, and the latter type 5.

We could have three other forms of delegation between the two extremes like: (2) Subordinate takes action, but tells the manager what he did. (3) Subordinate looks into the problem, tells the manager what he intends to do, then does it unless he says no and (4) Subordinate gets manager's approval before he takes action.

Recently I asked a group of 25 managers to identify criteria for determining what form of delegation along this continuum should be employed: Some suggestions appear in the chart.

Other factors that should be taken into account are: the competence of the manager, the workload of the manager and of his subordinates, the subordinate's vs. the manager's interest in the task, the effect on the morale, initiative and commitment of the subordinate, aspirations and personal goals of the manager and of the subordinate, the subordinate's need for independence (or his need for direction), the subordinate's readiness to assume responsibility, the size of the organization and the geographical dispersion of the subordinates.

Our recent article titled, "The Contingency Theory of Management" (*Design News* 9-19-77) states that, "The contingency philosophy is *not* unique to any one area of management theory. It is a basic process which should be applied to all areas." Clearly, the above discussion demonstrates that we should use a contingency perspective if we want to improve our practice of delegation. In a word, the proper delegation pattern *depends* upon many factors and there are no simple prescriptions.

Type 1 Extensive Delegation	*Type 5 Limited Delegation*
routine task	non-routine task
short-term task	long-term task
low-cost task	high-cost task
low-risk task	high-risk task
clear policy guidelines	no policy guidelines
experienced subordinate	inexperienced subordinate
easy task	difficult task
low coordination requirements	high coordination requirements
low personal risk	high personal risk
low task complexity	high task complexity
well-defined task	poorly defined task
Theory Y organizational climate	Theory X organizational climate

The Hawthorne Experiment: Man is more than a programmable robot

Dr. T. F. Gautschi, P.E.

Undoubtedly, many of you have heard of the Hawthorne Experiment and its influence on management theory, but probably few of you know much about the details. So to give you a better appreciation for this important event, we will devote this article to its description.

It all began during the spring of 1927 at the Hawthorne (Chicago) works of the Western Electric Co. The purpose of the experiment was to answer the folowing type of questions:

1. Do employees actually get tired out?
2. Are rest pauses desirable?
3. Is a shorter working day desirable?
4. Why does production fall off in the afternoon?

The basic thrust was to determine how production output could be changed as a function of such external factors as length of time at work and the number of rest periods.

Six women were selected. They were average workers. Their job was assembling telephone relays. A coil, armature, contact springs and insulators were assembled and secured together by four machine screws and the unit was then dropped into a chute. The test room was separated from the main department by an 8-ft partition. The women sat in a row on a long workbench which was identical to those in the main department.

The women did not have a supervisor in the usual sense. Instead, they had a test room observer whose duty it was

to maintain records, arrange the work and secure a cooperative spirit on the part of the women. Whenever any experimental change was made it was discussed with the operators, whose comments were requested, to make sure that they understood and could comply with the new plan. The women were frequently reminded not to strain but to work at a comfortable pace, that this was not intended to be a race or contest of any sort.

There were 13 test periods in all. Period I was an initial compilation of the operator's records (without their knowledge) over a two-week period in the main department. Then the experiment proper started with Period II, as depicted in the chart.

Period II conditions were the same

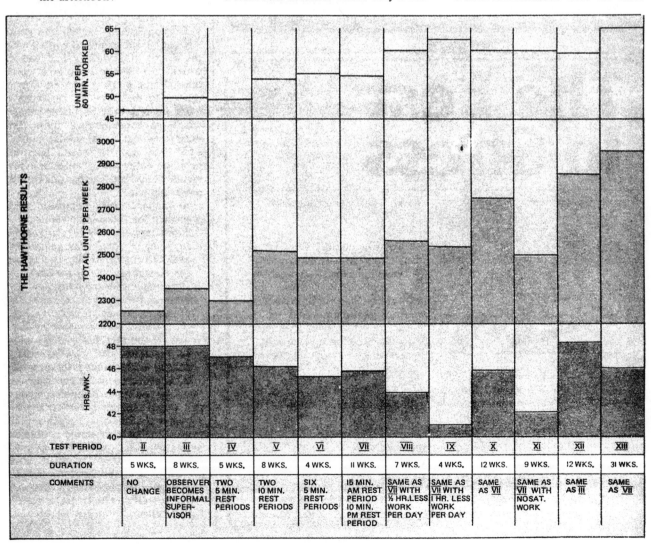

TEST PERIOD	II	III	IV	V	VI	VII	VIII	IX	X	XI	XII	XIII
DURATION	5 WKS.	8 WKS.	5 WKS.	8 WKS.	4 WKS.	11 WKS.	7 WKS.	4 WKS.	12 WKS.	9 WKS.	12 WKS.	31 WKS.
COMMENTS	NO CHANGE	OBSERVER BECOMES INFORMAL SUPERVISOR	TWO 5 MIN. REST PERIODS	TWO 10 MIN. REST PERIODS	SIX 5 MIN. REST PERIODS	15 MIN. AM REST PERIOD 10 MIN. PM REST PERIOD	SAME AS VII WITH ½ HR. LESS WORK PER DAY	SAME AS VII WITH 1 HR. LESS WORK PER DAY	SAME AS VII	SAME AS VII WITH NO SAT. WORK	SAME AS III	SAME AS VII

as in the main department. Everyone worked a 48-hour, 5-1/2-day week. The changes for the other periods are shown on the chart. Note that Period VII became a reference period for all subsequent periods except for Period XII.

Now let's look at the results for the experiment through Period IX. The total number of units produced per week showed a general upward trend and the production rate per 60 minutes worked showed a steady increase as rest periods were instituted and the work day was shortened. These results led the experimenters to believe that rest periods and reduced working time would result in higher production rates. Periods X and XI were variations on this theme and the production rate remained essentially constant.

Then, in accordance with sound experimental procedure, it was agreed, with the consent of the operators, that for Period XII a return would be made to the original conditions of work, with no rest pauses, and a full-length work week. *Here is where the surprise occurred*—both the number of units per 60 minutes worked and the total output rose to new highs! They were far above the results obtained during Period III where similar conditions were in effect.

The conclusions reached after Period XII can be substantiated by looking at the results of Periods VII, X and XII which had identical working conditions. If the output rate were directly related to the physical conditions of work (as originally postulated) then it would be expected that these three periods would have similar outputs. This was *not* the case. The only common pattern was that each experimental period had a higher rate than the preceding one.

A January, 1931 company report presented the following statement:

Upon analysis, only one thing seemed to show a continuous relationship with this improved output. This was the mental attitude of the operators. From their conversations with each other and their comments to the test observers, it was not only clear that their attitudes were improving but it was evident that this area of employee reactions and feelings was a fruitful field for industrial research.

It became clear to the experimenters that they had stumbled upon something that would encourage workers to make a greater contribution to organizational goals than that which could be obtained by simply manipulating their physical environment in accordance with rational scientific management principles. This concept has been characterized by the term INDUSTRIAL HUMAN RELATIONS.

6

Survey on employee loyalty

*Here's your chance to find out
why your associates change jobs*

Dr. T. F. Gautschi, P.E.

It's sad but true: employers often lose the employees they value the most—those highly skilled men and women who possess good potential for advancing into key positions of great responsibility. Why do they terminate? Why do other employees remain loyal to their employer for long periods? To what extent can management foster employee loyalty? This survey attempts to find the answers to these questions. As we have done with our previous surveys, we will tabulate and analyze your responses and report on the results as soon as we can.

Instructions.

Please be assured that all questionnaires will remain *strictly* confidential. Check or fill out the answers to the questions and mail the completed survey to me, **Dr. T. F. Gautschi, Design News, 221 Columbus Ave., Boston, MA 02116.**

Editor's note: Dr. Gautschi says he has tried out this survey on students in his management classes and the fill-out time averages only 12 minutes.

---

1. What is the total number of years you have been working full time? (exclude military service)
   _____ 0–5 years
   _____ 6–10 years
   _____ 11–15 years
   _____ 16–20 years
   _____ 21 or more years

2. During that time, for how many companies have you worked including your present job?
   _____ 1 company
   _____ 2–3 companies
   _____ 4–5 companies
   _____ 6–7 companies
   _____ 8 or more companies

3. In what type of industry are you currently working?
   _____ Public sector (e.g., utilities, non-profit organizations, etc.)
   _____ City, state or federal gov't
   _____ Private sector
   ☐ Check here if self-employed

4. How many years have you worked for your present employer?
   _____ Less than 1 year
   _____ 1–2 years
   _____ 3–4 years
   _____ 5–9 years
   _____ 10 or more years

5. What is the size of the company you work for?
   _____ Less than 100 employees
   _____ 100–499 employees
   _____ 500–999 employees
   _____ 1000–4999 employees
   _____ 5000 or more employees

6. What is your annual salary from your company?
   _____ $10,000–15,000
   _____ $15,001–20,000
   _____ $20,001–24,000
   _____ $24,001–28,000
   _____ $28,001 or more
   ☐ Check here if you have substantial other income (other than from spouse)

7. How many people do you supervise?

_____ 0 people
_____ 1-3 people
_____ 4-10 people
_____ 11-20 people
_____ 21 or more people

8. Are you satisfied with your present job?

_____ Definitely satisfied
_____ Somewhat satisfied
_____ Somewhat dissatisfied
_____ Definitely dissatisfied

9. What is the probability that you will voluntarily change employers in the next 2 years?

_____ 0%
_____ 1-49%
_____ About 50%
_____ 51-99%
_____ 100%

10. What is your job title? _____

11. Have you received a promotion(s) while working for your present employer? _____ no _____ yes. If yes, how many? _____ . Give dates of your last two promotions. _____

12. Almost everybody considers leaving their present employer from time to time. Suppose you were offered employment in another company. Considering each of the following factors independently, how important would each factor be to your decision whether or not to *accept* the offer?

	Definitely important	Somewhat important	Somewhat unimportant	Definitely unimportant
A. More recognition for doing a good job				
B. More socially relevant job				
C. More challenging work				
D. More highly regarded organization				
E. Opportunity for early retirement				
F. Greater job security				
G. Higher earnings				
H. Better fringe benefits				
I. Better physical working conditions				
J. Greater opportunity for advancement				
K. More time for personal and family life				
L. More opportunity to exercise leadership				
M. More opportunity to work with people rather than with things				
N. Other (Specify)				

13. Aside from the appeal of a new job offer, factors can exist or can arise in a person's present job that could lead him or her to seek a new job. Considering each of the following factors independently, how important would each factor be to your decision to actively *seek* a job elsewhere?

	Definitely important	Somewhat important	Somewhat unimportant	Definitely unimportant
A. If I were working for someone who is a poor manager				
B. If I were in an inefficiently run organization or department				
C. If I had no opportunity for creativity and originality				
D. If I were required to move to a new city				
E. If coworkers were not friendly and congenial				
F. If I did not have enough to do				
G. If the job required excessive travel				
H. If the job put me under too much strain				
I. If I did not receive a promotion				
J. Other (Specify)				

14. To what extent would the following considerations tend to *hold* you in your present company?

	Definitely important	Somewhat important	Somewhat unimportant	Definitely unimportant
A. Your investment in the company's pension and/or retirement plan				
B. The location of your company				
C. Your sense of the future of the economy				
D. Your age				
E. Your spouse's unwillingness to move				
F. You recently changed jobs and are reluctant to make another change at this time				
G. Your current salary				
H. You have an approaching promotion opportunity				
I. Opportunity for you to retire early				
J. Other: (specify)				

15. How satisfied are you with each of the following factors in your present job?

	Definitely Dissatisfied	Somewhat Dissatisfied	Somewhat Satisfied	Definitely Satisfied
A. Your knowledge of your career paths and promotional opportunities				
B. Recognition you have received for work you have accomplished				
C. Your knowledge of what is expected of you				
D. The sense of accomplishment that you get from your job				
E. Your opportunities to influence decisions made at higher levels				
F. Challenges you receive in your position				
G. The enjoyment you receive from your work				
H. The amount of information you receive about what is going on in your company				
I. The amount of time you have for personal and family life				

16. Age _____   Sex _____

17. Highest academic achievement: _____ high school degree   _____ 1-3 years college
                                                    _____ bachelor's degree   _____ master's degree
                                                    _____ professional engineer   _____ doctorate's degree

18. Marital status: single _____ married _____ divorced _____ widowed _____

19. Number of children _____ Ages _____

20. Spouse working with financial renumeration: full time _____ part time _____ not at all _____

21. _____ Check here if spouse earns a substantial contribution to family income.

Survey report on employee loyalty

Over 2500 of your associates let us have it right between the eyes—telling us of considerable dissatisfaction with their jobs, but also pointing the way to a more motivated and contented workforce.

Dr. T.F. Gautschi, P.E.

When our survey on employee loyalty appeared in the January 20 issue, the response from you, the reader, was immediate. Within a week we had received more than 1000 surveys, a deluge of mail so heavy on some days that our mailroom supervisor said "this guy Gautschi must be giving away free money."

We certainly weren't giving away free money, but we were giving readers a chance to communicate about something that is important to them—their relationship with employers. We struck a responsive note, but one that reverberates with some discord: according to our results, *nearly 35% of the respondents are dissatisfied with their present jobs.* Our respondents expressed dissatisfaction about a whole spectrum of employer-employee issues—the amount of information they receive about what is going on in their companies, their knowledge of career paths and

promotional opportunities, challenges they receive, opportunities to influence decisions, recognition for work accomplished, knowledge of what is expected, sense of accomplishment and the enjoyment received from work.

But amongst all these sour notes we can identify specific, concrete ways for employers to maintain the loyalty of their most valuable resource and enhance the effectiveness of their organization. Indeed, the response to this survey contains enough data for a book, and the summary that follows can only begin to scratch the surface. But it's a start.

Zeroing in on employee dissatisfaction.

If employee discontent is higher than employers might wish, is there any group that seems generally satisfied? Here the survey provides some interesting results. It shows that those in higher salary ranges tend

RESPONSE TO SURVEY ON EMPLOYEE LOYALTY*

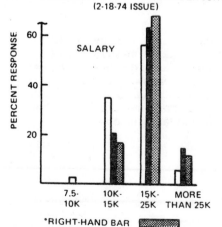

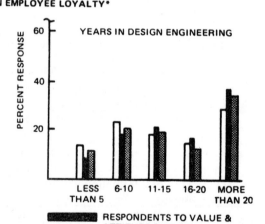

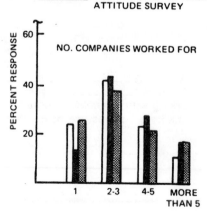

to be more satisfied with their jobs. Their probability of changing jobs is significantly less, but the degree of satisfaction and the probability of changing jobs did not correlate with the number of years worked.

To explain further, among the entire sample of respondents the percentage in each category of job satisfaction (definitely satisfied, somewhat satisfied, somewhat dissatisfied, definitely dissatisfied) was constant except for those with the highest salaries. Only 10% of the respondents making between $10 to 15 thousand were definitely satisfied with their jobs, but 33% of the respondents making more than $24

thousand indicated they were definitely satisfied.

On the other hand, total number of years worked didn't affect the level of satisfaction. Just as many "old-timers" were unhappy with their jobs as were the "young turks". So it's the money-makers, young or old, who seem most satisfied.

We see a similar trend in the probability of changing jobs within two years. I find it a bit discouraging to see that 72% of the respondents indicated that they might voluntarily change jobs within the next two years. Breaking this percentage down further, we find that the percentage of respondents who gave themselves a

Almost everybody considers leaving their present employer from time to time. Suppose you were offered employment in another company. Considering each of the following factors independently, how important would each factor be to your decision whether or not to *accept* the offer?

	MEAN	Definitely important (1)	Somewhat important (2)	Somewhat unimportant (3)	Definitely unimportant (4)
A. More recognition for doing a good job	1.65				
B. More socially relevant job	2.89				
C. More challenging work	1.57				
D. More highly regarded organization	2.32				
E. Opportunity for early retirement	2.70				
F. Greater job security	2.01				
G. Higher earnings	1.38				
H. Better fringe benefits	1.81				
I. Better physical working conditions	2.32				
J. Greater opportunity for advancement	1.49				
K. More time for personal and family life	2.05				
L. More opportunity to exercise leadership	1.75				
M. More opportunity to work with people rather than with things	2.37				
N. Other (Specify)					

Aside from the appeal of a new job offer, factors can exist or can arise in a person's present job that could lead him or her to seek a new job. Considering each of the following factors independently, how important would each factor be to your decision to actively *seek* a job elsewhere?

	MEAN				
A. If I were working for someone who is a poor manager	1.56				
B. If I were in an inefficiently run organization or department	1.65				
C. If I had no opportunity for creativity and originality	1.35				
D. If I were required to move to a new city	2.21				
E. If coworkers were not friendly and congenial	2.11				
F. If I did not have enough to do	1.73				
G. If the job required excessive travel	2.16				
H. If the job put me under too much strain	1.95				
I. If I did not receive a promotion	1.75				
J. Other (Specify)					

To what extent would the following considerations tend to *hold* you in your present company?

	MEAN				
A. Your investment in the company's pension and/or retirement plan	2.47				
B. The location of your company	2.10				
C. Your sense of the future of the economy	1.94				
D. Your age	2.43				
E. Your spouse's unwillingness to move	2.42				
F. You recently changed jobs and are reluctant to make another change at this time	3.05				
G. Your current salary	2.09				
H. You have an approaching promotion opportunity	2.18				
I. Opportunity for you to retire early	2.79				
J. Other: (specify)					

50/50 chance of changing jobs in the next two years decreased from 35% for those making $10 to 15K to only 8% for those making more than $28K. Those who gave themselves no chance of voluntarily changing jobs (0%) increased from 19% for the $10 to 15K range to nearly 50% for those making more than $28K. And again, these differences were unrelated to the total number of years worked.

Why do the respondents seek change? Higher earnings ranked high as a reason, followed by greater opportunity for advancement, more challenging work, more recognition for doing a good job, more opportun-

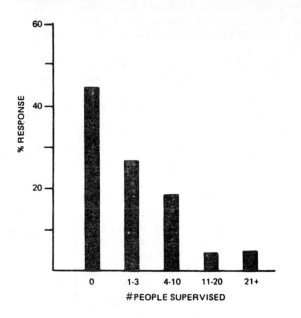

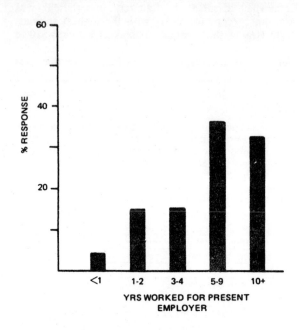

ity to show leadership and finally, better fringe benefits.

There was convincing data showing that the following factors would cause the respondent to seek a change:

- no opportunity for creativity and originality

- being part of an inefficiently run organiztion
- not having enough work to do
- not receiving a promotion
- receiving too much stress from the job

I feel strongly that the way a person feels about himself and about his job and his job environment

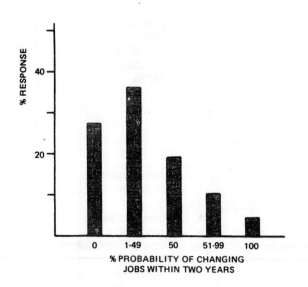

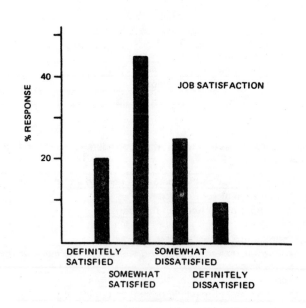

How satisfied are you with each of the following factors in your present job?	MEAN	Definitely Satisfied 1	Somewhat Satisfied 2	Somewhat Dissatisfied 3	Definitely Dissatisfied 4
A. Your knowledge of your career paths and promotional opportunities	2.78				
B. Recognition you have received for work you have accomplished	2.48				
C. Your knowledge of what is expected of you	2.28				
D. The sense of accomplishment that you get from your job	2.16				
E. Your opportunities to influence decisions made at higher levels	2.68				
F. Challenges you receive in your position	2.73				
G. The enjoyment you receive from your work	2.13				
H. The amount of information you receive about what is going on in your company	2.83				
I. The amount of time you have for personal and family life	1.92				

determines, more than anything else, his job performance.

Looking at the common thread.

Concern for higher earnings weave a common thread throughout this survey. For example, people with higher incomes are more satisfied and less likely to change positions. Also, the prospect of higher earnings is seen as the most important factor influencing a decision to accept an outside offer. And over 38% of the spouses have full or part-time jobs.

This emphasis upon earnings may well be explained by the fact that our average respondent is 38 years old, is in the middle income bracket, and has 2.25 children. This group carries a significant tax load. Many will want to send their children to college, but can't get any financial help. People in this group feel that they are entitled to have at least a bit of the "good life". With recent inflationary pressures it is very difficult to stretch the paycheck even enough to cover the "necessities", so I'm not surprised to see so much importance attached to earnings.

On the other hand, those receiving higher salaries are not more satisfied because they receive more money. They're more satisfied because their higher-level jobs provide higher-level satisfactions—greater responsibility, more authority, more status symbols and the like.

In reference to our 1/6/75 article, "Human Needs & Motivation," adequate earnings is a **BASIC** need, and can become such a strong concern that higher level needs (such as **BELONGING** and **EGO STATUS**) will have little or no influence on our behavior. This is a constant danger in the engineering profession because initial salaries are relatively good, but often they do not rise very rapidly with increasing years of experience. Technological obsolescence (see 11/17/73 DN) and inflation also have a depressing effect on salary.

In contrast, all but one of the other factors that would be important in a decision to accept a job offer can be classified in the **EGO-STATUS** or in the **SELF-ACTUALIZATION** needs categories. (The exception is better fringe benefits, which is a **SAFETY** need, and can be somewhat related with salary.)

These factors are under the control of management. Therefore, since the key to motivation is to make task performance a path to need satisfaction, managers can motivate their workforce by providing greater opportunity for advancement, more challenging work, more recognition for doing a good job and more opportunity to exercise leadership. After all, these are the factors that would be important to the respondents regarding a new job. So why not capitalize on these needs?

Further, the four most important factors in the respondents' present jobs that would cause them to consider other employment are: no opportunity for creativity and originality, working for a poor manager, working in an inefficiently run organization, and not enough work to do. These factors are also under the control of management, and tie in closely with the ego status and self-actualization needs discussed above. In fact, in a properly motivated workforce these negative factors would not exist.

Only one factor was considered important for holding the respondents to their present companies: their sense of the future of the economy. And this really doesn't relate directly to the job, but to the economic environment. Thus, we can draw the conclusion that for most employees pension plans, opportunity to retire early, company location, age and unwillingness of spouse to move provide almost no motivation. Improvement in these factors would probably have little influence on the efficiency of the work force. Per our 1/6/75 article, these are **HYGIENE** or **MAINTENANCE** factors. Their fulfillment provides little motivation to achieve organizational goals, but at the same time they're essential to avoid dissatisfaction and to prepare the workforce to respond to higher-level motivators.

Finally, there is dissatisfaction with all of the job climate factors that were listed—the knowledge of career paths, recognition for work performed, the sense of accomplishment and challenges received from work and other factors. The respondents expressed satisfaction with only one factor—they feel they have enough time for personal and family life.

Most dissatisfaction was expressed regarding the amount of information the respondents receive about what was going on in their companies. Surely an enlightened and committed management could reduce this dissatisfaction through a little positive effort.

The knowledge of what is expected and recognition for work accomplished could be improved by the implementation of realistic employee evaluation and counselling programs.

It is quite clear that the results of this survey indicate that there is lots of room for improvement and that there are some very specific actions that management can take if they want to develop a highly motivated, effective workforce. In future issues we will discuss these actions in greater detail. I would also be interested in your reactions, analyses and comments regarding the data presented.

Dr. T.F. Gautschi, P.E.

Factors affecting employee loyalty

Another look at the data generated in our employee loyalty survey

METHODOLOGY

As you may have guessed, our employee loyalty survey (*Design News* 1-20-75) provided much more information than could be presented in the initial report (*Design News* 4-7-75). Edward H. Getchell has completed a unique analysis of your responses for his masters thesis in the Sloan School of Management at Massachusetts Institute of Technology, and I would like to summarize his findings for you in this and the next issue of Management Forum.

To fully appreciate Getchell's analysis we should briefly review his methodology and definition of terms. The data base (your responses to the 1-20-75 questionnaire) was separated, filtered, and analyzed using the steps shown in the schematic diagram.

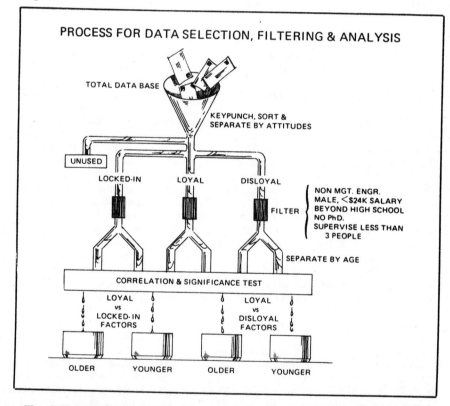

The first step was to divide the input into three major streams—LOYAL, DISLOYAL and LOCKED-IN.

LOYAL employees—Those who have the tendency to continue working for the same employer, as measured by a less than 50% response to question #9 ("What is the probability that you will voluntarily change employers in the next two years?"); and some degree of job satisfaction in response to question #8 ("Are you satisfied with your present job?").

DISLOYAL employees—Those who claimed to be somewhat or definitely dissatisfied with their jobs *and* whose probability of voluntarily changing jobs in the next two years is greater than 50%.

LOCKED-IN employees—The respondents who claim job dissatisfaction, *but* also claim less than a 50% probability of leaving their present employer.

These three categories are used because each contains a relatively large number of respondents, and those who are LOCKED-IN and DISLOYAL demonstrate certain behavior patterns opposite or contradictory to those displayed by the LOYAL employees.

The second step was to filter the data to isolate a group of employees with which the management process can deal, typified by the non-management engineer, who is male, receives less than $24,000 annual salary, has education beyond high school, does not have a Ph.D., and supervises fewer than three people.

On the assumption that the environmental needs of workers change as their age and careers progress, the data was further divided into younger (less than 35 years) and older groupings.

Finally, loyalty profiles were developed by comparing the *relative routings* by the LOYAL groups to the DISLOYAL and LOCKED-IN groups for the job factors contained in the survey questionnaire. The CLIMATE factors affecting loyalty are considered first, then the PUSH, PULL and HOLD factors affecting loyalty. The main thrust is focused on actions that management can take to reduce turnover and improve employee motivation.

RESULTS AND DISCUSSION

All comparisons are related to the "base line" LOYAL engineer under the following headings: for the CLIMATE factors

vs. disloyal younger engineer   vs. disloyal older engineer
vs. locked-in younger engineer   vs. locked-in older engineer

for the HOLD, PUSH, PULL loyalty factors

vs. disloyal engineer
vs. locked-in engineer

LOYAL VS. DISLOYAL YOUNGER ENGINEERS

The young LOYAL group was found to experience much more satisfaction with nearly all climate factors when compared with the young DISLOYAL group. That is, the DISLOYAL group expressed a relatively low level of satisfaction for the challenges, enjoyment, and sense of accomplishment they get from their jobs. *As managers, we should bear in mind that many workers derive a great sense of accomplishment and enjoyment from a job by being challenged by and successfully meeting difficult work assignments.*

The DISLOYAL group also expressed much lower satisfaction with their knowledge of what is expected of them and their knowledge of career paths and promotional opportunities. They seem to have the ambition and desire to advance, but are unclear as to what it takes to earn the right to move up the hierarchy, or exactly how the hierarchy will accommodate them should they get promoted.

Ambiguity in personnel review systems, and in company policies and opportunities for promotions, are elements that management could easily and effectively correct. Unfortunately, management often overlooks these factors, perhaps to avoid interactions with subordinates on "sensitive issues" such as accurate and candid performance reviews, and the identification of realistic career paths.

This position is supported by the DISLOYAL group, which expressed lower satisfaction regarding the recognition they receive for work they have accomplished and with the amount of information that they receive about what is going on in their companies.

The young DISLOYAL group was less satisfied with its opportunities to influence decisions made at higher levels than their LOYAL counterparts. They also desire more influence in the decisions that directly affect their daily work and their long-term career development.

LOYAL VS. DISLOYAL OLDER ENGINEERS

Although the climate factors that differentiate the older LOYAL vs. DISLOYAL engineers are the same as for the younger engineers, there is one striking difference. The order of the factors tends to be reversed.

For example, the most significant factors differentiating the satisfaction levels of the LOYAL vs. DISLOYAL *older* engineers are their knowledge of career paths and promotional opportunities, and recognition received for work accomplished. These factors rank fourth and seventh for the younger engineers.

Perhaps the older DISLOYAL engineers feel frustrated because they have not received credit and recognition for their achievements, which should earn them the right to advance in the organizational hierarchy, and are baffled by an ambiguous or vague system of rewards and promotions.

On the other hand, the sense of accomplishment from the job, which was the second most important climate factor associated with loyalty for the younger engineers, decreased to seventh most important for older engineers. Evidently, as engineers advance in their careers, the desire for the idealistic reward of a feeling of achievement and accomplishment diminishes as a differentiating factor (between LOYAL and DISLOYAL employees) while the desire for ego satisfying recognition of accomplishments from the organization and from the peer group becomes much more important. The knowledge of what is expected of an employee decreased in differentiation (between LOYAL and DISLOYAL) and supports the assumption that employees from both groups acquire an understanding and tolerance of the "norms" of the organizational environment, and learn to better cope with the system with increasing age and experience. Both the older and younger disloyal engineers are relatively dissatisfied with the challenge and enjoyment they receive from work.

In conclusion, the situation of the younger and older DISLOYAL engineer can be characterized by the following scenario:

Younger Disloyal Engineer: "I would like to be assigned more challenging work; I'm sure I could do it, and it really gives me a sense of pride and accomplishment when I complete a tough job. That's where a lot of my enjoyment in work comes from, and if I had the chance to prove myself more often I think I could get ahead a lot faster in this organization—although I don't really know what I would be promoted to, or where I would go from there."

Older Disloyal Engineer: "I would like to be assigned more challenging work; I'm sure I could to it, I've done it before. All I ask is that when I complete a tough job, I get credit for it—that would make work a lot more enjoyable. And I guess it would give me more opportunities to get ahead in this organization—although I don't really know what I would be promoted to, or where I would go from there."

In both cases the key to improving the level of satisfaction of the DISLOYAL group and thus reducing employee turnover would seem to be 1) a more equitable distribution of interesting and challenging work among a greater number of individuals, and 2) a well defined system for recognizing achievement and rewarding performance, and a commitment on the part of management to provide engineers with opportunities for personal and professional growth within the organization.

Dr. T.F. Gautschi, P.E.

Factors affecting employee loyalty—Part 2

This is the second and concluding discussion of a unique analysis of the information generated by our employee loyalty survey (*Design News* 1-20-75). Please refer to DN 5-10-76 for a description of the analysis approach and the definitions of LOYAL, DISLOYAL and LOCKED-IN groups.

LOYAL VS. LOCKED-IN YOUNGER ENGINEERS

The order of the climate factors in the loyalty profile for the LOCKED-IN group is very different from the loyalty profiles of the DISLOYAL group.

The first three factors of the loyalty profiles for the young engineers would imply that, relative to the LOYAL engineers, the young LOCKED-IN engineer feels as if he doesn't know what he should do, doesn't know where he is going in the company, and doesn't know what is going on in the company. In short, he appears somewhat bewildered and confused. Remembering that the LOCKED-IN employee does not require encouragement to stay with his present company but is likely to lack motivation, the needs of the LOCKED-IN employee would seem to be best satisfied by more information and by being made to feel more a part of things, of "belonging" to the organization.

The more personal and ego satisfying aspects of the jobs, such as the enjoyment and sense of accomplishment received from work, and the recognition received for work accomplished were all climate factors that were perceived as significantly less satisfying by the LOCKED-IN relative to the LOYAL group of younger engineers. However, these groups were not significantly different in their relative satisfaction with the challenges provided by the job. The relative dissatisfaction with the enjoyment and sense of accomplishment the younger LOCKED-IN engineers get from their jobs may well be a result of their relative dissatisfaction with the recognition they receive for their accomplishments.

Although management may not be able to directly affect the level of enjoyment and the sense of accomplishment an employee derives from his job, they can go a long way towards indirectly improving the environment for such feelings, particularly for the LOCKED-IN employees, by directing more effort towards rapidly acknowledging and rewarding accomplishments.

LOYAL VS. LOCKED-IN OLDER ENGINEERS

As was the case for the loyalty profiles for the LOYAL vs. DISLOYAL groups, a comparison between the younger and older engineers indicates a tendency for the climate factors to reverse orders.

The LOCKED-IN older engineer, relative to the LOYAL older engineer, seems to be less satisfied with his knowledge of career paths and promotional opportunities, the challenges and enjoyment he gets from work, and the opportunities to influence decisions made at higher levels. The LOCKED-IN older engineer seems to emerge as an employee who wants more influence in his company but does not see a clear career path in his organization to gain that influence. He is relatively dissatisfied with his knowledge of what is expected of him and what is going on in his company, both of which do not help his feelings of ambiguity towards advancement in his organization. He feels underutilized and, probably as a result of being unchallenged in his work, he is relatively dissatisfied with his job. Relative to the LOYAL older engineers, the LOCKED-IN older engineers are less satisfied with the recognition they receive for work they have accomplished, possibly because the tasks are not as challenging and therefore less deserving of recognition. The feelings of lack of recognition and challenge experienced by the LOCKED-IN older engineers must surely explain some of their relative dissatisfaction with the sense of accomplishment they derive from their jobs.

A scenario based on factors that most strongly differentiate the LOCKED-IN and LOYAL groups offers insight into the attitudes of the engineers classified as

LOCKED-IN and appears as follows:

Younger LOCKED-IN Engineer: "I feel confused, like I don't belong here. I don't know what is expected of me, or how to get ahead in this organization. I don't have any influence around here, nobody ever recognizes my achievements. I don't even know what is going on in this company."

Older LOCKED-IN Engineer: "I wish I knew how to advance in this organization. If I had some influence around here I might be able to get some of the challenging work that would make work more enjoyable and satisfying. I'm not sure what is expected of me. I don't get much recognition, and I don't know what is going on in this company."

In both cases keys to improving the level of satisfaction and motivation of the LOCKED-IN group seems to be 1) Better information and feedback about an employee's immediate task assignments and more information about what is going on in the company, 2) Allowing the engineers to have more participation and influence in the decisions that directly affect their work and careers.

Hold Factors

As might be expected, the investment in a pension or retirement plan becomes the most important HOLD factor differentiating LOYAL and DISLOYAL older engineers. This would strongly suggest that the LOYAL older engineer is voluntarily locked-in by his pension while the DISLOYAL older engineer is either prepared to leave it for the right opportunity, or else has insufficient pension benefits to act as a holding force.

Push Factors

Independent of age, the LOYAL employees indicated that the requirements to move to a new city would more strongly influence them to leave their present company when compared to the DISLOYAL employees. *Perhaps the selection of a "good" company location, which might represent a one-time cost somewhat higher than a less desirable location, may well repay itself over a period of years by attracting more desirable workers and reducing labor turnover.*

Two additional factors would more strongly influence the LOYAL employees to leave compared to the DISLOYAL employees. They are the requirement for excessive travel and the lack of friendly and congenial co-workers. The older LOYAL engineer appears to be comfortably embedded into a social structure at work and with his family and community life that is more important to him relative to his DISLOYAL counterpart.

In addition to the above PUSH factors, which act more strongly to cause the LOYAL employees to leave compared to the DISLOYAL employees, there are numerous other factors that have a stronger "pushing" effect on the DISLOYAL engineer. The tolerance level for not receiving a promotion or working for a poor manager or working in an inefficiently run organization or department was notably lower for the DISLOYAL young engineers than for their LOYAL counterparts. The DISLOYAL young engineers may well consider these three job factors as interdependent. He may consider that if his manager and his organization were better and more efficient, he would advance faster.

A lack of promotions, working for a poor manager and the lack of opportunity for creativity or originality are all differentiating factors less tolerated by the DISLOYAL older engineers than by their LOYAL counterparts. Compared to the LOYAL older engineers, the DISLOYAL older engineers are not particularly concerned with overall organizational efficiency as long as their own local environment is well managed, but they are sensitive to not receiving promotions and to work situations lacking the opportunity for creativity or originality.

Pull factors

The older engineers have an additional factor that is more attractive to the LOYAL group—the opportunity to retire early. These hardly would be considered aggressive job-oriented factors. On the other hand, those factors that attracted the DISLOYAL engineers relative to the LOYAL engineers are, for the most part, implicitly aggressive, job-oriented factors, such as the desire for leadership, recognition, advancement, and higher earnings. As previously discussed, the LOYAL employees are more satisfied with all the CLIMATE job factors than are their DISLOYAL counterparts. Perhaps the LOYAL employees are actually less aggressive and are satisfied with a much lower level of effort and challenge than the DISLOYAL engineers, who feel under-utilized, unchallenged, and frustrated in their achievement of career goals.

7

Management by Objectives: key concept, or the kiss of death?

A closer look at a powerful management technique; plus the solution to Critical Incident #1

Dr. T. F. Gautschi, P.E.

> *"What the business enterprise needs is a principle of management that will give full scope to individual strength and responsibility and at the same time give common direction of vision and effort, establish teamwork, and harmonize the goals of the individual with a common weal. The only principle that can do this is Management by Objectives and self control."*[1]

AT ITS BEST

At its best, MBO improves organizational effectiveness through: (1) integrating the manager's need to contribute and develop personally, (2) improving the planning and controlling process in response to organizational goals and (3) providing a vehicle for improved communications.

AT ITS WORST

At its worst, MBO becomes a hollow and frustrating exercise that consumes a great amount of time and energy, and contributes little or nothing towards improving organizational effectiveness of meeting organizational or individual goals.

REQUIRES TOP MANAGEMENT INVOLVEMENT

As with many other corporate activities, the success of MBO is related to the depth of top management involvement. It can *not* be slipped into the organization as part of a management development program, and be successful. It's not something that can be "added" to an organization. Rather it is a fundamental philosophy for integrating planning and control within the organization. It also requires a great deal of top management attention and interest to be successful. MBO is concerned with the totality of the business and its results and it must involve all levels of management. Since MBO is so pervasive, it usually requires two to three years to install and fulfill its intent.

Another major problem is that on the surface MBO looks so simple. After all, most managers already feel they know what is expected of them and that they have effective standards and control procedures. This attitude must first be recognized, and then corrected through a process of education.

The basic thrust in MBO is to quantify precisely what one is trying to achieve, as related to every key task and organizational objective. Generalized statements like "We will increase our profits next year" are not operational and should be replaced by "We will improve our profit before taxes from 6% to 7% of sales next year."

PROBLEMS IN IMPLEMENTATION

The unit of measurement is not always easy to define. For example, in a recent seminar with EPA representatives the question of goal identification was raised. Should the goals be dimensioned in terms of violations identified, when a major thrust of EPA is to try to help companies avoid violations through corrective action?

---

[1]Peter Drucker, *The Practice of Management* (New York, Harper and Row, 1954).

MBO must start at the top and be responsive to a strategic plan that specifies overall organizational goals and objectives. Every subsequent organizational level should establish related supporting goals—otherwise, the firm could end up accomplishing the wrong things.

THEORY Y VIEW

Successful MBO implementation generally requires that management have a "Theory Y" view of their workforce. That is, subordinates should be viewed as wanting:

- freedom to plan and control their own work without excessive detailed direction
- opportunities for creativity and originality
- to work in an efficiently-run organization
- to keep busy
- challenges
- recognition for work accomplished
- to participate in the organization's decision-making process
- to know the way their work fits into the organization's goals

Our recent survey on employee loyalty (DN April 7, 1975) indicates that these are the very factors that most of the respondents are looking for in their work environment. Since this is the case, implementation of an MBO philosophy and process in a professional organization should improve productivity because it would meet the motivational needs of the employee as well as provide a technique for improving the coordination of work activities with organizational goals.

In spite of its benefits, MBO is not without its problems. In fact, few managers are really willing to devote the effort and hard work that is necessary to integrate an MBO philosophy and program into their organization. As a result, there are many organizations that claim to be MBO-oriented, but are really putting up a facade, and at best are simply going through the motions.

MBO IS RESULTS-ORIENTED

Although the MBO process is very logical and reasonable, most managers have a difficult time applying it to their own situation. Because MBO is results-oriented and most managers are work-oriented, managers must learn to state objectives in terms of result and *not* in terms of work tasks or activities.

The installation of MBO may identify unsound organizational alignments and poor management practices. It also establishes clear-cut goals and measures of individual and group achievement. Some people clearly do not want this to happen. They prefer to keep things a little fuzzy.

Frequently, firms start to install MBO without a full realization, or commitment, to the concept or to the amount of time and resources required. This usually results in a situation where either the entire program is abandoned, or it is continued as a facade where it is simply given lip service.

In either case, organizational efficiency will suffer because of the resultant confusion, frustration, and just plain disillusionment.

Much has been written on the subject of MBO. In succeeding articles we will explore some of this literature and present some practical ideas for installing an MBO system in an organization.

Dr. T.F. Gautschi, P.E.

Management by Objectives: Its pros and cons in the 'real world'

The driving forces and restraining forces you may encounter—and a strategy for effectiveness once you're committed to MBO.

THE IDEAL MBO

MBO IN THE REAL WORLD

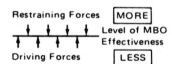

Restraining Forces [MORE]
Level of MBO Effectiveness
Driving Forces [LESS]

In a national survey of companies of various sizes, 83% of the respondents indicated that they manage by objectives. As discussed in our previous MBO article (DN 7-7-75), MBO appears to be such a straightforward and logical approach to management that, more than likely, many managers believe that they are using the technique when in fact they are not. However, a large percentage of companies must be using some variation of MBO in their management process.

Ideally, the MBO process is built upon a system of clearly defined and communicated goals. These are developed throughout the management hierarchy by a series of interlocking relationships—starting with the overall objectives of the organization and working down to the lowest level manager, or perhaps individual contributor. MBO concentrates upon measurable results, and not upon the manner in which the goals are to be implemented. Many tie performance evaluation in with MBO. In fact, some see it primarily as a performance evaluation technique.

To provide further insight regarding MBO and its implementation in the real world, I recently made a survey of several groups that report to vice presidents in a large international corporation that has been depicted in the management literature as a company that has done a good job in its application of the MBO process. The survey was conducted by asking a number of managers to analyze the level of MBO effectiveness using the Force Field Analysis Technique (see DN 5-19-75). The results were collected in terms of Restraining Forces, those that keep the MBO process from being more effective; Driving Forces, those forces that tend to make the MBO process more effective; and a Strategy to increase overall effectiveness by reducing the Restraining Forces and increasing the Driving forces.

The managers involved in the survey found it more difficult to develop the list of Driving Forces than to develop the list of Restraining Forces even though this is a company that has been widely discussed in the literature as being a model MBO organization!

DRIVING FORCES:
- Key management personnel are on a corporate financial incentive plan, which is based upon the satisfactory attainment of MBO goals. (Some managers indicated that they felt that this was the primary purpose for the MBO process.)
- MBO meets a need to clarify responsibility and define areas of responsibility.
- MBO provides for two-way goal alignment—top down and bottom up.
- MBO helps establish an acceptable level of mutual commitment.
- MBO is a formal process requiring a quarterly review of progress.
- MBO encompasses the typical management functions of planning, organizing, communicating, motivating and controlling.

RESTRAINING FORCES:
- No direct reward for MBO achievement, except for the executive level.
- Resources *not* allocated by objectives.
- Lack of clear-cut measurable top management objectives.
- Too much reactive planning in the face of budget and time restraints and changing requirements. (This survey was conducted during the Fall of 1974 and the Spring of 1975 when the business environment was characterized by uncertainty and rapid change—many indicated that MBO does not work well in such a crisis environment.)
- The goals are almost exclusively financially oriented—perhaps because financial figures are easier to collect and analyze.
- The goals are frequently shifting, and the process is not easy to update.
- Too many goals which, in turn, result in an over-detailed process that is cumbersome and too restrictive.
- Goals, along with implementation details, are directed from the top. There is very little negotiation and there is insufficient person-to-person dialogue.
- Top management believes that plans submitted "bottom-up" are not realistic.
- Lower management levels believe that top management wants more than the bottom can furnish.
- Oftentimes the goals are conflicting.
- There is a general lack of availability of good measurement data.
- The MBO process is not implemented to the same level of detail for each of the various management levels because there is no general agreement regarding how the MBO process should be administered.
- There is a lack of management involvement and support regarding the establishment, review and timely update of the objectives.

STRATEGY:
Present the facts to top management and secure a commitment establishing the degree to which they wish to integrate MBO into the operating management process. This commitment should be in terms of time and resources. Factors to be considered in this commitment include:
- Determine how far down into the organization the MBO process of implementation should extend.
- Stipulate who participates and ensure that the objectives are controllable by the participant.
- Define what is expected at each level. Limit the number of MBO's, and relate to the Long Range Plan.
- Establish an MBO planning process, which should include these eight points:
    1. consistent administration
    2. realistic time schedule for development, review and updating
    3. reliable process for assuring mutual discussion, understanding and commitment to the various goals
    4. link with budget development
    5. provide for timely MBO adjustment as the resource availability changes
    6. training program for all participants to assure a common perspective on the MBO process and its detailed implementation
    7. formalize the measurement process
    8. budget for MBO administration
- Work out a policy for relating compensation and other recognition for goal achievement.
- Establish an information system that will provide timely feedback on the status of goal achievement.
- Document and communicate the overall goals by means of the Long Range Plan.
- Integrate MBO reporting with other management reporting requirements.
- Establish an activity to audit the MBO process and provide educational and consulting support as required.

SYSTEMS VIEW

MBO, as you no doubt have quickly ascertained, requires a systems view of the organization. Most managers must operate in a complex network of vertical, horizontal and diagonal relationships, and success as measured by goal achievement is quite often dependent upon the communication, cooperation, and support of other managers in the network. This is especially true for staff managers.

TEAM MBO

In the last issue (DN 12-8-75), I suggested that an organization's effectiveness might be improved by viewing it as being made up of a series of teams rather than of individuals. French and Hollman [1] present some interesting arguments in favor of CMBO (Collaborative Management by Objectives) which is a participative, team-centered approach to MBO. They assert that one-to-one MBO does not account for the interdependent nature of most jobs, it does not assure optimal coordination of objectives, and it does not always improve superior-subordinate relationships. These deficiencies are in evidence in the above RF list. It is claimed that the CMBO approach can overcome these deficiencies by shifting the climate of the organization in the direction of more team work, more cooperation, more joint problem-solving, and more support. Their article concludes with a proposed nine-phase strategy for introducing more systematic collaboration into the MBO process.

CONSIDER THE RFs

If your firm uses some form of MBO (and according to our statistics, it probably does), you might find it helpful to use the above RF's and DF's as a check list to gain further insight into how your operation really works. My guess is that the RF's listed are fairly common throughout the industry and that they would be well worth some of your attention.

---

[1] *Management By Objectives: The Team Approach*, W. L. French and R. W. Hollman, California Management Review, Spring 1975, Vol. XVII #3.

Applying MBO theory

Specific guidelines for the practice of Management by Objectives

MBO THEORY

Management by Objectives is an approach to management in which specific goals (or objectives) are established for each manager on the basis of assigned responsibility and the results that must be achieved if the objectives of the company are to be realized. This process was discussed previously in "MBO: Key Concept, or The Kiss of Death?", DN 7-7-75.

APPLICATION

One of the reasons for the great disparity between MBO theory and practice is that although the theory is easily understood and accepted, it is very difficult to apply in the industrial situation. Part of the implementation difficulties may lie in the fact that MBO is so logical that everyone thinks he is an expert and follows his own version of the process.

In any case, I thought that it might be helpful to provide some guidelines against which you can measure the implementation of your MBO program. The list is probably not complete, but it should provide you with a good basis for thinking about the process.

Ask yourself two questions as you review the guidelines: (1) Is this currently true for our implementation? (2) Should it be true for our implementation? When the answer to the first question is different from the answer for the second question, there is an implementation gap, and steps should be taken to correct it.

GOALS—PART OF PLANNING

1. The entire process should begin with the overall corporate objectives as documented in the Long-Range Plan or some other suitable document that is approved by top management.
2. Goals should be discussed and negotiated on a face-to-face basis between the supervisor and the subordinate(s) until they are mutually understood and accepted. They should be in writing, along with any back-up or explanatory material that is deemed desirable.
3. Both short-range and long-range goals should be considered when establishing required results.
4. Line organization goals should be set first. Then compatible goals should be set for supporting staff organizations.
5. There should be four types of goals:
   - routine job-related goals
   - innovative job-related goals
   - routine personal development goals
   - innovative personal development goals

(The purpose of the personal development goals should be to delay or prevent the onset of technological obsolescence. These goals should be related to the firm's long-range requirements for developing managerial and/or technical skills and capabilities.

JOINT GOALING; CROSS CHECKING

6. Goals should be set for persons in all areas where they have strong influence on the results, even though they do not have full control. Joint goaling becomes more commonplace as the organization grows in complexity.
7. Not more than eight result goals should be specified for any one position during a particular period. More goals usually add unnecessary complexity and paperwork to the process.
8. All of the goals for the subordinates reporting to a particular manager should be cross-checked for compatibility. This can oftentimes be best accomplished through group discussion.
9. The goals set for each person should be considered to be reasonably achievable by those involved.
10. Every employee should have a written list of the results for which he is responsible.
11. The results expected of each manager should include the results expected of all the managers below him, but in less detail.

**DESIRED RESULTS—
BE SPECIFIC**

12. The subordinate should be held accountable for results, but should be free to choose those means to the desired end he believes most effective, as long as they conform to an overall company policy. (Too often supervisors try to control the "means" as well as the end results. This is one of the quickest ways that I know of to turn a professional off.)

13. The results should be stated in specific terms, including *what* must be accomplished and *when*. They should be measured in terms of dollars, ratios, amounts, percentages, or what ever is appropriate.

14. Resources should be allocated by results expected.

15. All persons should be expected (committed) to accomplish each of the results delegated to them until there is mutual agreement with the delegator to change them.

16. A specification should be prepared for each MBO result. It should state:
    - Key result elements
    - Descriptions of results and measurement method
    - Basic and "stretch" objectives
    - Decision limits (usually monthly, bimonthly, quarterly)

17. Decisions that are directly related to the accomplishment of the results expected of a manager should be his responsibility.

18. The information system should provide the necessary information to accurately measure progress vs. goals to each manager responsible for accomplishing results.

19. Some sort of compensation plan should be used to reinforce accountability stimulate motivation.

20. Appraisals of performance should be related to the results specified in the MBO process.

21. The information system should be designed to report deviations before they get beyond control.

22. Deviations from goals should be first reported to the responsible person who should take the required action to correct the problem.

MBO in the matrix organization

MATRIX ORGANIZATION

With the increasing complexity and rapid changes that are taking place in technology, more and more firms are turning to some form of matrix organization in order to cope with the situation. I would like to discuss the application of the MBO process and philosophy to such an organization.

As I have noted before, matrix organization includes the following points: (1) authority is shared between functional and program management, (2) functional manager has administrative responsibility for manpower resources; determines *who* and *how*, (3) program manager has planning and budget control; determines *what* and *where*.

VENDOR AND PM

In the matrix type organization the implementing functional organization can have a vendor-like relationship to the Program Manager, so I'll use the terms vendor and PM.

THREE MBO STEPS

The utilization of an MBO process involves three steps, each of which should be handled differently depending upon the relationship that has been established and on the readiness of the vendor to accept responsibility for his part of the program—especially as related to program cost, schedule, and system performance. The goal toward which the PM should work is the acceptance by the vendor of full responsibility for his contribution to the success of the program.

(1) OBJECTIVES

The first step is the *establishment of objectives*. A good way to begin is to ask the vendor to document and discuss his conception of the responsibilities that he considers to be primary in his task—essentially a contract proposal. This is often an instructive process for both parties, because even where there are detailed written specifications, vendors do not always perceive their responsibilities as the PM does, and vice versa. The proposal will provide the opportunity for modification and clarification in give-and-take discussion. For the purposes of management objectives, a list of the major responsibilities of the job as agreed to by both parties is required.

The requirements of the job should be determined by the situation; they should not be perceived as requirements established solely by the PM or the vendor. The ideal role for the PM in the discussion of the vendor's proposal is that of a collaborator. The PM's purpose is to help the vendor understand what the situation demands of him. This step may take some time, but the achievement of mutual understanding and joint agreement concerning the vendor's responsibilities is essential to the future of the whole program. By this process, the broad objectives defined by the situation are clarified and accepted.

(2) SPECIFIC TARGETS

Once the vendor, primarily through his own efforts but with such help as is needed from the PM, has arrived at a clear statement of the major responsibilities of his job, step two can occur. This step requires the vendor to *identify those targets or objectives that he feels are important for him to achieve during a specified period of time* (such as six months). These targets should be as specific as possible; i.e., tasks he plans to complete, new projects he wishes to undertake, tests he plans to complete, system performance goals, funding schedules, etc. They should, of course, be related to the responsibilities he has already outlined for his job. His targets, in turn, are determined jointly with the PM in a give-and-take fashion.

In establishing these targets, both parties should give careful consideration to ways of determining at a later stage to what degree they have been achieved. In some instances this will be easy; a job will have been completed, the funding schedule will not have been exceeded, etc. In other cases, careful thought may be required to determine whether the targets have been reached. The goal here is to have the vendor able to determine for himself whether he has reached his targets, rather than to have him in a situation where his accomplishment is determined solely by the judgment of the PM. The vendor needs to consider what evidence, what measures, what data will indicate his progress towards his goals, and how he can obtain this information for himself.

(3) TARGET EVALUATION

The third step takes place at the expiration of the agreed-upon period for which the targets have been set. However, this does not mean that the PM forgets all about the matter in the meanwhile. During the intervening time, the PM should seek out opportunities to work with the vendor. Here again, the nature of the PM's actions will differ from situation to situation. If the vendor is accustomed to complete delegation, he may operate relatively independently, coming to the PM to obtain advice or consultation only when he needs it and to keep the PM informed of progress. If, on the other hand, he has not operated with much independence in the past, there will be need for frequent interchange and guidance.

At the end of the stated period, *the vendor should make an appraisal of his performance relative to the targets that were set earlier.* Having done so, he should have another discussion with the PM. If he has achieved his objectives, the process can start over again, with new targets for the ensuing period.

MODIFYING TARGETS

If, however, he has failed in some respect or another to achieve his targets, the discussion should consist of an analysis of the reasons and of what can be done about them. With reasonable care on the part of the PM, this will not be a situation in which the vendor becomes unduly defensive. The purpose is not to force the vendor to rationalize his failures, but rather to encourage him to examine his performance and the program results to date in order that the progam can be modified as required by such results. The emphasis in on the future, not on the past.

In this discussion the PM, who is sensitive to the interdependent nature of the relationship, is likely to find that his own behavior has been a factor in the vendor's success or failure in reaching his targets. Thus, the planning for the future may well involve changes on the part of the PM also!

Further applications of MBO
in the matrix organization

TEAM TARGETS

Three steps for Management by Objectives in a matrix organization between Program Manager and vendor were described last issue. However, the process lends itself equally well to target-setting by a group of subordinates on a departmental basis, or between a superior and a single subordinate. The group departmental goals thus set can become the basis for a team effort (see DN 12-8-75) in which each individual has his own part to play. Actually, measures of accomplishment relative to objectives are often easier to set for a department than for an individual. Sometimes both individual and group targets can be established with the two processes supplementing each other.

**OBJECTIVES,
NOT ORDERS**

It is especially important to understand that what we have been considering is not a formula but a broad theory of management, the application of which must be adjusted and modified to fit the particular circumstances. Its basic value lies in the substitution of objectives for orders, and in the substitution of self-control for external control. To the extent that the vendor's goal can be related to the requirements of the program, this process can be used to bring about gradually the full acceptance of responsibility on the part of the vendor for system performance, schedules, and funding and their interrelation. To achieve this integration, the PM does not abdicate. The PM should not attempt to minimize the contractual relationship that pertains. The PM does not have to choose between a "hard" and a "soft" management; these concepts are simply irrelevant; nor is the process "democratic" so much as it is collaborative.

The use of this method of managing does not eliminate the administrative necessity for judgments by the PM concerning the performance of the vendor. These will be made independently, as required, for the purposes of establishing new relationships and management planning. It is probable, however, that the PM who is managing by objectives and self-control will acquire information and data with respect to the vendor's performance, which provide a more substantial basis for the judgments that he is called upon to make. The PM will also, in all probability, become more judicious in making them.

**POWER BASED
ON EXPERIENCE**

A supplementary approach for controlling vendor behavior merits discussion. Power can be defined as the capacity to secure dominance of one's values or goals. This power must be granted by the group or individual over which it is exercised. Authority, in turn, is generally defined as the right to command. An ideal situation exists when power and authority rest with the same person or group. In a matrix organization the reliance upon authority alone can have a detrimental effect upon an entire program. Once the relationship is established, the PM has few alternatives to enforce authority that are not extreme in nature. Further, scientists and engineers are an independent lot, and tend to ignore formal authority unless it is accompanied by power based upon expertise.

In an R & D project relationship, the primary basis for power should be expertise. Expertise that is perceived by those over whom the power is exercised must include both technical and managerial skills in the field in which the R & D takes place.

Critical Incident #5
"Too Late"

I recently was faced with the need for a senior engineer with expertise in vacuum technology and cryogenics for a three-month project assignment. A Principle Engineer named John was recommended from the Star Tracker Engineering Section. Recent budgeting cutbacks on research had brought John's project to an end.

During an interview I found John to be well qualified (Ph.D. Physical

Chemistry—MIT, and he had a number of significant papers and patents). Interaction with John occurred for a one-week period while he wrapped up his R & D projects. During a final scheduling meeting on a Tuesday afternoon we covered concepts, hardware, cost and schedules. John felt excited about the opportunity and agreed to tell his boss Jerry—Head of Tracker Design Section—the next morning. I was surprised that he had not kept Jerry informed prior to this.

The next morning before John could describe our assignment opportunity, his boss informed him that he was laid off. Reason: loss of R & D charter in the Tracker group. I later learned that John's boss and the Personnel Department had attempted for five to six months to locate a transfer for John to another division. Apparently John did not perceive the precarious nature of his position; maybe because he had a high degree of professionalism and always did a "good" job, he felt that he didn't have to be concerned.

John was shattered, obviously. Apparently he was not fully aware of the "signs" that might have forewarned him of this event. His boss was unaware of our project needs until my telecon later. Had he known this, he would have postponed the layoff.

In an attempt to salvage the situation, I reaffirmed our project need and reminded John that he still could have a three-month project during which time he could be developing other possible job opportunities on a spare-time basis. However, he was not mentally up to the idea and decided to leave.

What do you think were the problems in this situation? What can be done to reduce the likelihood of the same thing happening again?

Critical Incident #6
"Temporary Assignment"

Rapid growth in my area of responsibility required that six of my workers be temporarily assigned to a special developmental project under a new manager. Upon completion of this project, expected to last approximately six months, the new project was to be disbanded and the people returned to my group.

After an unsuccessful outside search for a manager for the new project group, I was asked to submit two names for the job. I offered my two top people, neither of whom had any previous experience in the new field of endeavor.

Tom had come up the "hard way", had eighteen years of service in the company and the reputation being a man who could be counted on to get things done, even under very adverse conditions.

Dick was new to the company. He was hired directly into management after being laid off from a responsible managerial job with another company that went bankrupt. He had demonstrated definite leadership abilities, even though he had less than six months service, and was one of my best workers.

Both men were interviewed by their new Departmental Head and Dick was promoted to the new position as supervisor. His responsibility was to bring the project to completion ASAP (not to exceed six months). He would then rotate to another assignment at the same level and his group of six would return to work for me.

This caused two problems for Dick.

(1) Dick was now Tom's supervisor and needed Tom's complete support to successfully complete the project within the specified time period.

Tom was very disappointed in not getting the job. He felt that his relative standing with his peers had been damaged by being "beat out" by a "new guy" in the organization. However, being well on his way to a pension, Tom had no intention of either alienating his new boss or of quitting the company. Dick's challenge was to motivate Tom to successfully meet his objective.

(2) Dick's other problem was to deal with the other five men reporting to him. These men were his co-workers until his promotion and were, in some cases, envious of Dick's rapid rise in the organization. They were aware that they were on a temporary assignment and would be returned to their previous group within a few months.

How should Dick deal with these problems?

8

Staffing and budgeting the productive operation

Dr. T. F. Gautschi, P.E.

STAFFING. A firm's most important resource is people; the staffing activity is concerned with the attraction, development and maintenance of these human resources. The staffing function may be designated by any of the following: Human Resource Management, Personnel, Employee Relations or Industrial Relations. But whatever the title, the key point is that line management is responsible for this function, and the staff organization that has the title is supposed to support the line managers through their expertise and coordination activities. For example, the Employee Relations department may prepare and assemble an employee policy manual as a coordinating function, but the contents should reflect decisions by line management.

Staffing functions generally include: recruiting, interviewing, hiring, firing, testing, training, career planning, benefit planning, performance evaluation, manpower planning, compensation, EEO planning, and implementation, job design and management development.

The quality of human resources is critical to effective and efficient performance. All other resources when utilized decline in value, while human resources have the *inherent capacity* to develop and become more valuable with use. Whether this happens and whether individual companies will have

sufficient numbers of qualified human resources is a basic, but sometimes neglected, management responsibility.

In the larger organizations the director of Human Resource Management is becoming a very critical source of influence on top management because of the increase in the impact of unions and government regulations on a firm's operations.

DECISION-MAKING. Most managers make a lot of decisions—that is, they choose one alternative course of action from among several. In this process they usually use some form of the traditional problem solving approach:

1. *Define the problem*—being careful not to be misled by a symptom. Oftentimes the manager does not spend enough time on the definition of the problem; this will prolong this process or even cause the manager to make an incorrect decision.

2. *Gather relevant information*—Depending upon the circumstances, this could involve listening, reading or observation.

3. *Identify alternatives*—This requires analysis, concentrated thought, and perhaps a bit of brainstorming either alone or with others.

4. *Evaluate alternatives and make a choice*—The key here is to establish evaluation criteria and to weight them according to their importance.

Management science (quantification) can provide useful inputs to our mental models of the problem situation. However, such application often involves too much simplification to yield operationally practical answers. It should be emphasized that this predicament is changing with improvement in information gathering and processing capability.

Most managers use mental models that they develop through experience and modify by management science as they think it is applicable. These mental models generally employ SATISFICING rather than a MAXIMIZING process. That is, the manager "tests" alternatives sequentially and chooses the *first* alternative that meets the evaluation criteria, whereas the maximizer would test all alternatives and then choose the one that *best* satisfies the evaluation criteria.

5. *Communicate the decision*—Without this step nothing would happen. Ideally, those involved in the implementation of a course of action would also be involved in some way in the decision process. This should not only produce a better decision, but it should also enhance the communication and commitment phase as well. The communication should be specific and unambiguous — even when viewed from the recipient's

point of view. Where possible the implementor should be able to view the decision as rational, and to his advantage; or at least, not to his detriment.

6. *Feedback*—After the decision is implemented, careful attention should be paid to the results to verify that in fact the correct alternative was chosen, or to gather information for modifying the decision.

It is interesting to note that when a group meets to make a decision, they invariably start with step 4, "evaluating alternatives and making a choice", without first establishing a common definition of the problem, sharing relevant information and identifying alternatives.

The amount of involvement by the manager's subordinates in the decision making process is a key variable. Such involvement should vary, and be determined by factors such as the importance of the problem, the subordinates' (and the manager's) interest and competence in the problem, the time and geographical situation, the organizational environment and the like.

DIRECTING. This is the activating function for the organization. After the previously described tasks of planning (and decision making), organizing and staffing are completed, the manager must take the initiative in starting operations and coordinating the various activities to assure that the objectives of the business are being met.

COMMUNICATION. This is the process of transferring a thought or concept in its entirety to another person. This very important task has been the subject of a number of Management Forum articles, so we will not dwell upon it here, except to mention some of the key concepts.

1. Verbal and non-verbal communication. Much communication takes place non-verbally—a good communicator learns to read the "cues".

2. One-way and two-way communication. One-way appears to be fast and orderly, but often it is very inaccurate. Two-way takes more time, it often is not orderly, but it can be very accurate. It usually has a side benefit of greater commitment on the part of the recipient.

3. Communication barriers—a good communicator is aware of the gateways and barriers to good communication.

4. Perception—different people perceive the same thing in different ways, and yet what they perceive is reality to them.

5. Communication is the cement that connects the members of the organization, serves to transfer information and to establish common purpose.

CONTROLLING. The purpose of the control function is to assure that the results and plans are compatible.

The controlling function involves:

1. Establishing standards (plans, budgets, quality level, etc.)

2. Comparing the actual performance against the standards.

3. And, where deviation is found, to initiate corrective action to make the actual performance comply with the established standard.

In practice, controlling, directing and planning are all closely related.

RESPONSIBILITY (The exercise of). Responsibility is being accountable for the organization, its resources and its activities. Although authority can be delegated, responsibility *cannot* be delegated. The manager cannot avoid taking the responsibility for one course of action among many uncertain alternatives, or of making mistakes and taking the consequences. In fact, one of a manager's major responsibilities is to resolve the uncertainties that are always involved in important decisions; and when necessary, to absorb the displeasure, and sometimes severe hostility of those who would have taken a different course of action.

BUDGETING. Budgets, usually expressed in dollars, are the means for documenting the targets involved in the planning and control processes. The budget, to be most effective, is viewed as an agreement or informal contract between the parties involved. Deviations from the budget usually serve as a basis for managerial initiative for identifying the cause and taking corrective action. As one proceeds down the organizational hierarchy, the budgets increase in detail.

CONTINGENCY PERSPECTIVE. The manner in which each of the activities is carried out should be determined by where the organization falls along the mechanistic-organic continuum. As discussed previously in *Design News*, all useful organizational forms can be viewed as falling along a continuum bound at the extremes by mechanistic and organic orientations. The mechanistic extreme perceives the organization as a machine-like system operating in a relatively stable environment with workers who are basically programmable robots. The organic orientation stresses organizational flexibility and the psycho-social aspects of organizations including human motivations and needs.

The essence of the contingency approach is that the best management style and organizational environment is that which best fits the situation. That is, a more mechanistic approach is best for the more mechanistic situation—such as a stable production line. And a more organic approach is best for the more organic situation—such as may be required in an engineering or marketing organization.

How to change jobs successfully

*First of a multi-part series
on the employment situation.*

Dr. T. F. Gautschi, P.E.

Changing jobs is not the uncommon experience it once was. Our employee loyalty survey (*Design News* 4/7/75) indicates that nearly 35% of the respondents are dissatisfied with their present jobs, and that 72% of all respondents might voluntarily change jobs within the next two years. The reasons given were the desire for higher earnings, greater opportunity for advancement, more challenging work, more recognition for doing a good job, and more opportunity to show leadership.

This situation is influenced by many factors, including: better education, better communications and transportation, and higher expectations. The current world economic situation is causing firms to readjust their workforce to meet new marketing requirements. Some say that the average person now changes jobs about every four years. Evidently individualism is beginning to dominate what were previously traditional feelings of corporate loyalty—especially among professional workers. And the dynamics of our society are such that jobs are just not as permanent as they were a decade or so ago.

BE AWARE OF THE JOB MARKET

In such an environment, the individual professional should always be aware of the job market in his, or her, field. For many, personal growth should be viewed as a matter of marketing talents and knowledge to implement long-range plans and goals. With this view we need not be fearful of losing, or changing, our jobs, and we shouldn't have to "trap ourselves" into unacceptable work situations on a continuing basis. Life is too short, and too dear, to spend it doing something that we do not enjoy—at least on a long term basis.

DON'T PANIC

But what about the individual who is actually faced with the possibility of a job loss? The normal reaction is to be very concerned when confronted with the prospect of being unemployed or having to locate another position. In this situation, it is important to your morale, and your future success in locating another position, that you do not panic and that you carefully and dispassionately list and consider all of your assets and liabilities. After all, you have a good product to sell—you.

BE PATIENT

Experience indicates that two or more months may be required to find a position that is reasonably commensurate with your interests and experience. The time varies directly with your salary requirements, age, background and experience, and the general employment situation.

You might have to make a tradeoff decision between your job requirements and your living location. So you may have to live on a "bare-bones" budget for a while. If you have lost your job, plan to work full-time looking for your new position. Don't get discouraged as the weeks go by—remember, you are looking for the right job, one commensurate with your interests and experience. Persistence will pay off.

IT'S A MATTER OF MARKETING

It's a matter of marketing—that is, matching up what you have to sell with someone who needs your services. Unfortunately, there is no central clearinghouse for those who are seeking positions and those who are looking for employees. Therefore, you must survey the marketplace yourself. The more good contacts you can make, the greater will be your probability of finding the right position. About 50% of your success will be determined by your background and abilities, and the other 50% will be determined by how you go about your job hunting task. You cannot change your past, so you should try to improve how you communicate it, and also try to improve your job hunting skills.

PERSONAL LETTER

Experience has shown that a brief well-written personal letter is a good introduction for your resume. These should be addressed by name to the vice-president in charge of your specialty.

Be brief. Tell him why you are writing. Convince him that by reading your resume his company will be interested in talking to you. Suggest a personal

YOUR RESUME

interview. You may wish to state that in a few days you will be calling to arrange the interview—that way when you call he'll already know something about you.

There is no such thing as a perfect resume—so always be on the alert for improvement. It is important to try to project your career as a progressive series of accomplishments and not a "hodge-podge" of unrelated jobs. Be sure to write for your audience, and don't be modest.

BE BRIEF

Your resume should be considered as a tool to encourage the reader to want to interview you. The average applicant sitting down to write his resume becomes fascinated by all the interesting work he's done and his life history. He tries to tell about it on paper. Actually what he's done for twenty years is serve as a test engineer, market researcher, or in some other capacity. Save the exciting anecdotes for the interview. The resume should be the main framework—primary structure— of your experience. The decoration and design detail can be hinted in your covering letter and explained at length in an interview.

STANDARD RESUME

Try to keep your resume to one page. Besides your address, telephone number, education, a history of past jobs and possibly your salary history, it should include your selling point—accomplishments in past jobs—professional societies, awards, etc. A recent college graduate should list academic achievements but the mature candidate with work experience should leave that out.

The standard "general" resume includes a specialty objective and a listing of qualifications, usually work experience in reverse chronological order.

FUNCTIONAL RESUME

But suppose there aren't many jobs available in your specialty? Write another one that is a functional resume. Your objective is a type or types of work. You back this up with experience in a variety of functions—kinds of work you've done that support your objective. You do not list specific employers, only the functions you've performed. When you go to an interview you can bring along your general resume and explain what you did.

It helps to tailor a resume for a specific job or company—make a rifle shot instead of a shotgun blast. These are harder to do, but they will often produce surprisingly good results. Emphasize the details of your work experience that apply to a specific job or company and ignore other areas. You can never tell it all anyhow so why not tell the things that will interest a specific target?

In the next Management Forum column I will discuss the art of face-to-face interviews. No matter what your qualifications, experience, or references, if you blow the interview you are likely to lose the job. To avoid this kind of catastrophe, read my next column for practical hints and advice on the employment interview.

How to survive the face-to-face interview

The second in a multi-part series
on the employment situation

Dr. T. F. Gautschi, P.E.

The most important part of applying for a job are those few minutes when you are face to face with the company's interviewers. No matter what your qualifications, experience or references, if you blow the interview, you are likely to lose the job.

Here is what you should do:

Appear interested and be familiar with the company. Bone up on its products or services, markets, competition, etc. Be sure to read the company's own literature if it's available.

BRING SUPPORTING MATERIAL

Take along appropriate samples of your work and records of achievement to support your job application. If you haven't supplied a resume in advance, bring one with you.

DO YOUR HOMEWORK

The interview shows your ability to handle yourself with other people. Don't be argumentative. You might argue yourself right out of the job. Even if the interviewer is offensive, you can't afford to lose your temper. In fact, he may be testing you. Some company interviewers evaluate the applicant on how he reacts to stress situations. Don't panic. Answer questions briefly and as naturally as possible. If you've done your homework, you're less likely to get rattled. The interviewer expects a certain amount of nervousness. Recruiters see a great number of candidates each year, and say that many survive even the most embarrassing moments. One eager young man, when invited to be seated by a recruiter, grasped the armrests of two chairs behind him and plunged to the floor between them. He got up, apologized and won the job, in part because he refused to let the momentary embarrassment panic him.

KEEP YOUR COOL

Many applicants get carried away with their own thoughts and in their quest for details about the position, make the recruiter feel as if he's the one being interviewed. Express interest without being too aggressive. Be a counter-puncher. Let the interviewer provide the leads and respond accordingly. Discuss what the interviewer wants to talk about.

DON'T INTERVIEW THE INTERVIEWER

Many applicants lose out because they simply don't know what they want to do. Others seek jobs for which they're unprepared—the engineer, for example, who applies for a position as an insurance sales manager though he has never had experience making personal contacts.

ESTABLISH YOUR OBJECTIVES

Try to enter the interview with realistic job objectives. Look ahead four or five years and establish career goals to match your interests, abilities, and past performance. Narrow down your choices. As an engineer, for instance, you should know whether you want to work in a production plant or in a research environment.

TELL IT AS IT IS

Boasting about your abilities is dangerous. Even if you have exceptional talents, the interviewer may consider you a braggart. Understatement will do more good. Exaggerations or false claims made to impress the interviewer may come back to haunt you. If he checks your story and finds holes in it, your chances for the job will evaporate. If your misrepresentation is discovered after you get the job, the results will not only be embarrassing, they might ruin your career.

EMPHASIZE WHAT YOU CAN DO

Interviewers say too many applicants have the attitude, "What rewards will you offer to get me to produce?" This cart-before-the-horse approach raises questions about the job hunters' motivation. An interviewer looks more kindly on those who take the position, "Here is what I think I can do for your company" and who assume they will be rewarded if they produce. When possible, try not to bring up the subject of money. Let the interviewer begin the salary talk. When the question of "salary requirements" arises, most agree it best to state that salary is "open" and is dependent on the position and potential of the position.

BE PROMPT

Don't be late for the interview and don't overstay your welcome. When it's time

JOB SOURCES

to go, leave briskly and confidently. Make your last impression a positive one. Avoid a bad beginning or ending and you will go a long way toward winning the job you're after.

Many sources and media exist and all should be utilized in seeking another position:

Newspaper Classified Ads—Examples: local papers, small town weekly papers, large city papers like *The New York Times, The Wall Street Journal*, technical publications, etc. Ads may be inserted by a company looking for an employee or by an individual seeking a position.

Employment Agencies—A good company-paid agency can sometimes unlock doors that would otherwise be closed to you. You pay them nothing since they receive a commission from the company once you are hired. Some are very reputable and are held in high esteem for their skills by many companies and employers.

Employment Offices of small and large companies

Associations—The IEEE would be a good example; and of course, there are many others to which you or your coworkers belong.

Friends and Relatives—Make it known to as many people as possible that you are seeking employment.

Consulting Firms

Alumni Placement Offices

State Division of Employment Security

Magazines—Technical journals may be helpful.

Don't panic, be patient, be persistent, and remember, you have a good product to sell—yourself.

How to conduct
a selection interview

*"... the first opinion which one forms of a prince, and of his understanding, is
by observing the men he has around him; and when they are capable and faithful
he may always be considered wise, because he has known how to recognize the
capable and to keep them faithful. But when they are otherwise one cannot form
a good opinion of him, for the prime error which he made was in choosing them."*
The Prince - *1513, Nicolo Machiavelli*

**IMPORTANCE OF
HUMAN RESOURCES**

A major point stressed throughout Management Forum is that the success of a manager and his organization is determined by the quality of its human resources. If the people are well trained, motivated and work together, the organization will usually be a success. Consequently, one of the major tasks of a manager is to develop a work environment that will attract, maintain, motivate and improve people.

Usually when a person is brought in to manage an organization he has to work with the human resources already in place. But once in a while the manager gets the opportunity to select a subordinate. And it is this selection process that I would like to discuss.

**SELECTION IS
A TWO-WAY
COMMUNICATION
PROCESS**

Selection is important because it has such a direct influence on the success of your organization, perhaps more than any other activity you will be involved in. You should give a great deal of thought and effort to it. It is far better to make a good selection in the first place than it is to try changing a person after he has become part of your organization.

The employment selection interview is a communication process that not only has a significant effect upon the organization, it also involves the hopes, aspirations and possible future directions that the life of the interviewee will take. Aside from selecting a mate for life, the acceptance of a job is one of the most important decisions a person makes in his lifetime. In this sense it has many of the characteristics of a marriage contract. Unfortunately, decisions are usually based upon the interviewer's impressions of you and your impressions of him in the all-too-brief association of the employment interview. This hardly seems fair to either party, yet it is the most often used method of selection.

**PROXIMAL CUES CAN
BE MISLEADING**

It is difficult to measure the suitability of a person for a given position. You are usually interested in the candidate's technical capability and such characteristics as honesty, willingness to work, ability to get along with others, emotional stability, self-confidence and ability to plan and organize. You cannot measure these characteristics directly. You usually have to resort to discernible symbolic representations of what you are interested in measuring—proximal cues (Lens model, *Design News* 2-3-75). These cues combine to form the "lens" through which you view the interviewee. For example, if the person you are interviewing has a nice firm handshake, good consistent eye contact, a warm and friendly voice, appears cleancut and is reasonably well dressed you are likely to judge that person as a good person for your organization—especially if he also has a reasonably attractive resume and you only have 30 minutes for your interview. The unfortunate thing is that these obvious proximal cues can prejudice your judgment regarding the candidate.

Try to avoid the "halo" effect in which you let one prominent characteristic or your initial impression overshadow all others. For example: some are turned off if the candidate has a low grade point average. Some are turned on by a high grade point average—especially if it is from a prestige school.

No matter how much you read about the subject of interviewing, nothing will help so much as planning and carrying out an actual interview yourself.

You can read some good books on how to play tennis, but you really cannot learn to play without spending many hours on the court hitting balls. Interviewing is the same way.

Most managers have the basic skills to handle an interview and with careful thought and preparation should be able to do a good job.

TWO MAIN FUNCTIONS

As interviewer, you have two main functions—to obtain information and to evaluate information. Some information will be clear-cut facts, but the balance will have to be inferred from clues and references.

It's a good idea to prepare a list of areas you are interested in exploring. This list should be based upon the responsibilities and requirements of the position to be filled.

Get information in chronological order—start with the first job and work up to the present.

Do *not* take notes during the interview—this can result in a loss of rapport you are trying to establish. Try not to break eye contact. Be sure to record your notes immediately following the interview—especially if you are conducting several.

Try to encourage the candidate to talk freely and spontaneously because that is when you learn the most about him. The challenge is to guide the discussion into areas you are interested in. Try not to talk too much. You should not take more than 20% of the total time (that's just 6 minutes in a 30-minute session).

Ask open-ended questions—not questions that can be easily answered by a yes or no response.

Try *not* to ask leading questions.

wrong: *"I assume your college grades were good."*
better: *"How were your grades in school?"*
wrong: *"Did you leave the XYZ company because of a lack of opportunity for advancement?"*
better: *"Why did you leave the XYZ company?"*
wrong: *"Do you understand what I am saying?"*
better: *"How do you feel about the situation?"*

Your "rejection filter" will be set by how truthful you believe the candidate to be—is he telling the whole truth or is he coloring certain aspects to make them sound better? His willingness to discuss his shortcomings and the consistency of his responses should give you some clues in this area.

DON'T TALK TOO MUCH

Try to get the candidate's likes and dislikes regarding the job you are discussing—this can give you valuable information regarding his capabilities.

The pattern of previous earnings is often a valid indication of job progress to date—a level salary profile could be probed by a question like, "How do you feel about your salary progress?"

Ask the candidate to discuss his achievements, his development needs, factors he feels are important to job satisfaction, and his present interests and hobbies.

ENDING INTERVIEW

Try to terminate the interview on a positive note. When the candidate is not the best qualified for your particular job try to remember his feelings and the company's reputation. When the candidate is well qualified, try to sell the job. Be specific regarding opportunities, salary and benefits.

Remember, the people that you hire today will determine the long-run success of your company.

Our next article will review the important subject of matching the employee's expectations with those of the organization. This could well be one of the most critical areas in the selection process—especially for the recent college graduate.

"Even if deceit were not as despicable to every right-minded man as it is, the negotiator will perhaps bear in mind that he will be engaged throughout life upon the affairs of diplomacy, and that it is therefore his interest to establish a reputation for plain and fair dealing so that men may know that they can rely upon him."

Monsieur de Callieres 1716

Dr. T.F. Gautschi, P.E.

Matches and mismatches in the employment situation

How to avoid disappointment in both employer and employee

MISMATCH AFFECTS JOB PERFORMANCE

I wonder if we give enough thought to the match or mismatch between an employee's expectations and those of the organization. We should, because the magnitude of the mismatch will have a direct impact on the employee's performance on the job. The time that we can do most about this is when we are bringing an employee into our organization, or when we are moving an employee to another position.

EXPECTATIONS

As managers, we and the employee have expectations about what the job entails—the career paths, its status, its challenges, the standards and rules to be observed, the amount of effort required, the overall job environment, and so

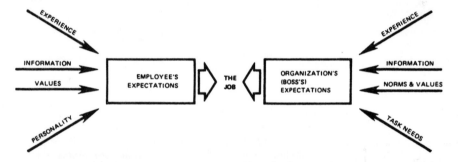

on—but we don't often talk about them in any detailed or systematic manner.

THE EMPLOYEE

An employee's expectations are influenced by past experiences, and their image of the organization as gained from their values, their personality, how they view the overall work environment and their interaction with representatives of the organization.

THE BOSS

In turn, the organization (the boss) has expectations based upon past experience, organizational norms and values, information that is available about the employee, the organizational environment, and the characteristics of the tasks to be performed.

MISMATCH IN ACTION

The problem is that the boss usually does not spend enough time with the person about to join the organization to be sure that there is a reasonably good match between the expectations of the organization and those of the employee. As a consequence, there is a high probability that there will be a certain amount of mismatch between how the employee perceives the job and how management perceives it. As time goes on both the boss and the employee will gradually become aware of these differences. The employee may very well begin to feel that the job was misrepresented and that the opportunities for creativity, challenge, promotion, discretion, and whatever else he thinks was "promised" was really a facade to get him to join the organization. Also he may feel that there are far too many rules, policies, procedures and standards to be followed that were never discussed. In turn, the boss may feel that the employee has not performed up to the expectations, and does not exhibit the enthusiasm, initiative and cooperation that was expected.

Mismatched expectations are inevitable. However, the earlier that the differences in expectations can be identified, the more effective will be their remedies. For example, a relationship that would involve a completely unacceptable mismatch should be terminated at the onset without further investment on anyone's part. Any other action would be mismanagement.

Too often neither the employee nor the manager has the motivation, awareness or the tools to really determine what their expectations are. So we tend to "play it by ear", and then try to correct the problems when they surface at a later date, often after there is considerable damage to the relationship. That is, the employee "hangs in there" trying to make the best of an unacceptable situation and the organization tries to accommodate the employee the best that it can under the circumstances; or the employee leaves the organization and the organization has to find a new employee and start the cycle over again—hopefully with better results. This can be an expensive process in terms of organizational effectiveness, as well as in recruiting and training costs.

One approach to identifying our expectations is to think about and list them in two classes: **core**—necessary ground rules, no compromise, needs; **non-core**—flexible methods, compromisable, wants.

The important thing for both the employee and the organization is to identify which of their expectations are **CORE**. Then, if agreement can be reached in this

area, more than likely the expectations in the other areas can be worked out.

For example, if the job requires extensive travel and the employee does not want to travel very much, there is probably no hope for the relationship and it should be terminated. On the other hand, perhaps something can be worked out when social contribution is a core factor for the employee and it has not been a particular interest for the organization.

CONTRACT SETTING

In a very real sense this matching-up process can be viewed as a contract-setting activity. That is, the manager and the employee each try to describe their core expectations to the satisfaction of the other, and then mutually agree that they can be fulfilled. In addition to providing a common base of expectations, this process should lay the foundation for a healthy relationship involving trust, candor and two-way communication.

POSSIBLE SOLUTION

Check lists or questionnaires for both the manager and the employee should be developed to guide the implementation of this contract-setting process. Recent *Design News* Management Forum articles on Motivation and Employee Loyalty should be helpful in this activity. Such a questionnaire should provide a basis for both the manager and the employee to compare their expectations regarding the job. This can be accomplished by asking each party to respond to the questionnaire; then they should compare and discuss their responses. Some areas where differences are likely to be identified are those relating to career path opportunities, personal development opportunities, job security, ability and interest in working with groups, opportunities for creative and innovative activities, freedom to make decisions, and the social relevance of the job.

CONTRACT REVIEW

Over time it is quite likely that the expectations of the employee and the organization will change. So the better managers will review the "contract" with the employee periodically to keep it up to date, and to keep the lines of communication open.

NOTE: The basic concept, and some of the terminology discussed in this article were picked up at a seminar presented by Dr. Alan Frohman of Pugh-Roberts Assoc., Cambridge, MA. Dr. Frohman has developed a set of questionnaires, which are available on a fee basis, to help companies improve their "joining-up process".

The management assessment center

Dr. T. F. Gautschi, P. E.

The quality of human resources is critical to effective and efficient performance. All other resources when utilized decline in value, while human resources have the inherent capacity to develop and become more valuable. Whether this happens and whether individual companies will have sufficient number of qualified managers depends upon management action now.[1]

The assessment center is a technique which has been used by a number of companies, both large and small, to identify management potential and individual management development needs. Basically it consists of a series of realistic situational exercises in which a number of participants take part while being observed by several raters. Depending upon its purpose and the organizational level of the participants, an assessment center will last from one to about two and one-half days.

Simulated managing

The exercises are simulated management tasks and may include group analysis of case studies, individual fact-finding and decision-making situations (such as case studies or 'in-basket' exercises) and participation in computer supported business simulations in competition with other management teams.

The case studies are based upon real life situations and usually involve several problems and generally do not have one best solution.

The in-basket exercise is supposed to simulate the contents of a typical manager's in-basket. The participant

1. "Management Development Can Be More Effective", P. R. Cone and R. N. McKinney, *California Management Review*, Spring 1972.

is instructed to go through the basket's contents as he would in real life—establishing priorities, solving problems, answering questions, scheduling, planning and communicating as appropriate.

The business simulation involves several management teams. Each team manages a different corporation—together they make up an industry. They compete against each other in the same markets. The teams make various management decisions —such as product price, product quality, advertising expenditures, plant investment, R&D investment, the number of units to be produced, etc. These management decisions are then processed by a computer program, and each team receives a printout covering certain general industry information and their own decisions and their consequences.

Participation in an assessment center program can also be a useful management development experience in itself—both for the participants and for the raters, who are often a management level or two above the participants.

Management potential

The assessment center is especially helpful for identifying the management potential of non-management people—for example, the professional engineer who thinks he may want to go into management. Participation in such a process will give both management and the participant useful information regarding his interest, competence and perhaps his potential for operating as a manager. It may also identify areas where the potential manager has needs for further training. Management acceptance of the assessment center is often high because the technique looks valid and

"makes sense".

When participation in an assessment center is offered early in a person's career—perhaps during the second or third year of employment —it can provide valuable input regarding career interests and potential, and appropriate administrative action can be taken at an early date. In some firms assessment center candidates are nominated by their supervisors; others also encourage their employees to volunteer when they think they are ready.

The assessment center report should not be some sort of go or no-go document. Rather it should indicate the participants' strengths and weaknesses in relation to what the firm has identified as areas that are important to the firm's success.

Assessment center weaknesses

A potential weakness in the assessment center concept is the difficulty of determining what factors are important for success. There is always the potential for inbreeding in this technique. For example, what is useful for a firm just starting up may not be useful for the mature firm. Also, there is the self-fulfilling prophecy problem. That is, when certain people are identified as good management material they become so because everyone treats them that way—or, what may be worse, someone who does not fare well in the assessment center may never be given the opportunity to prove otherwise.

Assessment center evaluation should not be the primary criterion for career path selection and potential, but it does appear that if it is used properly it can provide some very helpful insight into the situation both for the participant and for management.

Dr. T.F. Gautschi, P.E.

Performance appraisal

A vital element in every manager's job

APPRAISAL PITFALLS

Terms like performance appraisal, merit rating, counseling, performance reviews, development reviews, and the like, often generate strong reactions.

- They involve assessments of a person's contributions and abilities, which can have a strong impact upon their self-image and subsequent performance.
- Bosses are often uncomfortable when they are put in a position of evaluating another person—in a sense playing God.
- The organization can suffer a loss in productivity due to deterioration of interpersonal relationships.
- Employees receiving low evaluations will often respond with a reduced level of performance.
- For many, a performance appraisal has proved to be a very frustrating experience, or one that turned out to be simply a hollow exercise. The purposes for the appraisal are not always clear, and the techniques utilized are not always appropriate.
- Standards and ratings tend to vary widely and often seem unfair.
- Bosses do not always know how to conduct an appraisal.
- Personal values and bias sometimes distort organizational standards.
- Often too much emphasis is placed upon the form and not enough emphasis is placed upon the content of an appraisal.
- Sometimes attempts are made to compensate for poor initial selection by enforcing a formal appraisal program.
- Performance appraisals may interfere with more constructive coaching relationships by emphasizing the boss's role as judge.
- In some cases, due to lack of communications, employees do not know how they are rated.

APPRAISAL SIGNIFICANCE

In spite of all these problems, managers cannot escape the responsibility for making judgments about subordinates—judgments that will have a significant influence upon their assignments, their salary levels, and perhaps their overall career paths. Such judgments may vary from not being written down, or following any rational procedure, to a very formal over-documented mess of red tape.

The purpose of this article is to explore some of the fundamental issues relating to performance appraisal, and to provide some guidelines for dealing with this most important, but often misunderstood subject.

The vast majority of U.S. companies claim to have some sort of performance appraisal program. However, in actual practice many programs have yielded unsatisfactory or disappointing results. Some critics have even suggested abandoning all performance appraisal procedures as a lost hope. (This would be like burning my tennis racket because it doesn't make good shots. What I should do is select the proper racket and learn to use it correctly—that is, if I want to continue to play tennis.)

A major problem is created by confusion regarding objectives.

- Management usually wants a system that will identify and motivate high performers to do even better—and to identify low performers and cause them to improve or be removed from the organization.
- Managers, and employee relations people, want accurate and complete back-up data for decisions involving salary levels, promotions, pay increases, transfers, training needs, dismissals and the like.
- Top management sometimes requires an assessment of human resource capability for long-range planning purposes.
- Subordinates want to know how they are perceived by their bosses, how they can increase their value to the organization and what the future holds for them in the organization.

IDENTIFY OBJECTIVES

Thus, the first step for management should be to identify specifically what their objectives are for the appraisal program. Then they should plan to employ the appropriate techniques to assure that the objectives are met. This planning should be approached like any other major project and involve widespread discussion and agreement, and adequate training for all supervisors.

GIVE APPRAISALS HIGH PRIORITY

A major shortcoming for most programs is a lack of commitment and understanding by those involved regarding the purposes for which the program is being established. Performance appraisal is an important element of every manager's job and should be given priority in terms of time and energy. They are *not* easy to conduct, and what makes them especially critical is that unless they are properly carried out, they can cause more harm than good. Another important point to remember is that, in most cases, the boss is the link between the employee and the company, and the boss should conduct himself accordingly.

REACTION APPRAISALS

When adequate plans are not established, and a recognized performance evaluation is not implemented, the evaluation process becomes very muddled.

- Subordinates try to interpret their value to the company on the basis of what they think the boss thinks about them, the assignments and salary they receive, bits and scraps of information picked up in conversations, peer analysis, self-analysis, and perhaps how they feel their subordinates regard them.
- Management makes 'guesstimates' regarding who are the high and low performers based upon visibility and personal contact.
- Back-up data for employee relations actions will often be subjective and incomplete.
- Assessment of human resource capability is generalized without specific back-up information.

These are all basically *reaction* appraisals, and managers make them every day in their encounters with people—and properly so, because they help to refine the mental models that managers employ when they think about themselves and others. However, these are quite different from career-influencing well-planned *managerial* appraisals that provide the balance and rationality that is required by today's organizational environments. A discussion of current appraisal techniques will be the subject of the next issue of "Management Forum".

Dr. T.F. Gautschi, P.E.

Performance appraisal techniques

Match the technique(s) to the objectives

In the previous issue of Management Forum (*Design News* 7-19-76) we discussed four major issues associated with performance appraisal:

- The strong reactions generated by the concept.
- The confusion regarding objectives.
- The necessity for commitment and understanding by those involved.
- The requirement for using appropriate techniques to fulfill the objectives.

OBJECTIVES DETERMINE TECHNIQUE(S)

Today's organizational environment requires the introduction of well planned *managerial* appraisal programs to add balance and rationality to the *reaction* appraisals that most managers make intuitively. These programs should be approached like any other major project and involve widespread participation in terms of defining objectives and selecting alternatives. The selection of the appropriate combination of appraisal techniques should be dictated by the objectives that management establishes for the program. For example, it has been my experience that it is not good practice to confuse salary review sessions with coaching and career planning discussions.

APPRAISAL TECHNIQUES

Seven alternative techniques that are available for management's consideration, listed roughly in order of popularity include:

1. graphic scale ratings
2. narrative appraisals
3. critical incident appraisals
4. forced-choice ratings
5. management by objectives
6. ranking techniques
7. assessment center evaluations.

EMPLOYEE'S CHARACTERISTICS

Graphic scale ratings

This is the most widely used rating method. Basically it involves rating the individual on a number of characteristics according to some sort of scale. The characteristics may relate to quality of work, quantity of work, job knowledge and education, work attitude, cooperation, punctuality, initiative, dependability, and other job-related factors. The scale may consist of a number of points (like 1 to 10), or involve descriptive phrases (like outstanding, above average, average or below average).

This technique does not provide a great deal of information, but generally it is consistent, reliable, and easy to use. In some applications the boss never shows the employee the rating sheet, but in most cases the boss and the subordinate discuss the rating and then both of them sign it—especially if one of the objectives is to improve communication between the boss and the subordinate.

An interesting variation for the application of this technique is to have both the subordinate and the boss complete the form independently, and then get together and compare ratings in order to arrive at agreement.

INDIVIDUAL'S STRENGTHS, NEEDS

Narrative appraisals

In this situation the evaluator prepares a paragraph or two covering such factors as the individual's strengths, development needs, potential capability and accomplishments. Narrative appraisals are often used to supplement graphic scale ratings—especially when they are unusually high or low. They are also used in employee selection situations—such descriptions often carry significant weight when prepared by former employers, associates or teachers. Although narrative appraisals often reveal important factors regarding the person being evaluated, they are difficult to combine or compare.

FACTUAL INCIDENTS

Critical incident appraisals

This technique requires the boss to document actual factual incidents that involve the employee being rated—they should include incidents of both favorable and unfavorable behavior and cover the entire appraisal period. In theory this is an excellent technique because it permits the appraisal interview to concentrate on facts and not upon the traits and characteristics of a person. In some organizations such back-up information is almost indispensible when the boss wishes to discharge an employee. The critical incident technique can also be used to supplement the graphic scale rating technique.

Unfortunately, the critical incident method has shortcomings:
—It takes a significant amount of the boss's time to jot down the critical incidents as they occur.
—It could generate an undesirable work environment, especially if the incidents are stored up and not discussed at their time of occurence.

TYPICAL STATEMENTS

Forced-choice ratings

This method requires the rater to choose from among a group of statements the ones most typical of the individual being rated, and the least typical. The results are then scored in accordance with some sort of weighting table which is not available to the rater. Quite a bit of time and care is required to prepare the necessary statements, but it may be worth it to reduce bias and establish some sort of objective standards. This method often generates more heat than light in performance appraisal interviews, and as a consequence is not often used.

EMPLOYER-EMPLOYEE EVALUATION

Management by objectives

The general MBO concept is discussed in previous "Management Forum" articles (*Design News* 7-7-75, 1-12-76, 1-26-76, 2-9-76 and 2-23-76).

Briefly this program involves three steps:
—The individual and his boss discuss and agree upon the content of the job and the relative importance of the major duties as related to the objectives of the organization.
—The individual then proposes and negotiates with his boss goals to be attained by a specified date; and appropriate intermediate checkpoints are established.
—The individual and his boss then meet at the end of the specified period to evaluate the results vs. goals and to start the cycle over again.

It is important that the individual and boss have a common understanding regarding the things the employee is being paid to do and what he is responsible for. This concept should be applicable to any appraisal technique.

Experience has also revealed that employees at the lower levels are not always comfortable with setting their own goals, and in some applications MBO can become a kind of manipulative form of management in which participation is a facade, and management ends up imposing its standards and objectives upon the employee.

SUBJECTIVE JUDGMENTS

Ranking techniques

This method is useful for "totem-poling" the members of an organization for purposes of identifying the high potential members and the low potential members; and it is sometimes used to develop lay-off lists when force reduction is necessary. It involves overall subjective judgments. The two most commonly used methods are alternation ranking and paired comparison ranking.

Alternation ranking involves alternately choosing the most valuable and least valuable employee from a random order list.

Paired-comparison ranking compares every person on a random order list with every other person in accordance with the chosen criteria. Then the person with the most marks (favorable comparisons) is number one, the next most is number two, etc.

FUTURE PERFORMANCE

Assessment center evaluations

All of the above methods stress past performance as a basis for predicting future performance. The assessment evaluation is intended to predict future performance, or potential, on the basis of an assessment center evaluation.

Usually, the employees under consideration are brought together, and spend several days in a work-like environment completing individual and group tasks under the observation of trained observers. A combined judgment of the observers is then used to prepare a rank ordering of the individuals involved.

9

Organization for the dynamic environment

Dr. T. F. Gautschi, P. E.

Less than 100 years ago the horse was our fastest individual mode of transportation. Thirty years ago the fastest airplane had a speed of about 500 miles per hour. Today man travels to the moon and back at thousands of miles per hour. The power of weapons has increased from the bow and arrow to the multi-target thermonuclear bomb. The number of books and papers published is increasing dramatically, as is the energy consumption per capita. This is the dynamic environment for organizations.

DYNAMIC ENVIRONMENT

There is no sure way to corporate security and sustained success in this kind of environment. No corporation or product line is completely immune to obsolescence, and a company can fail quickly if its management is not sensitive and skillful in recognizing and dealing with technological change, and relating it to the other forces in the business environment.

Indeed, a single technological improvement can overpower almost any degree of productivity or make a product line obsolete. The atomic bomb, computers, guided missiles, nuclear power and transistor are all examples of this.

In short, we operate in a dynamic technological environment. It places unique burdens upon us to assure that the products we develop are technologically current—especially in performance and cost—and yet do not push the state-of-the-art too hard.

NO FIRM IS IMMUNE TO OBSOLESCENCE

I remember a TV manufacturer whose chief engineer was a genius; yet his company went broke. The problem was that when production got tooled up and the company could start deliveries, the chief engineer would come up with a change to improve product performance. As a result, the company had the best performing TV on the market; but it was also the costliest; and unfortunately production couldn't meet delivery commitments.

POPULATION CONCENTRATION

We have not always worked in such a changing environment. At the end of World War I the United States was the world's foremost industrial power, yet over half its population lived in rural areas and small towns. Today, two-thirds of the people in the United States live in 312 urban sprawls extending thirty-five miles or more out from each central city. These population concentrations have developed because our economy, driven by technology, requires large concentrations of specialized labor.

BRAWN TO BRAIN

During the past fifty years the population and the working force has doubled; so has the proportion of white-collar workers to blue. The average work week has shrunk from fifty to forty hours. Yet total product has multiplied five times. This has been made possible by a significant increase in productivity, or output per man-hour, the result of better management and applied technology. In fact, as our society becomes better educated, and automation increases, our strategy for raising productivity has shifted from brawn to brain.

**ADOLESCENT
ECONOMY**

Early in our history management was geared to meet the needs of an adolescent economy—the development and acquisition of machines and tools. Later it shifted

**ADVANCED
ECONOMY**

to the needs of a growing economy—the development of more effective power sources and communications facilities. In recent years the objectives of management have been directed towards the needs of an advanced economy—research, product development, and managerial efficiency. Each successive achievement in technology builds upon what has gone before and opens up, in turn, new developments beyond it. Engineering and scientific progress, and their impact upon our society, is thus like a snowball rolling downhill. It gathers mass and momentum at an accelerating rate. Increasing amounts of time, money and knowledge are required to produce successive products. At the same time their useful life is decreasing.

**SHORTER
PRODUCT LIFE**

For example, Lord Nelson's flagship was forty years old at Trafalgar and was still a first-class ship of the line, but Halsey's Enterprise, which cost more, was obsolete within a few years after its construction. The B-36 bomber took ten years to design and develop, but was operational for less than four years.

**MANAGEMENT
CHALLENGE**

The challenge is rapidly becoming one of managing highly educated people; of managing technological innovation; and of managing highly complex social organizations.

To cope with this challenge, I believe there are some significant steps a company can take:

FLEXIBILITY

- The firm must be organized for timely and effective decision-making. This requires flexibility and quick reaction. Organizational "constipation" can not be tolerated. A company must be able to "read" the situation and take the appropriate action—much like the quarterback on a football team who reads the defense and calls an audible play change at the line of scrimmage.

TIMING

- The firm must have a good sense of timing—especially since the opportunity windows (the time period when value exceeds cost) are becoming shorter. If a firm tries to enter a product market too early, it will experience high costs. When it enters too late, profits are too small.

- The firm must have short effective communication links and patterns. Two approaches involve ad hoc task forces, and a minimum of management layers.

- Management must be knowledgeable about the firm's products and business, and must be involved in what is going on.

WILL TO SUCCEED

- There must be a strong will to succeed at all levels of management. Self-perception is as important to an organization as it is to an individual. When a football team goes onto the field expecting to be beaten, it usually is. When a firm does not expect to succeed, it usually doesn't.

GOALS

- The firm must have a good sense of direction and specific goals. Objectives and strategies must be based upon a realistic analysis and forecast of the market and a realistic assessment of the company's total resources.

- The firm has to decide whether it will be a technological leader or follower. There is a certain prestige associated with being a successful technological pioneer, but this does not automatically result in business success. On the other hand, the follower may never catch up when the technological time scale is short.

- The firm must invest the proper amount in R&D, as well as in manpower development, production resources, market penetration, and the like.

KEEP INFORMED   We, as engineers and engineering managers, must remain fully aware of the significant technological trends that can affect our business, and keep management informed so that they can properly factor the trends into our company's planning activities.

Managing the engineering spectrum

Our place within the broad spectrum of engineering activity should influence how we manage.

For purpose of analysis I have found it convenient to divide engineering into eight categories under the major headings of research, development and support engineering.

1   2   3   4   5   6   7   8
Research-Development-Support

Research
1. Work producing knowledge for its own sake.
2. Exploratory work in the field of interest with the objective to advance the state-of-the-art.
3. Exploratory work in a field of interest prerequisite to the development of a component or system.

Development
4. Design, fabrication and test of a component to be used as part of a larger system, e.g., gyroscopes, relays, valves, special film circuits.
5. Design, fabrication and test of a new system, e.g., centrifuge, computer, communication system, a nonpolluting gasoline engine.
6. Preparation of a major improvement to a current product.

Support Engineering
7. Production support and the preparation of minor improvements to a current product.
8. Troubleshooting and maintenance of a current product.

ENGINEERING SPECTRUM
Using this categorization several observations can be made that should influence the engineering manager's perception of his job.

The risk involved in completing a product that meets the specifications decreases as the project moves from research to support.

The cumulative resource requirement increases rapidly as a project enters the development phase.

At the research end, planning should not be very detailed and should be tentative at best.

At the support end there is no question about the feasibility of the project, and its planning can be very detailed and specific. The performance, schedule and cost

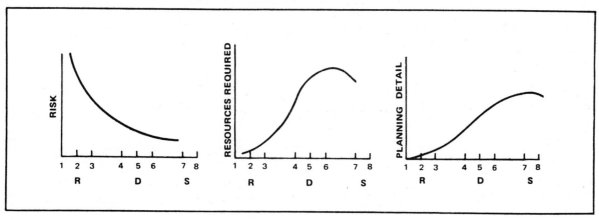

factors can also be closely predicted.

The number of people involved in a program increases dramatically as the project moves into the development phase. This places greater emphasis upon planning and control, organizing, communication and leadership perspectives.

The engineering manager must determine where his project is along the engineering spectrum and conduct his management process accordingly. Planning and coordinating research too tightly could be a mistake.

**NINE WAYS TO
REDUCE CREATIVITY**

Dr. W.B. McLean, an eminent Navy Laboratory Director, supports this position by listing nine ways to change a creative research laboratory into one doing only routine work.

- Coordinate work carefully to avoid duplication.
- Keep the check reins tight; define mission clearly; follow time scales. (New and interesting ideas may not work and always need extra time.)
- Concentrate on planning and scheduling and insist on meeting time scales. (New and interesting ideas may not work and always need extra time.)
- Insure full output by rigorous adherence to the schedule. (The creative man sometimes remembers his ideas, but his delay in working on them helps to dissipate them.)
- Insist that all plans go through at least three levels of review before starting work.
- Sub-optimize to insure that each component is as nearly perfect as possible.
- Centralize as many functions as possible. (This creates more review levels and cuts down on direct contact between people.)
- Strive to avoid mistakes. (This increases the filter action of review.)
- Strive for a stable, successful, productive organization. (This justifies opposition to change.)

On the other hand, lack of adequate planning, organization controls, and communication when required during the development phase can be even more serious because of the significant resource commitments involved. No one wants a program that costs too much, takes too much time to develop and doesn't meet the performance requirements.

We must match our management approaches to the position of the program on the engineering spectrum.

Functional and program organization

Our advanced economy requires that the efforts of many people be blended together in a meaningful and coordinated fashion to produce its goods and services efficiently—we call this *organization.*

My purpose, in this and the succeeding article, is to explore two basic organizational forms that relate to engineering and engineering management—functional and program—and to describe the phases that an organization experiences as it matures.

Organization design must keep pace with technological development—otherwise we will find ourselves faced with the problem of trying to deal with complex, dynamic situations with outmoded tools.

Under the functional organization, personnel are grouped by the function they perform—marketing, finance, manufacturing, engineering. These may be further divided by subfunction—mechanical, electrical, systems and the like.

**FUNCTIONAL
ORGANIZATION**

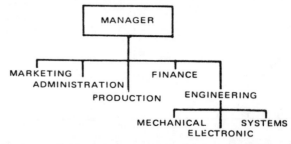

The traditional functional organization assumes that there will be a continuous flow of products or services, without major deviation in the performed tasks. This organizational form is sometimes termed *bureaucratic,* and is characterized by: a well-defined hierarchy of authority, systems of rules and procedures for dealing with work situations, and promotion and selection based upon technical competence.

In contrast, the program orientation groups personnel by major programs. Typically, the program organization is an adaptive, problem-solving, temporary system of diverse specialists linked together by a common goal. As such, it is responsible for completing a unique and specified objective on schedule and within the resources allocated—a batch type of process.

PROGRAM ORGANIZATION

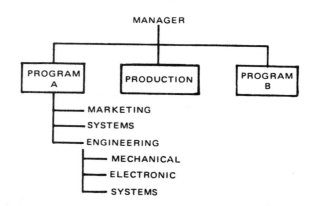

ORGANIZATIONS COMPARED

A multi-product company will usually have some combination of functional and program organization, because there are advantages (and disadvantages) to both types of organization in their pure forms:

Program advantages
(batch processing)
- Stimulates innovation
- Better program control & decision making
- Better customer relations
- Shorter product development time
- Greater employee satisfaction
- Lower program costs
- Improved quality & reliability
- Higher profit margins
- Better control over program security
- Better response to priorities

Functional advantages
(repetitive processing)
- Better long-range planning
- Better personnel career paths & technical depth
- Better utilization of key personnel, facilities & previous developments
- Better application of design standards & company policies
- No major disruptions when a program is completed

The appropriate type of organization usually changes as a program proceeds through the R&D spectrum.

At the research end the essential creativity and innovation is usually best achieved by a minimum of "co-plan" activity (control, coordination, communication and planning).

During the development phase, which usually involves risk, innovation, and significant resource allocations, co-plan activities become important—it is usually during this phase that a program manager can be of greatest use in the multi-product company.

The support phase, which involves production and production support, field maintenance and related functions, tends to be organized on a functional basis because the tasks involved are likely to be repetitive.

The program/functional interaction usually exists in one of three basic combinations: *Autonomous, Matrix* or *Influence.*

ORGANIZATIONS INTERACT

Autonomous

- Program manager has virtually full authority within the company to complete the assignment
- For large programs this organization structure approaches being a separate company or major division

Matrix

- Authority is shared between functional and program management
- Program manager determines *what* and *where*
- Functional manager determines *who* and *how*
- Program manager has planning and budget control
- Functional manager has administrative responsibility for manpower resources.

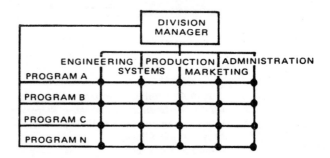

Influence

- Staff to the general manager
- Program management has no direct authority over the work being done in the functional organizations
- Functional management has budget control
- Program manager is basically a progress/status reporter

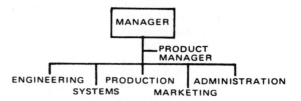

WHAT SHOULD YOU USE?

General Observations

1. A very large program should be organized around an *Autonomous* program manager.
2. A multiple-product line company should use some form of *Matrix* organization.
3. A single-product line company should use the *Influence* type of organization.

Program characteristics

- Is critical to the company, relatively large in scope, or is unique to the existing organizations
- Has a defined end-product
- Involves the participation of organizations outside of program manager's control
- Has a high proportion of professionals
- Involves some uncertainty and innovation
  Essentially "R & D on schedule"
- Has a terminal date
- Is usually task-oriented
- Is complex with respect to detail task interdependencies

Program Management Task Overview
Functional Tasks
- Planning
- Organizing
- Directing
- Controlling/coordinating

Operational Tasks
- Communications
- Decision Making

TASK REVIEW

These two functions above overlay all four management functions (planning, organizing, directing and controlling) and are essential for effective management. They are about equal in importance. Program managers give slightly more emphasis to decision making. Subordinates tend to stress communications a little more. Face-to-face communications are given primary emphasis by program managers.

In an attempt to use the advantages of both the functional and program type of organization, most firms combine the two—with the upper levels of the organization having a functional orientation and the lower levels using the program or adaptive orientation.

"We trained hard . . . but it seemed that every time we were beginning to form up into teams we would be reorganized. I was to learn later in life that we tend to meet any new situation by reorganizing; and a wonderful method it can be for creating the illusion of progress while producing confusion, inefficiency and demoralization."

Petronius Arbiter, 210 B.C.

The advantages of program organization

Although program management (or adaptive) organization is a relatively recent innovation, it has been gaining favor because it has advantages over a purely functional orientation in a dynamic environment as discussed in the last issue.

I would like to continue my discussion of program management by listing representative tasks, some program manager characteristics and some qualifications for success.

PROGRAM MANAGEMENT TASKS

1. Prepare program proposals and negotiate with customers/marketing
2. Develop and maintain program plans
3. Develop and maintain a system for management control
4. Provide for system analysis, system engineering & the preparation of system specification
5. Be sure that there is a balanced system test program
6. Maintain system configuration management
7. Allocate funding
8. Identify interface and system problems and initiate corrective action
9. Keep top management informed of progress and status
10. Verify requirements and participate in overall design
11. Act as focal point for all project related information
12. Balance performance, schedule and resources
13. Serve as the person between the technologist and management

The degree of responsibility for implementing these management tasks is determined by where the program management function is along the *Autonomous, Matrix, Influence* spectrum.

SOME PROGRAM MANAGER CHARACTERISTICS

- Coordinator of activities
- Person of action
- Person of thought
- "Front man"
- May carry responsibility with little formal authority

By authority, we mean legal and formal authority, conferred by position in the organization. This is in contrast to power, which is influence in an organization other than that related to authority. Power factors can be such things as status and respect inside the organization, persuasive ability, reputation, program authority, rank, and specialized knowledge.

- Must use power to accomplish objectives in the *Matrix* and *Influence* forms of organization.

SOME QUALIFICATIONS FOR PROGRAM MANAGEMENT SUCCESS

1. Must have knowledge in the various technological and specialty fields involved in the program.
2. Must understand general management problems, marketing, control, field service, finance and financial analysis.
3. Must be able to perform an integrative function between the various organizational inputs.
4. Must be highly motivated.
5. Must require little direction—should be a "self starter".

The qualifications for a program manager are much like those of a general manager with slightly different emphasis: the program manager emphasizes short-lived programs and day-to-day activity, whereas the general manager emphasizes the life and health of the organization over the long run.

SOME CRITERIA FOR EVALUATING PROGRAM MANAGEMENT

- The program manager must be evaluated on the basis of project results and not by trying to identify his individual contributions.
- The program manager's job is catalytic in nature i.e. music is made by the orchestra, not by the conductor. In fact, he is the only participant who does not contribute some sort of sound.
- Evaluation should be made on how well the program meets its schedule and lives up to its performance and cost goals.

In this and the previous article we have looked at some aspects of two basic organizational forms—functional and program.

The functional form is more efficient when there is a continuous flow of products or services and change is uncommon. Some form of program, or adaptive organization, is better suited to dynamic environment that is characterized by rapid technological change and diversification.

When this fact is not recognized, a functional organization, in an effort to cope, may be subjected to almost continuous change, especially at its lower management levels. The resulting climate of uncertainty can result in low morale, low output and excessive employee attrition.

To be effective, the organization form must be compatible with the task and the environment in which the task is performed.

Just as an architect must take into account the qualities of the various building materials—bricks, steel and glass—the organizational architect must take into account the characteristics of the personnel he works with.

The life cycle of an organization

As an organization matures, it can move through five combinations of functional and program (adaptive) organizational phases. As engineering managers we must be able to recognize which phase our organization is in, and conduct our activities accordingly.

ENTREPRENEURIAL

In the beginning an organization is mostly concerned with developing, manufacturing and selling a product. There are only a few participants, usually highly motivated by the prospect of significant financial reward. Everyone interacts with everyone else, and there are no formal organizational lines. The facilities are often makeshift, temporary and inadequate.

MANAGEMENT EMPHASIS:
MAKE & SELL
ORGANIZATION:
INFORMAL & ADAPTIVE

Through the application of much effort by this highly motivated group, both a product and a market are somehow created, and pressures for efficiency and additional resources start to be felt.

EFFICIENCY

During this phase the organization is functionalized under the direct control of the key men who originally created it—perhaps with a few additional technical specialists. Efficiency techniques are introduced:

- Accounting systems
- Inventory and purchasing procedures
- Incentives, budgets, & work standards
- Additional facilities
- Formal communication lines
- Lower level managers chosen for their technical skills

MANAGEMENT: OPERATIONAL EFFICIENCY
ORGANIZATION: CENTRALIZED FUNCTIONS

MANUFACTURING   ADMINISTRATION
ENGINEERING   MARKETING

As the organization continues to grow, the upper-level managers start to lose contact with day-to-day problems and it becomes difficult for them to continue to exert direct control over everything that is going on—even when they work long hours and take home bulging briefcases. The eventual solution is some form of delegation of responsibilities together with decentralized organization.

DELEGATION

The day-to-day details are delegated to plant and market managers, with specified annual goals that they periodically report upon to top management, and by which their performance is judged. Top management concentrates on acquisitions and overall strategies.

MANAGEMENT: MARKET EXPANSION
ORGANIZATION: DECENTRALIZED

PLANT A   PLANT B   MARKETING
ADMINISTRATION

Many of the entrepreneurial managers leave the organization or are shunted to the side because this phase requires more conceptual skills and fewer technical skills than the earlier phases.

As the phase matures, top management makes fewer visits to the production line, communication becomes even more formal and tends to become one-way, and top management perceives that it is losing touch with what is really going on.

COORDINATION

To counteract this loss of control and improve efficiency, top management institutes special coordination techniques. These usually include:

- Product grouping in some sort of matrix organization
- Formal planning procedures and reviews
- Numerous central staff personnel to install and operate programs and procedures to give top management control
- Careful review of all budgets & capital expenditures
- Centralization of certain key technical functions
- Stock options
- Formal communication lines and administrative procedures
- Emphasis on form as well as content

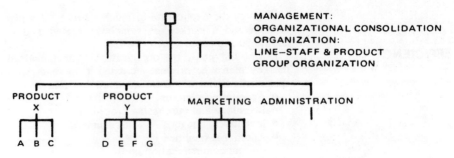

MANAGEMENT:
ORGANIZATIONAL CONSOLIDATION
ORGANIZATION:
LINE—STAFF & PRODUCT
GROUP ORGANIZATION

The eventual consequence of this phase is rigor mortis—procedure begins to take precedence over problem solving, and red tape makes the organization so stable that it is no longer able to react to change.

ADAPTIVE

This phase emphasizes greater flexibility in management action by using adaptive, problem-solving, temporary systems of diverse specialists linked together by coordinations and task evaluations within an overall functional organization. The goal of this phase is to combine efficiency with the freewheeling, highly motivated attributes of the entrepreneurial phase, and with the economies of scale of the large organization.

The emphasis is on:
- Rapid problem identification and solution through team action.
- Matrix type organization
- Teamwork & conflict resolution
- Fewer headquarter staff experts
- Real-time information-gathering systems that are integrated with the daily decision-making process.

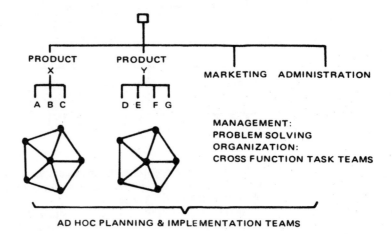

MANAGEMENT:
PROBLEM SOLVING
ORGANIZATION:
CROSS FUNCTION TASK TEAMS

AD HOC PLANNING & IMPLEMENTATION TEAMS

Matrix management: key to the two-boss system

Dr. T. F. Gautschi, P. E.

If the reorganization was a landmark event, it was in some ways less important than another change wrought in 1974—the adoption of the project center, a new concept in engineering management, devised to coordinate the efforts of the five automobile divisions. A G.M. project center, made up of engineers lent by the divisions, has no exact counterpart elsewhere in the auto industry—and perhaps in all of U.S. industry.

C. G. Burch,

"How G.M. Turned Itself Around" Fortune, Jan. 1978

The project center, or matrix structure, was adopted by General Motors to make it responsive to the special demands created by its decision to reduce the size of the automobiles in its product line in order to decrease their fuel consumption. These special demands included: the implementation of new design techniques and new technologies across the entire line in a short period of time without requiring excessive resources or redundancy.

The traditional functional organization simply was not adequate for such a dynamic task. The project centers were established to work through the engineering problems associated with parts that were common to all divisions—such as frames, electrical systems, steering gears, and brakes. The project centers were not permanent organizations; rather they were temporary and were disbanded as soon as their tasks were completed.

This matrix form of management is compatible with the traditional functional organizational form, but to be effective, it does require a special perspective, which we will discuss later in this article.

In an effort by upper management to get out from under the paper crush and speed up deci-

sion making, growing numbers of companies are trying a still-evolving organizational form, commonly called matrix management.

"How To Stop The Buck Short of the Top", Business Week, 1-16-78.

Utilized properly, matrix management is intended to push decision making down to more people and restore a measure of small company flexibility to the large complex organizations using it. According to *Business Week* the users of the matrix organizational form include: General Electric, Equitable Life Insurance, TRW Systems, CITICORP, Dow Corning and Shell Oil.

The challenge of the matrix management approach is to accommodate the requirement of having two different lines of authority exercise influence over the same resources. In the traditional functional organization conflicts between the two lines of authority are either unilaterally solved, are ignored, or are elevated to a management level that can exercise authority over the conflicting lines of authority.

As shown in the figure, the functional divisions of a matrix organization—such as engineering, production and marketing—form vertical chains of authority; the product-line divisions form the horizontal chains which cut across the functional groups. The people at the intersections of these two chains are consequently subject to two lines of authority—functional and product.

With that background, we are now ready to describe the key perspective that is required to enable an organization and its people to use the matrix approach effectively. This key is necessary to help those involved sort out their respective responsibilities. Here it is: *The functional manager should be responsible for WHO and HOW.* That is, he is responsible for designating *who* will be assigned to the various product lines from his organization and for their availability. He is also responsible for *how* they carry out their assigned responsibility in terms of technical competence.

In turn, *the product manager should be responsible for WHAT and WHEN.* That is, he must designate *what* they work on and *when* it is required. That's it. It is simple, but it is important.

In addition, the functional and product managers should get together from time to time to assure that they are not working at cross purposes; and that the functional manager and the product manager are each properly implementing their respective responsibilities of: WHO & HOW and WHAT & WHERE.

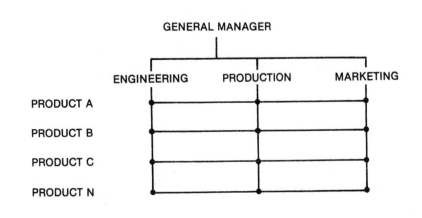

Maintaining individual creativity within R & D

A philosophy for program management

MAXIMIZE PRODUCTIVITY

Large complex projects are necessarily dependent upon team effort, but often significant advances in technology have resulted from ideas originated by individuals. In a study relating to the creativity of the individual and the large organization, it was found that about one-half of the major commercially important inventions, discoveries or innovations of the twentieth century came from individuals; that is, scientists who were working as both entrepreneurs and scientists. Included in those inventions credited to individuals were: air conditioning, automatic transmission,"Bakelite", ballpoint pen, catalytic cracking, cellophane, chromium plating, cotton picker, cyclotron, domestic gas refrigerator, electric precipitation, electron microscope, gyrocompass, hardening of liquid fats, helicopter, and insulin. Among those credited to the research laboratory were: acrylic fibers,"Scotch" tape, DDT, lacquers for fluorescent lighting, and the transistor.

An important R & D management challenge, then, is to maximize group productivity by preserving within the framework of large groups the creativity and productivity of the individual while at the same time providing the organization and coordination that is necessary to accomplish the objectives of a large project.

In the general field of management we are learning that the optimal use of human resources in organizations requires a different set of conditions, assumptions, and skills from those associated with "scientific management" and traditional bureaucratic patterns. The central emphasis of this new orientation is:

1. Wide participation in decision-making, rather than centralized decision-making.
2. Mutual confidence rather than authority as the integrating force in organization.
3. The supervisor as the agent for maintaining intragroup and intergroup communication rather than as the agent of higher authority.
4. Growth of members of the organization to greater responsibility rather than external control of the members' performance of their tasks.
5. Tasks that enable the enterprise to meet genuine needs of society (for goods, services, purchase, and income), and provide opportunities for satisfying the whole range of personal needs (physiological, safety, belonging, recognition, self-esteem, self-fulfillment) of the members.
6. Flexible planning that can accommodate the unforseen elements that occur in every situation and provide for the discrepancies between predetermined plans and outcomes.

TEAM OF INDIVIDUALS

In their early stages complex projects must of necessity be carried out by groups of scientists and engineers, even though the emphasis is on creativity, and most significant advances in technology have resulted from ideas originated by individuals. To be most effective, these groups should operate on a teamwork basis that maximizes the individual's contribution. Such teamwork must encourage interaction and mutual stimulation and help between top-flight scientists; it should *not* mean a closely directed project with assigned division of labor in the form of tasks and schedules for each of the team members; and since it is difficult to predict the course of new knowledge or plan ahead to assure the procurement of necessary skills at the right time, a very informal decision structure should be encouraged that will permit cooperative response to changing ideas and knowledge. For example: the success of the semiconductor research project, which produced the transistor, may be attributed to the close interaction of a group of top-flight scientists, a great deal of freedom in the course of research, and an extremely strong interest on the part of at least one member of the group in inventing a practical device.

COPLANNING— WITH FREEDOM

Once the feasibility of the system concept has been demonstrated with hardware and testing, and the design and development phase has begun, it would seem desirable to pursue this informal teamwork approach to permit the engineer to continue to make his maximum contribution. Unfortunately, many additional people are required in the program at this point to provide a variety of skills and to meet schedule commitments. At this juncture the emphasis moves from the creation of concepts by a small team to the design, fabrication, test and documentation of hardware by many. This effort of necessity requires some formal coplanning—planning, coordination, communication, cooperation and control— other than that which is accomplished through the informal teamwork relationship. To be most effective, this coplanning should be of such a nature that the individuals involved are given the maximum amount of freedom and self-determination compatible with program requirements.

As the program progresses from the research end of the R & D spectrum toward the production end, these program requirements increase, and more rigorous coplanning must be employed. The amount of coplanning necessary also increases with program complexity. Concepts such as management as a communication link, wide participation, mutual trust and confidence, flexible planning, sequential learning, expertise, management by objectives and the fusion of goals describe various aspects of this philosophy of operation. These concepts can be employed to create a relationship approaching that of a teamwork arrangement, wherein there is close interaction among the participants, a great deal of freedom, an acceptance of responsibility, and a very informal decision structure.

In addition to the above, the following guidelines are proposed:

(1) Place greater *emphasis upon the identification and encouragement of the unique designer,* around whom relatively small teams can be created to perform basic exploratory and feasibility investigations leading to potential developments.

(2) Provide more *competition between design groups.*

(3) Utilize new types of contracts that will *reward efficient performance.*

(4) *Be selective and critical* when choosing which R & D programs should enter into the production phase.

Dr. T.F. Gautschi, P.E.

Team organization benefits the system *and* the individual

Efficiency, creativity can blossom in a well-planned team

**EXPERIMENTS
IN TEAM WORK
. . . AN AUTOMOBILE
ASSEMBLY PLANT**

Perhaps you have heard, or read, about the successful attempt being made by Volvo in their Kalmar, Sweden plant to improve worker satisfaction and productivity by restructuring the work so that groups rather than individuals are the basic organizational building blocks.

As Volvo describes it:

Instead of spreading out the work units along a line with regard only to technical matters, jobs that have some kind of relationship between them are brought together, and a group of workers is given the task to take the responsibility for a complete function or component of the car. Thus we have teams comprising 15 to 29 operators, which are each responsible for special items such as the electrical system, instrumentation, upholstery, engine compartment, wheels, brakes, etc. Altogether there are about 20 such teams. It is up to the team members to decide how they want to distribute the job between them.

By these arrangements we are arriving at creating good conditions for job identification, a wider range of working knowledge, flexibility in working rhythm, communications between fellow workers and with foremen and engineers, increased job satisfaction and motivation.

Apart from the assembly work, the employees are directly responsible for material supplies within their own team area and they play an active part in continuous quality inspection work. The activities of the foreman have been modified. His major function has moved towards comprehensive planning and activity coordination.

**. . . UNMANNED
LUNAR
SPACECRAFT
OPERATION**

Similarly, the successful landing and operation of the unmanned Surveyor spacecraft on the lunar surface was the result of an emphasis upon team activity, rather than upon individuals. The various operations and technical teams worked closely together to achieve a common goal that everyone accepted and could relate to. The overall flight operations were coordinated by a team of Space Flight Operations Directors (SFOD's) who worked with four operations teams:

Space Flight Analysis and Control (SFAC) was the equivalent of a flight engineer on an airplane. This team was responsible for the technical status and health of the spacecraft.

Flight Path Analysis and Control (FPAC) was the equivalent of the navigator on an airplane, and was responsible for determining what path the spacecraft was on, what path it should have been on, and the determination of any maneuvers that the spacecraft should make in order to achieve the mission objectives.

Space Science and Analysis Control (SSAC) was responsible for operating all of the scientific experimental equipment that was on board the spacecraft. (This included TV cameras, particle detectors, soil analysis equipment and a lunar surface digger.)

The operators of the Deep Space Instrumentation Facility (DSIF) maintained and operated all of the ground support instrumentation such as the 85-ft antennas, communications facilities, and computer equipment, and provided the necessary administrative support.

Each of these teams was, in turn, supported by the technical experts who designed the spacecraft, the flight path analysis programs, the scientific instruments, and the deep space instrumentation facility.

One last team was made up of all of the secretaries to the people involved in the operations. They performed all kinds of duties to help keep things rolling smoothly—from "running" pictures or other data from place to place, making extra copies of key data, typing "quickie" reports, administering food or aspirin, conducting tours for visiting VIP's and much more. They worked all kinds of hours, and their only reward was "being in on what was going on."

Communications was emphasized throughout. For example, at all times we maintained a communications line over which all operations were described and discussed as they were actually taking place. This line was accessible to everyone in all of the Surveyor support facilities around the world. This capability was operated by the highly qualified people who controlled the pre-flight testing activities and data. In addition, periodic daily bulletins were published for the use of the general press and all employees associated with the organizations who were responsible for the Surveyor project.

A unique aspect of this operation was that it was not a continuing program. We took about five years to develop and build the spacecraft, the associated ground equipment, and to set up and train the operating organization. The actual flights were conducted over an 18-month period, and after the program was completed, the organization was disbanded, with some of the participants going on to new space programs, and others either going on to other company activities or leaving the company or the industry entirely.

These illustrations of the Volvo plant and the Surveyor Flight Operations team have a number of common characteristics as a result of their emphasis upon teams rather than the individuals as the basic organizational blocks.

TEAM CHARACTERISTICS

- They are not simply arenas wherein the individuals compete with one another; rather they somehow channel the competitive behavior of the various individuals in the interest of an overall common task.
- The participants are able to satisfy important membership needs as part of a group. It was "our" team, and "we" did this or that. "We" landed the first unmanned spacecraft safely upon the lunar surface.
- The team provides a relatively wide range of activities for challenge and opportunity for growth for each of its individual members.
- The team members can provide support and understanding during times of stress and crisis because everyone is more or less in the same boat and is dependent upon each other.
- The teams are good vehicles for promoting innovation and creativity; and when the relevant information is distributed among its members, they make better decisions than individuals do.
- The team is an excellent tool for implementation because once a decision is worked out, it is by definition acceptable to all, or most, of its members. (See recap of Consensus Thinking and "Lost on the Moon".) This commitment results in control and discipline of the individual members by the other members of the team in a manner that would be very difficult to achieve by individualistic methods. In fact this self-management capability of the well-developed team makes the traditional role of supervisor somewhat redundant, provided there is a congruence between the goals of the team and those of the overall organization.
- There seems to be less emphasis and concern within the team upon differential status symbols than within the traditional organization. This enables the participants to concentrate more of their emotions and efforts upon the accomplishment of the tasks for which they were established.
- Generally, the teams are more efficient than traditional organizations, they have less waste, and lower absenteeism and turnover.
- In a very real sense the team becomes experimental in nature where everyone feels free and responsible for recommending changes that might improve meeting the team's goals.
- The teams are responsible for scheduling outside interface relationships, solving production problems, and screening new team members.

I understand that the General Foods plant in Topeka, Kansas is also carrying on a team experiment. There, the general manager selected his immediate subordinates from people with whom he had worked previously and with whom he had good rapport. This team then screened the various applicants to select the appropriate first line supervisors. There were six positions and the final 12 candidates were invited to a weekend session in which they participated in role play situations and case discussions to help make a final assessment of their people orientation. The supervisors who survived this unusual process started out with a good idea of the team and its goals and probably felt part of a special group embarking upon a unique adventure.

- The information systems are designed to provide operating information to the team so that they can do their thing. This is true whether it be the box-score and batting averages for a Little League team or the complex thermal information program that is required to keep a spacecraft operating.
- The team encourages true participation where the various members are intimately involved in the key decisions that affect their lives. This goes well beyond the "Hawthorne effect", which postulates that people will be more cooperative and work harder if you just pay a little attention to them.

APPLICATION TO ENGINEERING MANAGEMENT

In summary, the team approach has some interesting characteristics and could make a significant contribution to the management of engineering in terms of productivity and effectiveness for the company. Satisfaction, challenge, a sense of accomplishment and greater financial rewards are the benefits for the employees that are involved.

CHALLENGE

Perhaps some form of team organization is an answer to the problems identified in our recent employee loyalty survey. Why don't you be an experimentalist? Give it some thought.

RECAP OF CONSENSUS THINKING

Design News/7-21-75

DISCUSSION PROCESS

Some groups used the "discussion process" and some used "consensus thinking". The "discussion" groups tackled the problems head on and spent a great deal of time and effort arguing about the relative merits of the various possible alternatives. Their solutions were generally far from optimal.

CONSENSUS THINKING PROCESS

(1) The consensus thinking groups took a different approach and their solutions were much closer to those of the experts. First, they defined the problem in terms that were specific and reasonably acceptable to everyone.

By the way, consensus does not require total agreement by all the contributors, but it does require general acceptance by everyone. When significant disagreement exists, it probably indicates that all of the inputs have not been adequately considered, and that further interaction should take place.

(2) Second, they pooled their information regarding the problem being considered. They were especially careful to include everyone's inputs to assure that they would develop a common data base.

(3) Next, they set about developing a hypothesis, or model, that would accommodate the information that they had.

(4) Finally, they "tested" their model to assure that it was compatible with the information they had and that it best addressed the problem they had defined.

Does this process sound familiar? It should. It is the process that anyone should go through when trying to solve a problem or make a decision.

The significant point here is that together the group should go through the same process an individual does, one step at a time. But what usually happens is that the participants assume that the first three steps are somehow covered and immediately skip to the fourth step—testing solutions. This often results in a great deal of argument and misunderstanding because everyone is pushing for his own solution in a win-lose contest. The problem has not been defined and the "contestants" are not working from a common data base.

FACILITATING CONSENSUS THINKING

In discussing the consensus thinking process, we always stress that the team should go through a four-step process, one step at a time. They are also urged to:

- Avoid arguing for their own positions
- Avoid getting trapped by the win-lose syndrome
- Avoid changing their minds simply to reach agreement and harmony
- Avoid "cop-outs" like coin flipping, averaging and trading
- Seek out differences in opinion as being natural and helpful
- Present their information and other contributions as clearly and objectively as possible
- Perceive their team as one that could excel in the task that they're undertaking. They were urged not to let a negative self-concept defeat them before they could even get started.

The procurement function

Dr. T. F. Gautschi, P.E.

The basic productive system model has three major functions: input, transformation and output.

The input includes labor, financial resources, information and materials. In this article we are concerned with the procurement of input materials—that is, the acquisition of raw materials, supplies, machines, finished components, tools and services. These materials are required to establish, operate and maintain the productive system which, in turn, transforms the form of the input materials to an output form that is desired by the customer. Materials procurement can have a major influence upon the cost of operating a business. Its importance is determined by the ratio of the materials cost to the total value added by the transformation process. This ratio is typically between 30% and 60%, so the procurement function is usually very important.

This importance can be demonstrated by the following example:

Consider a situation where profits are 10% of sales revenue, and the procurement costs are one-half of sales revenue (see Fig. 1). A 4% reduction in the procurement cost will increase the percent profit from 10 to 12%. This translates into a 20% increase in profits.

The principle task of procurement (purchasing) is to obtain the things that the transformation function requires at the quality level desired, when they are needed, and at the lowest possible price.

In a sense, vendors can be viewed as departments of the procuring organization. This is a modern view, and when adopted, the purchasing agent will usually have interests beyond just placing a purchase order and waiting for the specified material to be delivered. The purchasing agent should (when appropriate) be familiar with the vendor's key management people and receive periodic reports regarding quality, priorities, problems and schedule status. He should also be aware of the vendor's costs, productive process, quality assurance program and production problems. When viewed from this perspective the procurement agent is much more than an "order taker"—he is an important member of the management team.

The effective organization will prepare tradeoff analyses comparing the relative costs and desirability of outside procurement as compared to producing the product internally. These tradeoffs are termed "make/buy decisions". These are an important class of decisions and should involve management because such decisions can have significant influence on an organization's profitability and stability and the nature and size of its work force and productive facilities. At one extreme an organization could purchase the entire product from an outside vendor, and only perform the marketing and sales functions internally. This would result in product flexibility, and would not require production personnel or facilities. However, it probably would also result in a low profit margin. The grocery store is a good example of this type of organization; their profit mar-

gins are typically only 2 or 3% of sales.

At the other extreme, the organization could own the source of raw material and perform all of the necessary processes to convert the raw material into the finished product, which the organization would then market. A large paper products company grows its own trees, then harvests and processes the mature trees into pulp, which it then processes into various finished paper products. This type of firm is described as being vertically integrated.

Vertical integration occurs when a single company brings together the various process and production steps starting with the raw materials and ending with a finished product. It is more predominant in high-technology industries, such as petrochemicals, and lumber and wood products. Vertical integration can produce large profit margins, but it usually requires substantial investments in facilities and personnel, and it has the potential of reducing the technological flexibility, and the innovative competition that is encouraged by using outside vendors.

Often a firm in a particular business has unique capabilities that dictate the make/buy decisions. Sometimes a second source for a special or critical component or process may be desirable to cover the situation when difficulty is anticipated with either the inside or the outside source. When the requirements for certain materials fluctuate overtime, it is often appropriate to accommodate the fluctuation through outside procurement. Also, sometimes outside

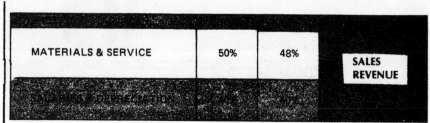

MATERIALS & SERVICE	50%	48%	
			SALES REVENUE

FIG. 1

competition is brought in to keep an internal department competitive in terms of technology, quality, cost or delivery.

Next issue we will discuss the duties of purchasing, policies for purchasing, purchasing classification, centralization vs. decentralization of the purchasing functions, and the modern trend in the buyer's activities.

The purchasing department

Dr. T. F. Gautschi, P.E.

Companies that purchase a great deal of their materials usually have a materials manager to coordinate everything having to do with materials, starting with the purchasing function and continuing until the material is delivered to the production line. However, even in these cases, the purchasing department is usually not very large—as a consequence some buyers are responsible for spending up to perhaps $5 million a year. Only in the larger companies that procure perhaps 10,000 to 50,000 items from nearly as many vendors (sources) can the buyers specialize. The smaller firms usually cannot support such specialization, even though they must procure a large number of items from a large number of sources.

Duties of purchasing

The principle duties of a purchasing department involve:
1. Locating and selecting suitable sources.
2. Requesting quotations and conducting negotiations.
3. Verifying quantity and quality received.
4. Advising engineering and others regarding materials available on the market, possible substitute materials, cost estimates, trends, etc.
5. Following up with vendors to assure that the desired quantities are delivered when specified and at the required quality level.
6. Maintaining appropriate records.
7. Disposing of scrap and surplus materials.

Policies for purchasing

A company should establish general procurement policies to assure that management's intent is in fact being met. Such policies usually cover: (1) a definition of purchasing's authority and responsibility, (2) relationships with source vendors and their representatives, (3) negotiations and competitive bidding guidelines, (4) reciprocity, (5) employee purchases, and (6) ethical practices.

The maintenance of an ethical posture is one that the buyer must constantly be alert to. Vendors are often "testing" various forms of bribery and the buyer should try to avoid any sort of personal obligation to the vendor. Not only should the buyer maintain a totally ethical position, his position should also have the *appearance* of being totally ethical. To be most effective the buyer should try to maintain an open and unbiased position regarding the choice of vendors and maintain an environment of competitive fairness.

Purchasing classifications

The purchasing process falls into four classifications:

(1) *Big and steady-use items*

These are usually negotiated annually on a blanket contract basis. Then, to keep inventories at a minimum, actual delivery dates and quantities are worked out between the buyer and seller to meet the buyer's needs. Once the contract is let, the purchasing firm's factory planning department usually coordinates directly with the vendor.

Except for basic raw materials, these large continuing contracts do not move around unless a major change or problem occurs. There are many examples of this classification in the auto industry where the assembly plants purchase tires, batteries, spark plugs and the like from outside vendors.

(2) *Large one-time procurements*

This type of procurement is used for purchasing special facilities, tools or equipment. Examples of this type of procurement are the design and installation of oil refineries, chemical plants, hydroelectric power generating systems, computer systems or perhaps the acquisition of a major machine tool or processing capability. Also, the federal government often lets large R&D and weapons procurement contracts in this manner. The engineering organization is usually involved, and each contract is individually handled on a competitive basis.

(3) *Middle-sized procurements*

Middle-sized procurements are usually made in response to the receipt of a purchase requisition from someone in the organization. Most procurement activity is of this type. Each requisition describes the product desired along with a required delivery date. It is then the buyer's task to shop around and get the best price that is compatible with the specified requirements.

(4) *Small orders*

Often this material is listed in standard catalogs. Here the cost of processing the paperwork may be more than the cost of the material being requested. One way to alleviate this problem is to encourage the requesting department to go to the vendor when the price is, say, less than $30.

Centralization vs. decentralization in the purchasing department

Dr. T.F. Gautschi, P.E.

As with many activities there is a tradeoff between centralized and decentralized purchasing. When a company has all of its facilities at one geographical location, it should have centralized purchasing. But when its facilities are spread over a large geographical area, some combination of centralized and decentralized purchasing is usually best. In this situation it is usually good practice to centralize those procurements where large amounts of money are involved and/or special technical expertise is required, and to decentralize to the individual locations the procurement of the other materials.

Factors that favor centralized procurement are:

(1) It permits specialization of the buyers.

(2) Larger quantities can result in lower cost and better priority considerations—especially in a seller's market.

(3) It reduces the number of purchase orders requiring processing.

(4) It can reduce investment in inventories.

(5) It enhances the enforcement of management procurement policies and standardization of specifications and material.

There are also factors that favor decentralized procurement:

(1) It reduces coordination and internal paperwork costs. However, the availability of more extensive data processing and communication facilities may remove this consideration.

(2) It may reduce freight costs.

(3) It permits local control over unique or small items that tend to be problems for a centralized purchasing organization.

Modern trends in buyer's activities

Until relatively recently, much of the buyer's time was occupied by semi-clerical activities such as searching for a copy of an order, trying to discover whether a delivery was received, determining where a particular material was previously procured, or gathering data on how a particular vendor performed in the past. These activities detracted much from the buyer's image. More importantly, they reduced the time that the buyer could spend on his primary task—that of analyzing data and making trade-off decisions to assure that the required quantity of material is delivered by the date specified and at the lowest possible price consistent with the required quality level.

Computer application programs are now available which relieve the buyer from most of the tedious and time-consuming chores of gathering, filing and retrieving data. These programs provide a means for maintaining data on what items the various suppliers can furnish, their available capacity and their historical price, quality, and delivery performance, and perform routine analyses of such data.

As a result, the modern purchasing organization can be more effective because the buyers can now devote much more of their time and energies to the evaluation and analysis of the data, and negotiations with suppliers rather than be submerged in the detailed clerical activities of the past. In addition to allowing for a more efficient use of the buyers' time, such programs have the potential for upgrading the buyer's job in terms of job satisfaction and other personal motivational factors, by enabling him to operate at a more professional level. This, in turn, can have significant ramifications regarding educational and training requirements, and the career paths for people into and out of the procurement organization.

Computer purchasing programs

Computer purchasing programs generally have a close tie-in with receiving and inspection activities. In addition, they are often related to an overall control and information system, usually through a common data base.

The purchasing programs maintain supplier and quotation data in an easily retrievable form to help the buyer compare and evaluate alternative suppliers. They monitor supplier responses in fulfilling orders by measuring quality, delivery and price performance and developing supplier ratings so that a recommended supplier can be selected for each order. They usually have "action files" for presenting purchase requisitions to the buyer in priority sequence.

Automatic supplier selection and purchase order generation is often instituted for low-value orders. This relieves the buyer of much repetitive activity, and allows him to spend more time on large-volume and high value items.

The computer program can be designed to do most of the purchasing department's routine clerical work. In addition, quotation renewal, as well as the acknowledgement and expediting of orders, can be automatically initiated and controlled.

Cash requirements for accounts payable can also be developed from "purchase orders placed" information.

The receiving function includes those processing and controlling steps that accept materials and place them into storage or distribute them to the production floor. The proper coordination of the receiving function can significantly reduce the time that elapses between initial receipt of a material and the time it can be used. This will also reduce inventory requirements and space requirements in the receiving department.

Conclusion

In summary, the procurement function should be an important aspect of most organizations. In recent years this function has been upgraded through the introduction of computers to accomplish the routine clerk-like tasks so that the procurement people can devote their time to their principal function of acquiring the specified materials at a reasonable cost and to the time schedules required. This total function can often have a significant positive impact upon profits when handled efficiently and effectively by qualified people. Finally, involvement in the procurement function can be very helpful experience for assuming general management responsibilities.

11

Distribution (marketing) inventory

Dr. T.F. Gautschi, P.E.

Distribution (marketing) inventory is made up of those finished or completed items that are available for meeting customer demand either directly, or as modules that are assembled into various configurations to constitute the final product. For example, one can purchase a complete hi-fi system or purchase various components, which can be assembled into an overall system. Complete computer systems can be purchased. Computer systems can also be assembled from various modules including central processing units memory, and peripheral devices such as tape drives, disc drives, punches, display units, etc. The complete systems and the various modules are considered distributive (marketing) inventory.

Distribution inventories can be in various forms. For example, they can be carried by the manufacturer as finished goods, by the supermarket as various grocery and other products, by the bank as lendable funds, and by the gas station as oil and gasoline.

Fig. 1 is a typical logistics system for a distribution type organization. The decision center operates in accordance with certain programmed rules and procedures and in accordance with top management policy. In the past these functions were established and implemented by lower and middle management with clerical and administrative system support. Since the early 1960's there has been a trend toward having more and more of the clerical and administrative type support provided by computer systems. This doesn't take people out of the loop—to the contrary—the computer's vastly superior data processing capabilities has greatly expanded man's ability to perform the basic programming and decision making functions because he is no longer limited by the sheer magnitude of the detailed mechanics associated with the operation. Now a person can do the thinking and the computer will operate as a slave to carry out his decisions exactly as he programs it to do.

The distribution logistics system can be changed to one for manufacturing by adding the product design and manufacturing activities as shown in Fig. 2. Some fail to recognize the great similarity between the two types of systems. Often service function are organized too organically without recognizing that greater organizational effectiveness can be gained through some mechanization of the distribution and service functions. This lack of parallelism in management's thinking probably arises from the fact that our mental models often picture service as being performed by individuals for other individuals, and usually out in the field away from the factory. On the other hand, manufacturing is viewed as being performed primarily by machines that are under human control and spew forth great quantities of consistent, high quality products for a collective customer base. This same mental model then proceeds to view the manufacturing environment as being one that is, and should be, quite mechanistic; and the service function as being performed in an organic environment where the working conditions are high-

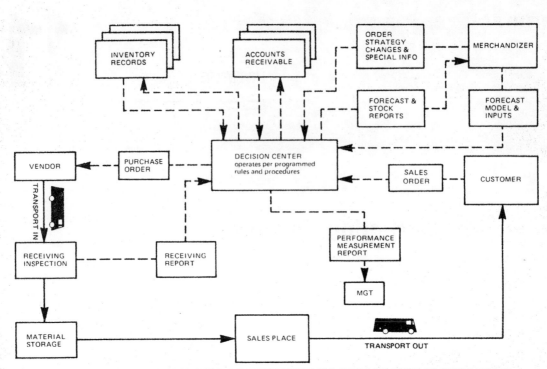

FIG. 1 TYPICAL LOGISTICS SYSTEM FOR A DISTRIBUTION (OR SERVICE) TYPE ORGANIZATION

ly variable, and where few, if any, manufacturing methods can, or should, be used. Oftentimes the quality and efficiency of a service could be significantly improved by applying technology that has been, and is being, developed by manufacturing to replace the high-cost erratic elegance of the individual craftsman.

An obvious example of such application is the supermarket, which substitutes fast and efficient self-service for the slow, inefficient, and often erratic clerks of the traditional service store. The automated cash register offers opportunities for even greater efficiency in terms of establishing and maintaining minimum inventory levels and provide an improved service, because the type and description of each transaction with the customer can be recorded in real time. In the past, such transactions were determined some time after the fact, by counting what was left in inventory and subtracting it from the quantities that were ordered and received. In terms of Fig. 1, the automated cash register can now provide a copy of the sales order to the decision center as the transaction is taking place (real time). This, in turn, will provide the data for more accurate trend analysis, and forecast models, as well as allowing the reduction of time between sales and preparation of purchase orders to replace the goods that are sold. All of this activity will result in a reduced inventory level and the related cost factors. A further step

could be to mechanize the grocery business at the distribution end. This could be accomplished by a warehouse-to-home delivery system where customers make selections from the company's catalog and place their order to a computer via a touchtone telephone in their homes. The computer would then control a mechanical warehouse, which would assemble the material that was ordered. Delivery would be made by a delivery person or pick-up by the customer.

The banking business can be viewed as one of borrowing money and then renting it out at a greater rate of interest. All of the various services, such as free checking accounts, are intended to attract the lender's money. When analyzed from the perspective of Fig. 1, the customer is the person or organization to which the bank lends money, and the vendor is the person or organization which loans money to the bank. In this situation the same person or organization could be both a lender and a borrower for different transactions. The "inventoried product" is cash. This cash inventory is increased by borrowing from vendors and it is decreased by lending to customers. The basic task is to assure that the cash inventory is sufficient to meet all loan demands and at the same time not be so large that income is lost because it is not invested in some sort of interest bearing loans or securities. This same problem exists in every productive organization, except that it is not so

easily recognized when the inventory is in materials and products.

The customer demand for distribution or marketing inventory tends to be erratic and of somewhat limited predictability. The total demand over a period of time is made up of the demands originating from the various separate customers.

The investment in distribution inventory should be governed by marketing considerations, and the sales forecast; and it should be in accordance with top management policy. The tradeoff is between investment on the one hand; and the sales revenue and customer satisfaction (or dissatisfaction) that can be realized through product availability. Large inventories clearly require greater financial investment but they also provide the capability for meeting fluctuating customer demands on a more timely basis.

The responsibility for the sales forecast function, and the related distribution inventory, should be assigned to a marketing, distribution or service organization and be reviewed by top management. When the distribution inventory and sales forecast functions are separated, the forecast is often too optimistic because the sales force wants to be sure that it will have adequate quantities of the product to sell. When the sales forecast is perceived as being a purchase order placed upon the production organization, the forecasts tend to be more realistic.

Manufacturing (work-in-progress) inventory—Part 2

Dr. T.F. Gautschi, P.E.

Prior to the availability of high-speed data processing equipment, it was usually more cost effective to use estimated usage rates and carry extra inventory on a statistical basis than it was to determine specific usage requirements for all inventory items for each period of time. Three concepts were especially useful in the precomputer era:

(1) Stock replenishment and reorder points strategies
(2) ABC inventory classification schemes
(3) Economic Order Quantity (EOQ) concepts

Stock replenishment strategies compensate for not knowing precisely what quantities of a particular item are required, and on what schedule. This is accomplished by attempting to carry sufficient inventory at *all times* so that items will always be available when needed. Various reorder strategies are used for implementing the stock replenishment concept. Generally, these strategies try to forecast demand on a statistical basis for a particular period of time, and then attempt to provide sufficient items to meet this demand. Safety stock is often employed to compensate for any fluctuations that may occur in the forecasted demand. Unfortunately, in addition to increasing inventory levels, stock replenishment strategies can still have shortages unless the safety stock is very large or the demand rates are relatively stable.

Oftentimes it is found that a few items are responsible for most of the cost of all the materials and parts carried in inventory. This is an application of Pareto's law, which addresses itself to the significant few and the insignificant many. In practice it is usually found that 80% of the cost of carrying an inventory (unit cost times quantity) is related to only about 20% of the items carried in the inventory. (See Fig. 1) *The ABC inventory classification* scheme is based upon this distribution characteristic. The limited 20% of the items are labeled "A" items. The remaining 80% are similarly divided into "B" & "C" classifications.

The A items are then given the tightest control, the B items next and the C items the least control. With this strategy, the number of tight-control items would be relatively small, and even a non-computerized information system could probably:

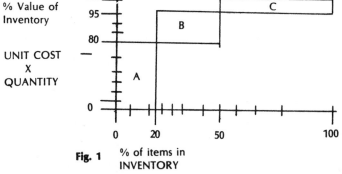

Fig. 1 % of items in INVENTORY

(1) **Determine inventory demand by calculation**
(2) **Keep detailed records of receipts and use**
(3) **Keep a close check on schedule and design revisions**
(4) **Support continual expediting**
(5) **Permit a low safety stock level.**

The B items, which might involve 15% of the inventory value and perhaps 30% of the items, could be subject to moderate control involving:
(1) Basing inventory levels upon past usage
(2) Keeping records of receipts and use
(3) Making some checks on major schedules and design revisions
(4) Expediting only for identified or expected shortages
(5) Carrying larger safety stocks.

The C items, which would involve the final 5% of the inventory value and the remaining 50% of the items, would be subject to relatively loose control:
(1) Order more when the inventory level gets low
(2) Don't keep records of receipt and use
(3) Don't worry about revisions
(4) Do not employ expediting
(5) Carry large safety stocks

The ABC system is an effective strategy for dealing with the manufacturing inventory problem when a firm only has a limited data processing capability, because it concentrates this limited capability on those items that involve the greatest cost or whose absence would create sizeable problems. Even with automated data processing, the ABC system continues to be a useful strategy for dealing with physical inventory control—inspection, storage, and frequency of checks because it tends to focus one's efforts on the higher priority items.

The economic order quantity (EOQ) concept is based upon the idea that production or procurement quantities can be determined that will result in the lowest cost per unit. EOQ is basically a tradeoff between acquisition costs per unit and costs of possession per unit. Acquisition costs include the costs of placing a purchase order or setting up a process to be operated in-house. The acquisition per unit cost decreases as the number of units is increased. The unit possession costs increase as the number of units is increased, and include inventory carrying costs, shelf wear, handling costs, and obsolescence.

In addition to these factors the EOQ can be effected by special quantity discounts and periodic variations in cost. The EOQ assumes that the item is used at a fairly constant rate throughout the year, and this is not always the situation. Further, the EOQ concept tends to suboptimize in favor of the item being procured. This may not result in the firm's best use of its capital. EOQs are most useful for the B-type items. A-type items require more careful attention and the C's usually require less attention.

Interrelationships between manufacturing and distribution inventories

Dr. T.F. Gautschi, P.E.

Whether a business involves the sale of groceries, a museum, a blood bank, a hospital or a manufacturing firm, it should be concerned with inventory policy, planning and forecasting. These functions are important because they drive the overall input-transformation-output system.

Generally, forecasting should be a formalized process. It should be based upon a projection of actual past events into the future as modified by forecasts of general economic conditions, competitive activity, customer expectations, state of the technical art, and other relevant external factors. The availability of extensive data processing capability provides the possibility of making much more accurate forecasts than before.

In order for any inventory management system to operate satisfactorily there must be a disciplined approach for:

1. Transaction reporting
2. Physical control over inventories
3. Procedures governing engineering changes and product releases
4. Product identification
5. Maintaining bill of material data
6. Generating and maintaining the master production schedule

The cost for carrying inventory is often a major expense. Typical values for manufacturing firms range between 15% and 35% of the average inventory value. For this reason, it is important to keep the average inventory level as low as possible within the constraints established by marketing and manufacturing in-process demands. The carrying cost is made up of a number of elements, including: interest on the investment in the inventory, storage charges, taxes and insurance, physical deterioration and/or its prevention, handling and distribution, record-keeping costs, and obsolescence.

The natural tendency of most firms is to carry too much inventory—in that way production will not run out of anything, purchasing doesn't have to expedite late shipments, and marketing can meet unanticipated heavy customer demands. However, the cost associated with carrying too much inventory is simply a wasted resource.

Management must be alert to the pressures that encourage excessive inventory levels, and provide the necessary discipline and controls to keep them from becoming profit drains on the organization.

Inventories are primarily a necessary investment expense to provide the firm with products to meet its customer demands as documented in sales forecasts and master production schedules. In addition, resources may be invested to carry inventories at levels higher than those dictated by the forecast because either quantity discounts are available, or material shortages are anticipated, or higher costs are anticipated. These situations should be considered as investment opportunities, and should be treated accordingly. The order size has a significant impact upon the average inventory level, and lead times too play an important role in inventory control. When materials are ordered too soon, excessive investment in inventory results.

A common index for inventory control is that which results from dividing the value of the product shipped by the average investment in inventory for the same period.

$$\frac{\text{Inventory}}{\text{Turnover}} = \frac{\text{Value of Product}}{\text{Average Investment}}$$

Large index numbers can result from either low investments in inventory or short manufacturing cycles. Since inventories do represent a financial investment, the determination of the proper ratio of this investment to operating profits can be used to establish and measure optimum inventory levels for many classes of inventory.

There are four alternative methods to price inventories for accounting purposes:

(1) FIRST IN-FIRST OUT (FIFO). This method prices all issues at the unit cost of the oldest lot until that lot has been completely issued. Then the cost of the next oldest lot is used, and so on.

Let's assume that we have an inventory of 100 units, and that they were acquired chronologically as follows: 20 units at $10 each, 50 units at $12 each, 30 units at $15 each.

Using FIFO the first 20 units to be issued from inventory would be priced at $10, then the next 50 units at $12 and then 10 units at $15. The remaining 20 units would be shown to be worth $15 each or a total of $300. FIFO results in lower cost figures during periods of price increases. This, in turn, results in more apparent profit and in higher income taxes, and values inventory at today's higher prices.

(2) LAST IN-FIRST OUT (LIFO). Under this procedure all issues are priced at the cost of the newest lot until that lot is used up. Then the price of the next newest lot is used, and so on. For our example above, using LIFO the first 30 units to be issued would be priced at $15, then the next 50 units at $12. The remaining 20 units would be shown to be worth $10 or a total of $200. LIFO boosts apparent costs, and thereby holds down profits and taxes, but it values inventories too low.

(3) AVERAGE VALUE. This method determines the value of the various issues by using a weighted average of the cost of material in stock. As new material is received at different costs, a new computation must be made. For our example above, the 100 items in stock cost $1250 or $12.50 each on the average. This method results in apparent costs that are higher than those determined by FIFO and lower than those determined by LIFO.

(4) STANDARD COST. Here a cost standard is established for each item of material and all issues are charged out at this standard regardless of the actual price paid for the material. This method is often used for items a company makes because no two lots ever cost exactly the same. Differences between the standard cost and the actual cost are then carried in a variance account. For our example above, assume that the standard cost is $12.00. Then all 80 units issued would be charged at $12 each, with the actual differences being carried as a variance account.

These are pricing methods and have nothing to do with the chronological order of actual disbursements. The FIFO and LIFO pricing procedures have the greatest application in industry. Generally FIFO is desired during periods of deflation, and LIFO is desired during periods of inflation because of the manner in which they treat apparent costs. American firms require IRS approval to shift from one system to another.

Quality control as a strategic function

Dr. T. F. Gautschi, P.E.

Quality is an important, but difficult, concept to define. However, in general, we can say that a product's quality is measured by the expectations of the customer, and includes such characteristics as function, reliability, serviceability, useful life, maintainability, and appearance.

These quality characteristics are determined by:

1. the pattern (or detailed product definition), which is usually established by engineering and approved by management. Generally the pattern is documented in terms of drawings and/or specifications; and
2. fidelity, which is a measurement of how accurately the final product conforms to the pattern.

The choice regarding the quality of the pattern (design) is only made occasionally, generally when a new product is being developed or modified. On the other hand, the maintenance of product fidelity (conformance) is a continuing struggle for as long as the product is being produced.

The quality level to be achieved by the pattern is a management decision and should be responsive to the organization's strategic objectives. For example, for years the level of Sears quality was pegged for the middle and lower income levels' tastes and incomes. Recently, the quality level has been drifting upward, and this has created problems for Sears. The trend towards higher quality (at a higher price) is putting Sears beyond the means of the lower and middle income classes, but at the same time it has *not* attracted the higher income customers because they perceive Sears as catering to the lower and middle income customer.

The perceived quality level of a company's products is a major image determining factor. In fact, if an organization has a reputation for high quality, the customer looking for high quality will tend to purchase its products without questioning the quality level of the specific product being purchased.

Quality and price have a direct interrelationship. Generally, most customers want the best quality that they can get for the money they are willing to spend. The more successful productive systems recognize this, and try to produce the "best" product that they can for the price that the customer is willing to pay. As a general rule, the higher the quality, the higher the cost. Costs usually increase at a faster rate than quality—at least beyond the ideal quality-cost relationship, i.e. a little extra quality may cost quite a bit more money. See Fig. 1. A good example of this is first-class vs. tourist class air flight fares.

Often when customers are faced with making a choice between two unknown products they will purchase the product with the higher price because they believe that the higher price indicates higher quality. This is especially true when the customer cannot detect any real differences between the two products, and the customer cannot be sure of the quality level of the product being purchased. Hi-fi sound systems and shoes usually fall into this category.

Quality characteristics are of major importance to the marketing organization because they have a direct effect upon the saleability of the product. Since customers usually want the highest quality they can afford, the percep-

tion of quality differences between competing products is often the determining factor in a purchase decision. Because of this factor, firms try to differentiate their products from those of their competitors in their effort to attract customers. Often these differentiations are superficial. Examples of this are the packaging of toys or record albums.

Although there are few universally accepted quality standards, three general classifications are often used to define quality—grade, satisfaction and consistency.

Grade implies certain product attributes such as closeness of fit; purity of color, taste or odor; smoothness; number of flaws; reliability; operating characteristics; and the like.

Unfortunately, there are few standards in this area beyond those used for designating grades of meat, grades of lumber and grades of bonds.

Satisfaction refers to the degree that the product or service satisfies the user. This is generally determined by the user's perception of the product grade level, the consistency of the quality level within that grade and how well the item functions, along with such factors as reliability and maintainability.

Consistency has to do with the repeatability of a product's conformance to its design requirements, or the repeatability of a service function. The customer is more likely to purchase the product, or service, when he can be reasonably sure that each new purchase will be of equal or better quality than the previous purchase.

There is an ideal relationship between a product's quality, its produc-

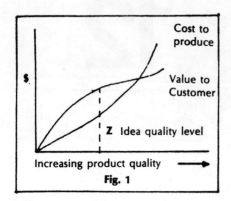

$ Cost to produce

Value to Customer

Z Idea quality level

Increasing product quality ⟶

Fig. 1

tion cost and its value to the customer. See Fig. 1.

The ideal quality is that which would result in the greatest profit to the firm—when "the difference between the value to the customer" and the "cost to produce" is maximized. Unfortunately, in practice these relationships are difficult to define. First, the quality concept is subjective, and secondly the incremental value to customer vs. incremental cost to produce cannot be reliably determined without extensive research or experimentation. Nevertheless, an understanding of the relationship as shown in Fig. 1 will help the manager improve his mental model of the organization, even if the relationship is not quantitatively accurate.

The fidelity phase of quality control

Dr. T. F. Gautschi, P.E.

The different functions within an organization may have different perspectives on quality:

- The technologist generally wants to have every product be of highest possible quality—the smoothest surface, the purest color, etc.

- The marketer wants a high quality product at the lowest possible price. He also wants the product to have some distinctive "quality features" that will differentiate his product from those of competitors. As mentioned before, these distinctive quality features may or may not be superficial, but they must be perceived by the customer as being important.

- The manufacturing, or fabricating organization, wants a standardized product with the lowest quality requirements possible so that the product will be easier and cheaper to manufacture or fabricate.

- Management's responsibility is to assure that the quality-price levels for its products are pegged to result in the greatest profit to the firm and at the same time be more acceptable to the customer than competing products.

Fidelity is a measure of how well the product conforms to the product pattern and its achievement is a continuing problem as long as the product is being produced. Because there is usually pressure to cost reduction, it can usually be achieved by producing a product that just barely meets the pattern requirements.

In the past, to assure product fidelity, a great deal of time and effort was often devoted to the chore of manually calculating various quality control factors, such as sampling plans, and various statistical analyses. Now, with the increasing application of computers, the time and effort required and devoted to these activities has been reduced significantly. This gives the quality control organization more time to consider some of the basic issues of quality control and its management.

The fidelity phase of QC generally includes three activities:
1. incoming material control
2. special support studies
3. product control

Incoming material control applies to all items that enter the productive organization from the outside environment. This includes material, components, parts and services. Acceptance criteria must be established along with the applicable procedures and sampling plans to assure detection of materials that do not comply with the specifications at an acceptable economical level. Techniques used in this activity include vendor rating, evaluation, or certification, and acceptance sampling plans of various sorts.

Special support studies involve analysis, testing, experiments and investigations with the purpose of identifying major quality problems and their causes.

Product control takes place at the product transformation level and its purpose is to identify and evaluate deviations from the product specifications and assure that timely corrective action is taken. See Fig. 1. This applies to all parts, materials, tooling, operations and processes involved in the transformation of the product. Generally this control is accomplished through the utilization of some sort of inspection process.

As mentioned before, the output of the pattern (design) phase for a product is a set of drawings and/or specifications describing the product and its component parts in detail. These documents specify such factors as dimensions, weight, materials, finish, color, texture, appearance and shape. Services are described by specifications that are sometimes written, but often they are verbal or even implied or assumed. Fidelity is measured against these pattern descriptions. Since products *cannot* be produced exactly to the designated pattern, specifications are provided with a tolerance factor. That is, the amount of deviation that the product can have from the pattern and still be acceptable. Generally, the tighter the tolerance factor is, the more it will cost to produce a product. So production continually pushes for the largest tolerance factor possible. Loose tolerances make the product less costly to produce and keeps the reject (scrap) rate to a minimum.

On the other hand, part standardization and requirements for having to fit several product components together dictate a fairly tight tolerance situation. So, as in many areas, there is a trade-off relationship between cost and the specified tolerance level.

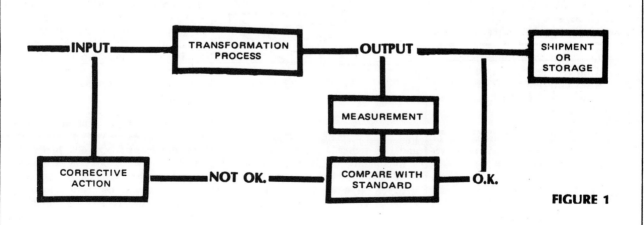

FIGURE 1

The inspection process in quality control

Dr. T. F. Gautschi, P.E.

The purpose of the quality control (QC) management function is to assure that the organization does develop and produce the product and provide product service in accordance to the quality objectives established by top management. This requires the development of an effective system for integrating the efforts of all those in the organization which influence product quality. It generally involves three major areas of activity—establishing standards, appraising performance against the established standards and taking corrective action when the product does not conform to the standard.

The inspection process includes those inspections and tests that are required to substantiate product conformance (fidelity) to the specifications.

Every inspection process should consider the following five points:

1. *What* is to be inspected—what characteristics or attributes are to be measured against the pattern? For example: length, hardness, weight, color, smoothness, taste, odor, etc.

2. *Where* is the inspection to take place? This is especially pertinent for vendor supplied materials, and for lengthy transformation processes which add significant value to the input material.

3. *How* is the inspection to be performed? This includes tools, instruments and techniques.

4. *What* are the *units* of measurement? This is closely related to the answers to the what, where and how questions. Typical examples are inches, pounds, and color comparisons.

5. *What* are the *criteria* for acceptance or rejection? What elements must be measured and found to be within specification to constitute our acceptable product?

One hundred percent inspection of every element (attribute) of every part is not often used—except for one-of-a-kind items that are very costly to produce. For example, all spacecraft receive a complete overall inspection because they are basically one-of-a-kind, and are very expensive, and failure of any function is unacceptable.

Most products just do not warrant the time and expense of 100% inspection. So various sampling plans are employed. Through careful statistical design, and reasonably accurate process control, sampling plans can be made nearly as reliable as 100% inspection, and at a fraction of the cost. Most sampling plans are progressive in nature—they proceed to smaller sample sizes as the product demonstrates its conformance (fidelity) to its specifications, and to larger more frequent sample sizes when the product conformance to specification is erratic or drifting.

The concepts of sampling and statistical control are based upon the fact that although variations between certain attributes of the product and the pattern are to be expected, they are predictable, when produced under controlled conditions. Seldom, if ever, does a product conform to its pattern in all respects. However, the variations in these attributes constitute a frequency distribution that can be measured.

For example, the hole in the plate shown in Fig. 1 is designated as 1.00 ±0.01 inch. This means that any hole

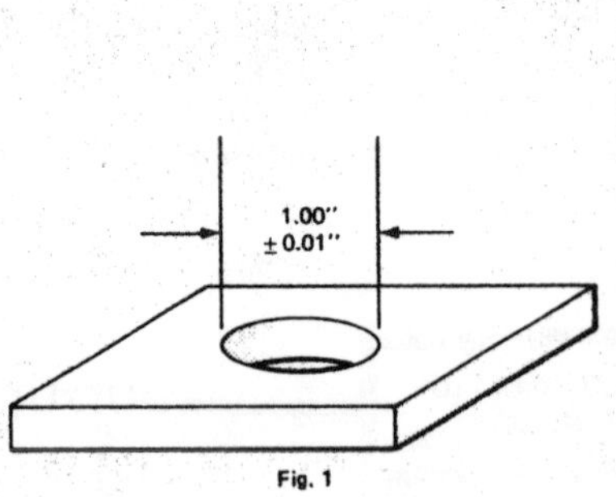

that has a diameter between 0.09 inch and 1.01 inches is acceptable.

In actuality, the diameter of the hole in a large number of parts will vary between these two dimensions in some fashion. These can be measured and plotted as a frequency distribution. See Fig. 2.

You will note that the frequency

distribution is skewed towards the larger sized hole. More than likely, the mechanic or operator started with a hole size near the larger tolerance so that as the drill becomes smaller through use, it will continue to produce acceptable parts.

In addition to reducing inspection costs, sampling plans are utilized when the product must be destroyed to assure that it conforms to specifications. This is the situation when one

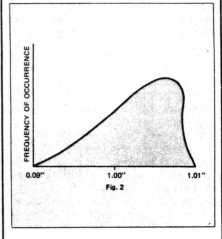

Fig. 2

tests foods by taste or tests fuses or squibs by detonating them.

Sampling may also be used in a service function to assure that the service meets the specified standards. For example, the amount of ice cream that is put into a cone, or the quality of service by a bank teller or the quality of service that is provided by the stewardess on an airplane. The quality of these kinds of activities are usually 'spot-checked' (sampled) in some manner to measure and control adherence to the required standards.

This sample inspection concept is often referred to as process control, and is used extensively in transformation processes where quantitative values for the variations can be obtained. Generally there are three sources for such variation: the condition of the incoming materials, the variations among people conducting the operation, and the tools or equipment used to perform the transformation. The varia-

Fig. 1

tions from each source can usually be identified and "controlled" separately. The usual technique involves some sort of control chart upon which the variation contributed by each source is plotted for each copy of the product tested. Then the measured data is compared to some standard.

For example, the process depicted in Fig. 3 is well within the control limits. However, there is some bias towards lower values.

The process charted in Fig. 4 is out of control, and some sort of corrective action should be taken to bring it back into control.

The quality level for a given product is really established by the basic patterns (specifications) that are developed and the transformation processes that are used. Beyond these two areas, inspection processes—no matter how elaborate—are simply checks to assure that the quality level that has been specified has in fact been achieved. Therefore, a good quality assurance program should put its primary emphasis upon the creation of an initial pattern that is responsive to customer requirements, and upon the transformation processes utilized to achieve the product.

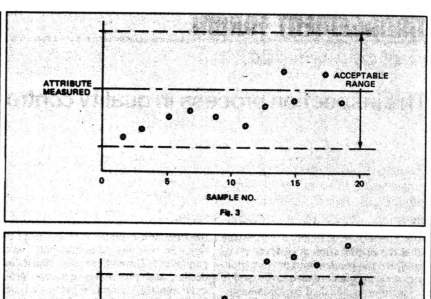

Fig. 3

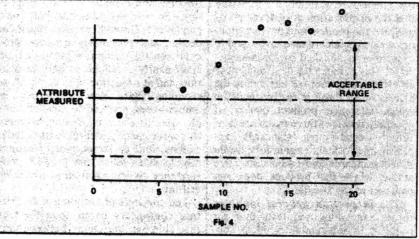

Fig. 4

Reliability–an important facet of quality control

Dr. T. F. Gautschi, P.E.

Reliability is an attribute of quality. In the past, this term was used rather loosely, but in recent years it has come to have a specific meaning. Reliability is defined as the probability that a system will perform satisfactorily for a given period of time when used under certain stated conditions. Thus, reliability is a probability and should be stated in probabilistic terms. Secondly, satisfactory or non-satisfactory performance must be clearly specified. A specific time period of life span is involved—an hour, a day, a week, a year or whatever. Lastly, the stated conditions refer to both how the product is used, and the environmental conditions that are associated with the life span over which the product is used.

A fact of life

Most military and governmental contracts have a reliability specification as part of their quality requirements. Such requirements were not introduced into the consumer product field until the early 1960's when consumer awareness started to gain momentum. Now, reliability is a recognized fact of life in most industries, especially with the ever-increasing emphasis upon product liability.

Life testing techniques are used to determine reliability characteristics for various products. At times these tests are accelerated (foreshortened) to save time, especially when the life span is relatively lengthy. This is accomplished by increasing the stress levels of such variables as temperature and vibra-

tion levels, or by simply operating the product at a rate faster than real time. (Typically when a large number of products are tested they respond in accordance to a "bathtub"-type curve.

As a result, once a product has gotten past the infant mortality time range, it will have a probability of being more reliable than one that has not gone through the infant mortality range. This is especially true for electronic circuits that utilize discrete components, so most applications require that the electronic devices go through a burn-in period to catch the infant failures.

Measuring quality

The quality of a product or service is not always easy to specify or measure. It is a management decision and should be determined by the interaction between customer requirements, technological considerations and processing requirements.

Quality should have a total life cycle perspective—including prod-

uct design, process selection, materials procurement, product inspection and process control. It should continue on through the delivery of the product, and include feedback of the customer's experience with the product, and appropriate corrective action.

Quality control concepts are applicable to all types of productive organizations—manufacturing, banks, schools, service activities, insurance companies, hospitals, etc. Many non-manufacturing organizations could reap significant benefits through the implementation of quality control concepts and techniques to assure that the product or service that the customer receives is in fact that which was intended. Quality is an important, but difficult, concept to define. However, as we said before, a product's quality is measured by the expectations of the customer, and includes such characteristics as function, reliability, serviceability, useful life, maintainability, and appearance.

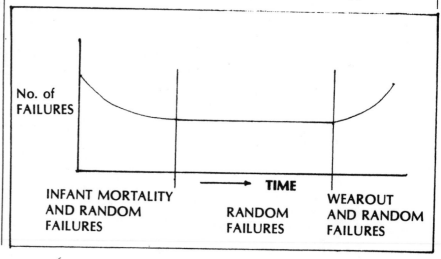

A series of mental models: The Productive System

Dr. T.F. Gautschi, P.E.

ASSIMILATION FRAMEWORKS

Our purpose for this, and several more articles, is to develop a series of realistic mental models for analyzing and operating modern organizations.

It is useful to think in terms of mental models. We use them to interrelate the concepts that we hold regarding a particular subject, and to serve as frameworks for assimilating related new information. We are not always aware of the mental model that we are using, but they exist nevertheless. In fact, we could not cope with our complex environment without them. The world would be just too confusing. As we pursue any subject, we:

(1) try to fit any new input into our existing model

or (2) modify our mental model to be compatible with the new input

or (3) reject the new input as being irrelevant.

As managers, each of us has mental models regarding how we think our organization operates and how it should operate. As such, these mental models guide our thoughts and actions and provide a framework for assimilating new information.

We will initiate this series by discussing the Productive System concept because it is useful for analyzing overall organizations.

THE PRODUCTIVE SYSTEM

A productive system can be defined as any organization that has an input, a

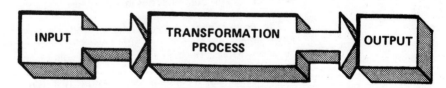

transformation process, and an output. The inputs generally include resources in the form of raw or finished materials, technology, money, people and facilities. The transformation process then operates on these inputs to produce the desired output, which is usually in the form of a product or a service.

College

A college is a productive system where the *inputs* are high school graduates, teachers, facilities and literature. The *transformation* process involves imparting knowledge, skills, and attitudes, and the *output* is an educated person.

Hospital

The *inputs* to a hospital include sick people, nurses, doctors, service personnel, medicine, equipment and facilities. The *transformation* process involves the combination of these inputs to produce the desired *output*—a well person.

Automobile assembly plant

An automobile assembly plant has *inputs* of automobile parts, people, equipment, materials and facilities. The *transformation* process involves the assembly of the various parts into a completed automobile—the *output*.

Engineering department

The inputs to an engineering organization include marketing requirements, technology, engineers, drafters, test equipment and facilities. These inputs are then transformed into the output—a set of specifications and other documentation that describe the component or a system that meets the marketing requirements.

SYSTEM INFLUENCES

The concept of the modern productive system is an evolving one, and is being influenced by a number of streams of activity. These include:

1. An early and continuing emphasis upon manufacturing processes.
2. The ever-increasing proportion of resources being applied to service and other non-manufacturing activities.
3. The changing work force, especially in terms of increasing education and greater expectations.
4. The introduction of electronic data processing.
5. The continuing refinement of quantitative analysis.
6. The availability of advanced communication techniques.
7. An increased understanding, acceptance, and formulation of planning and control concepts.
8. Better understanding of concepts such as leadership, motivation, power factors, group interaction, and organizational forms.
9. The challenge of having to cope with an environment that is characterized by increasing complexity, technological innovation, and increasing government control.

These streams are all converging against a backdrop of ever-increasing complexity and change.

CLOSED-SYSTEM PERSPECTIVE

As one considers a particular productive system, there is a tendency to try to explain, and understand, everything within the context of the system as defined—without much regard for its interaction with the overall environment. This is a closed-system perspective. When we define a system's limits with the exclusion of the external environmental factors, we remove a great deal of uncertainty and complexity. This permits us to concentrate on internal factors such as the definition of goals, improved efficiency, orderliness, and predictability.

A century ago when we did not have telephones, radio or T.V., and the horse was our fastest mode of transportation, most productive organizations were local in character and the closed-system concept was very appropriate.

Up until the 1950's, this closed-system perspective was generally adequate—at least for those organizations that were in relatively placid environments. However, times are changing!

Today the apparent world is much smaller, and it seems to be shrinking with each passing year. Now we can communicate, in real time, using sound and video pictures, with nearly any place on earth. A person can travel at thousands of miles per hour, and the computer has made possible the collection and rapid processing of enormous amounts of data.

The predominant characteristic of today's environment is change. In this environment there are no sure ways to corporate security and sustained success—witness the bankruptcy of Grants, and General Electric's and RCA's exit from the computer business. No corporation or product line is immune to obsolescence, and a company can fail quickly if its management is not sensitive and skillful in relating it to the forces in the business environment.

The sudden availability of large-scale integrated circuit chips and their significant impact upon the calculator and wristwatch worlds is a good example of this kind of pressure. Another example is the dramatic and sudden emergence of the energy shortage a year or so ago and its effect upon our entire economic system. Thus, we can sense the growing inadequacy of the closed-system model for the modern productive system.

OPEN-SYSTEM PERSPECTIVE

As with many issues, it is far easier to criticize and identify problems than it is to develop solutions. However, modern management thought is in the process of developing an alternate strategy to the closed-system perspective for analyzing organizations—some term this alternative strategy the open-system perspective; others, the contingency model; and still others, the adaptive model. This strategy takes into account the interaction between the various components within an organization as well as the organization's interaction with appropriate elements of its environment.

**PLAN YOUR
STRATEGY**

The challenge of this strategy is to learn to manage highly educated people and technological innovations to meet the goals of the productive system in a highly volatile and complex socioeconomic environment. There are some basic steps that a company should take to cope with this challenge:

1. Establish objectives, strategies and specific goals that are based upon forecasts of the marketplace and a realistic assessment of the company's resources.
2. Organize for timely and effective decision making. This requires flexibility and quick reaction. Organizational "constipation" cannot be tolerated. The management must be able to "read" the situation and take appropriate action—much like the quarterback on a football team who reads the defense and calls an audible play change at the line of scrimmage.
3. Strive for a good sense of timing—especially when the product opportunity windows (the time period when value exceeds cost) are becoming shorter. If a firm tries to enter a product market too early, it will experience high costs. When it enters too late, the profits will be too small.
4. Develop short, effective communication links and patterns.
5. Make sure that management is knowledgeable about the firm's products, its business, and is involved in what is going on.
6. Motivate management to become fully aware of the significant technological trends that can affect the business and factor these trends into the company's planning activities.
7. Apply both modern behavior and operation's management concepts, including advanced information processing.

Every organization is in a continuous state of change. Sometimes the changes are great, sometimes small, but change is always taking place. The conditions requiring these changes arise from both within and from without. As a consequence, there is a never-ending need for decisions which guide adjustments to change. The adequacy of these decisions for meeting an organization's current and developing internal and external situations determines the well being, power, and future of that organization.

Rensis Lickert, *The Human Organization*

Dr. T.F. Gautschi, P.E.

A series of mental models: tools for decision aiding

The increase in the numbers and applications of decision-aiding tools is one of the major trends in modern management practice. Although a detailed description of these tools is beyond the scope of Management Forum, it is becoming increasingly important for the manager in any modern productive system to at least be familiar with the more common ones. Few of these tools can be used to provide the final decision, because often we cannot describe the situation in precise enough terms. However, the tools are very useful for improving the manager's mental model—especially when a large number of factors are involved and their interaction is complex.

TYPE OF FORCE

Force-field analysis

This technique provides a framework for determining how to implement a change in the level of a particular activity, or for comparing alternate solutions to a particular problem. It is based upon the fact that in any situation where the level of activity is the resultant of a number of forces, these forces can be identified and resolved into those that promote the occurrence of the particular activity—DRIVING FORCES, and those that inhibit, or oppose, the occurrence of the same activity—RESTRAINING FORCES.

The force-field analysis technique is applicable to a number of problems: financial performance levels, employee turnover rates, management effectiveness levels, morale levels, production cost, expense levels, relationships with customers, and many more. Generally, it is difficult to quantify the magnitude of the various forces, but we can gain significant insight by just being able to identify the various individual forces and their relative magnitudes.

Decision Grid

This involves a display in grid form of the possible alternatives for a decision in relationship to the various factors or constraints that influence the decision. The alternatives can be listed across the top and the factors relating to the decision can then be listed down the left side. The cells at the intersection of these two dimensions can then be used to indicate how well the factors meet the constraints for the various alternatives. The decision grid is simple in concept, but it can be very useful in the analysis of a complex situation because it graphically displays all of the significant factors in an easily understood and communicable form.

An illustration of this tool is shown in Fig. 1. In this case the student is trying to determine which job alternative he will choose. He has offers from companies A, B and C, and he is considering the factors as listed on the left side of the grid. He is assigning grades of 1-10 to each factor, with 1 being unacceptable and 10 being very acceptable.

WEIGHTING FACTORS

If all of the factors were of equal importance, he could simply total each column. This would result in A=49, B=54, and C=53. On this basis he would choose alternative B. However, if he were to "weight" the various factors in terms of their importance, he might get a different answer as shown

		ALTERNATIVES	
FACTORS	A	B	C
SALARY	10	7	6
GEOGRAPHICAL LOCATION	7	10	8
COMPANY IMAGE	8	10	10
TYPE OF INDUSTRY	7	9	10
CAREER PATHS & OPPORTUNITIES FOR GROWTH	8	9	10
FRINGE BENEFITS	9	9	9
TOTAL	49	54	53

JOB DECISION GRID

FIG. 1

in Fig. 2. Here the answers are: A=408, B=429 and C=434. On this basis, C is the more logical choice.

The assignment of probabilities to the various outcomes for each of the alternate decisions can make the decision grid even more useful to the decision maker. These assignments are usually based upon historical data, or the judgment of people who are knowledgeable in the field (an interesting technique that has been developed for gathering such judgment is the DELPHI method, which will be discussed in a later article.)

PRODUCTION POSSIBILITIES

For example, suppose that the production manager is concerned about how much of a special material he should order each week. Assume that the probability of using 500 lb is 80% and the probability of

FACTORS	WT.	ALTERNATIVES		
		A	B	C
SALARY	10	100 / 10*	70 / 7	60 / 6
GEOGRAPHICAL LOCATION	5	35 / 7	50 / 10	40 / 8
COMPANY IMAGE	3	24 / 8	30 / 10	30 / 10
TYPES OF INDUSTRY	5	35 / 7	45 / 9	50 / 10
CAREER PATHS & OPPORTUNITY FOR GROWTH	20	160 / 8	180 / 9	200 / 10
FRINGE BENEFITS	6	54 / 9	54 / 9	54 / 9
TOTAL		408 / 49	429 / 54	434 / 53

*RAW EVALUATION WITHOUT WEIGHING (WT) SEE FIG. 1.

JOB DECISION GRID WITH WEIGHTING FIG. 2

using 700 lb is 20%. (These estimates could be based on past history.) Costs can be assigned to the two alternatives. Storage space for the additional special material will cost $5/week; if he runs out of the material, there will be a $15 delivery charge. The unit price for this special material is $1/lb for either amount. Fig. 3 graphically displays the alternatives and their consequences.

If 500 lb are purchased and 500 lb are used, the cost would be $500 as

		PROBABILITIES	
		500 (.8)	700 (.2)
ALTERNATIVES	500 POUNDS	A $500	B $715
	700 POUNDS	C $505	D $703

FIG. 3

shown in block A. If 500 lb are initially purchased and 700 lb are required, then the cost will be $500 + $200 + $15 (delivery charge) for a total of $715. See block B.

If 700 lb are purchased and 500 lb are used, the cost in that week would be $500 for the material used, plus a storage charge of $5 for the surplus 200 lb. See block C. If the 700 lb are purchased and the 700 lb are used, the cost would be $700 for the material used, plus $3 for additional storage cost until all 700 lb of the material is used. See block D.

Expected cost if 500 lb are ordered = 500(.8) + 715(.2) = $553.00 Expected cost if 700 lb are ordered = 505(.8) + 703(.2) = $544.60.

Thus, the purchase of 700 lb would save $9.40 per week, even though 700 lb would only be needed 20% of the time.

Both the force field analysis and decision grid techniques are useful for portraying considerable data in a form that is easily communicated and understood.

Tools for decision aiding

Decision trees, cost benefit analysis and break-even analysis

RELATING YOUR DECISIONS

Decision trees are useful for graphically relating decisions that are linked together over time with various possible outcomes. The decision tree starts with a decision point and proceeds to follow branches representing the various possible alternatives, each of which has a probability associated with it. A simple example will best illustrate this approach.

Suppose it is 8 a.m. on a rather overcast Saturday morning and you have scheduled a Little League baseball practice with 15 boys for 10 to 12 a.m. You have four basic choices: conduct the practice whether it rains or not; call off the practice; assume that it will not rain, and terminate the practice if it does rain; or conduct a "chalk-talk" in your basement.

This particular decision can be represented in the form of a pay-off table.

Choices	Events and Results	
Conduct practice rain or not	Rain (1) unhappy players & parents, possibility of injury	No rain (2) good practice conditions
Call off practice	Miss practice (3) but no one hurt & no discontented parents	Miss practice (4) players unhappy
Terminate practice if it starts to rain	Miss part (5) of practice, logistics problem for parents and coaches	Good practice (2) conditions
Conduct chalk-talk	Useful, but not as much fun (7) for players	

The various factors can also be presented in a decision tree form. The tree is made up of a series of nodes and branches. At the first node on the left, the manager has one of three choices. Each branch represents an alternative course of action or decision. At the end of each branch (or alternative course of action) is another node representing a chance event— in this case whether it will rain or not. Each subsequent course to the right represents an alternative outcome of this chance event.

For the example described above, either the payoff table or the decision tree is useful. However, when the situation is complex, involving interactions between the alternatives, uncertain events and future choices, the decision tree is usually more appropriate.

Cost-benefit analysis

CHOOSING BETWEEN ALTERNATES

This tool can be useful when a decision must be made between alternate expenditures of resources. The manager compares the respective cost-benefit ratios, each of which is expressed as:

$$CBR = \frac{\text{present value of benefits}}{\text{present value of resource costs}}$$

Conceptually this is a simple process. In reality it is usually straightforward to determine present value of resource cost, but it is sometimes difficult to determine the value of the benefits. For example, how can a manager place a value on the results of an executive training program, or how does one place a value on a higher level of health or education? However, there are many situations where a value can be placed on the benefits. For example, when the purchase and operating costs of alternate machines are being considered, the benefit is simply the production capacity of each machine.

Break-even analysis

VOLUME AND COSTS

This technique is used by management for examining the relationship between the volume of operation and the costs associated with operations at different levels of output. Basically it is a graphical representation indicating the relationship between total cost (the sum of fixed costs and variable costs) and total revenues (the product of output and price). The break-even point occurs where the total costs equal the total revenues.

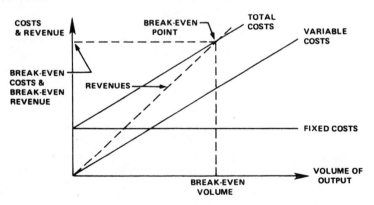

In this analysis fixed costs are those costs that do *not* vary with output volume (for example, building depreciation). Variable costs are those costs that do vary with output volume (for example, raw materials cost and direct labor).

The figure shows straight lines for variable costs and for revenues. In reality, costs and revenue relationships are rarely linear. Costs generally decrease with increase in output until total plant capacity is approached, at which point they usually start to increase. Price sometimes must be reduced with increasing volume to sell more units.

Tools for decision aiding

Operations research and Gantt charts

QUANTITATIVE STRUCTURING

"Operations research" is a term used to indicate that systematic body of knowledge that uses quantitative methods for structuring and resolving problems confronting the managers of productive systems. It is also described as management science, operations analysis, operational research and decision analysis.

OR has four distinguishing characteristics:[1]
1. A primary focus on decision making
2. An appraisal resting upon Economic Effectiveness Criteria—in a commercial firm these would include: variable costs, revenues, cash flow and the rate of return on incremental investment
3. Reliance on a formal mathematical model
4. Dependence on an electronic computer

An operations research model can never supply all of the information that is required for a decision, but it can influence and refine the executive's mental model. An important application of OR models is the determination of the sensitivity of the "solution" to the model specifications. This is especially useful in simulation analysis of long-range plans. Here the various inputs to the long-range plan—such as sales forecasts, prices, costs, profit requirements, inventory levels, etc.—can be modified until the organizational goals are satisfied. Then it is up to the manager to decide whether the resultant values are achievable!

OR models are generally categorized as linear models, transportation models, dynamic models and stochastic models.

JUDGMENT ENTERS IN

Unfortunately, most decisions do *not* lend themselves to quantification. Instead they usually contain qualitative characteristics and must be based upon a certain degree of judgment and intuition. Also, the employment of OR techniques can give the impression of rigor and accuracy. We must never forget "GIGO" (garbage in, garbage out), no matter how fine we grind it.

Gantt charts

Conceptually the Gantt chart technique is rather simple. In fact, most people use some form of Gantt chart without realizing it. In a Gantt chart the activities involved in a particular project are listed on the vertical axis of a grid-like chart and the time required to perform the activities is shown on the horizontal axis (See Fig.1). Each rectangle represents a task to be accomplished and the numbered circles represent milestones to be accomplished within each task. The entire project is the sum of the tasks as shown on the chart.

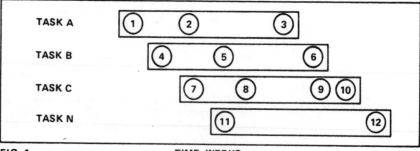

FIG. 1   TIME, WEEKS ⟶

Four important items are graphically illustrated on the Gantt chart.
1. The times necessary for the completion of each task and the completion of the milestones within the various tasks.
2. The time required to complete the entire project.
3. The sequence in which the various tasks should occur.
4. The interdependencies between the milestones that are related to an individual task.

MILESTONE PROGRESS

Progress vs. plan can also be easily indicated by filling in the completed milestones (See Fig 2). The vertical "time now" line indicates the date that the progress vs. plan was reviewed. Milestones 1, 2 and 4 are completed on schedule, milestone 7 has not been completed, and is therefore behind schedule. Milestone 5 was completed ahead of schedule. All of the other milestones are scheduled to be completed after the "time now" line.

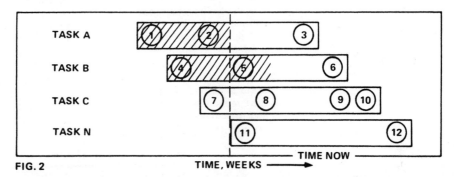

FIG. 2

The major shortcoming of the Gantt charting technique is that it does *not* show interdependencies between tasks or between the milestones for different tasks. For example, there is no indication of any interdependence between milestone 1 and milestone 9 in Fig. 2. Further, there is a communication gap between most management practitioners and the staff specialists who understand and can utilize OR techniques. This gap is gradually closing.[2]

Even with its limitations, the Gantt chart is perhaps the most widely used technique for planning and monitoring activities within the modern productive system.

[1]See *Principles of Operations Research* (2nd ed.) by Harvey M. Wagner, Prentice-Hall (1975), Englewood Cliffs, NJ, p.3.

[2]*The New Management* by W. H. Gruber & J.J. Niles, McGraw-Hill, NY, 1976 is devoted to a discussion of the interface problems that exist between staff specialists and line executives and their solutions. It focuses on the utilization of existing OR knowledge that is readily available to increase the effectiveness of management decision making.

"While one can identify many factors influencing organizational effectiveness, some of which are outside the direct control of those in positions of leadership, the critical importance of executive functions and of those persons who carry them out to the survival and effectiveness of the organization can not be denied."

V.H. Vroom and P.W. Yetton,
Leadership and Decision Making,
University of Pittsburgh Press, 1973

Dr. T.F. Gautschi, P.E.

Tools for decision aiding

Program Evaluation and Review Technique (PERT)

NETWORK PLAN

The Program Evaluation and Review Technique (PERT) is a method of planning and controlling non-repetitive projects. PERT applications range from the very complex and extensive program for landing the first man on the moon to something as "simple" as the construction of a building, the planning and launching of a new product or even moving a production process from one plant to another.

The basis for PERT is a network (or flow) plan. The network is composed of a series of related events and activities. *Events* are identifiable accomplishments that occur at definite points in time. *Activities* encompass the work required to complete the events. Events do *not* consume any time, they simply signify the beginning and end of activities. Events are usually drawn as boxes or circles and activities are represented by arrows joining them.

For example, suppose a firm is planning to install a new computer system. A number of events and activities will have to take place. Among them would be: the renovation of an existing room, selection of equipment, installation of the new equipment, hiring and training people to operate the computer installation, and many more. When many events and activities are involved, as in this example, PERT can be very useful in planning and controlling them. Fig. 1 illustrates the application of PERT to this project.

The numbers shown with each activity (the arrows) are an estimate of the time to complete the activity (usually specified in weeks). Some activities are shown in parallel. This indicates that they can be performed independently from one another. For example, hiring operators, getting the room, and ordering equipment are parallel activities. Interdependencies between the appropriate activities are shown as series relationships. For example, operators must be hired before they can be trained, or equipment must be received before it can be installed.

PATH THROUGH NETWORK

Perhaps the most useful characteristic of PERT is that it identifies the critical path for a project. That is, the series path through the network that takes the longest time to complete. In our example the critical path is shown by a heavy line, and its total length is 27 weeks. The other two parallel paths take 19 weeks and 24 weeks respectively—these are non-critical paths. The time differential between the scheduled completion of these non-critical paths and the critical path is termed *Slack*. Thus, one path has eight weeks slack time and the other has three weeks slack time. Any action to shorten the total project time should be applied to the critical path. When excessive slack time exists in a project, it should probably be reprogrammed.

PERT both encourages and permits managers to plan each major project through in its entirety, and in some detail. It identifies possible delays, and aids in the resolution of difficulties. Early in the planning process it identifies those activities that have long lead times. It helps managers achieve their schedules because of continuous and effective control. PERT contributes to the optimization of resources. It is also an excellent communications tool.

The DELPHI technique

Some form of group decision making process is indicated when the appropriate knowledge and expertise for solving a problem is divided among several people. Generally, the consensus thinking process (*Design News* 7-21-75) is best for this situation. However, there are circumstances when the Delphi Technique can be useful. These include:

(1) When a high status or strong individual tends to dominate the discussion and

the decision is liable to be some form of compromise rather than consensus.

(2) When the experts are separated from each other geographically.

(3) When the experts come from outside of the organization.

(4) When the experts are a collection of individuals from diverse backgrounds, and who have only a temporary relationship with each other.

(5) When the number of experts is too large for meaningful face-to-face group discussion.

LONG-RANGE PLAN

The Delphi Technique (named after Apollo's Oracle At Delphi) was developed by the Rand Corp. for long-range technical forecasting. It was used to collect, evaluate and integrate the inputs from a collection of expert individuals from diverse backgrounds. It replaces group face-to-face interaction with a structured program of individual interrogations. As a result, it can be utilized when all, or some, of the circumstances described above pertain.

A key element in this technique is that the participants are *not* identified to each other in any way. This eliminates all open discussion and any undue influence by a high-status individual, and it permits the participants to change their opinions without concern for face-saving. It also produces a better result than any one expert could make.

The basic process is one where a coordinator solicits each expert's opinions through a series of questionnaires or one-on-one discussions. The first round is completed when the opinions from all of the experts are gathered and tabulated (anonymously) by the coordinator. Everyone is then sent all of the information that has been gathered and tabulated. They are then asked to modify or change their inputs as they may desire, and to justify any significant deviation from the majority. Round 2 is completed when the second input from each expert is collected and tabulated. The process is continued through as many rounds as are necessary to obtain a sufficient convergence of opinion to make a decision.

SAMPLE QUESTIONS

The following is a sample list of questions that could be used in the Delphi Technique.

1. By what year do you believe that the majority of homes will have computer terminals tied in with a general computer utility?

(a) 1980   (b) 1990   (c) 2000   (d) 2010   (e) 2020

2. How desirable is the event in question #1?

(a) very desirable   (b) desirable   (c) not very desirable

3. What is the feasibility of the event in question #1?

(a) highly feasible   (b) likely   (c) unlikely, but possible

4. What is your familiarity with the subject in question #1?

(a) poor   (b) fair   (c) good   (d) excellent

When the coordinator does not have sufficient information to develop a meaningful questionnaire, the first round may consist of a tentative questionnaire or list of factors. The responses from round 1 can then be used to develop an appropriate questionnaire.

The Delphi Technique is an effective multipurpose tool that can be used by nearly any organization to determine the value of an uncertain event. Its accuracy can be improved by increasing the number of experts, and by continuing the number of rounds until the results from the last round do not significantly change

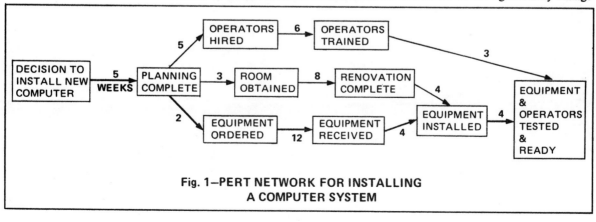

Fig. 1—PERT NETWORK FOR INSTALLING
A COMPUTER SYSTEM

those from the previous round. Although Delphi was developed as a long-range forecasting tool, it has been adapted to topics related to product lines; possible educational innovations; technological evaluation and its ecological impact; setting goals and priorities for education, business and government; and establishing management information system requirements. It can also be used to gather or validate the required inputs for the decision grids and decision trees discussed earlier in this series (*Design News* 1-17-77).

LIMITATIONS

The Delphi Technique does have some drawbacks.

(1) The calendar length of time required for each round can be excessive.

(2) The experts must be carefully selected and motivated to assure them continuing participation through perhaps three to five rounds of activity.

(3) Particular attention must be exercised in the design of the questionnaire—otherwise excessive bias can easily be built in.

(4) Usually, the expert is not the implementator for the resulting decision. As a result, special efforts may have to be made to achieve a high level of commitment on the part of those who will implement the decision.

CONCLUSION

A number of decision-making tools are used by management: force-field analysis, the decision grid, decision trees, cost-benefit analysis, break-even analysis, linear programming, Gantt charts, PERT charts, and the Delphi Technique. The results from such analysis usually do not provide the final decision, but they can be used to influence the manager's mental model of the situation, and as such, provide useful guidance. As the utilization of these, and other, decision-making tools increases, we will learn better how to use them, and they will become a more important aspect of the manager's decision-making process.

Force field analysis

A way to implement problem-solving change

Dr. T. F. Gautschi, P.E.

Kurt Leven proposed that in any problem situation where the level of activity is the resultant of a number of forces, these forces can be resolved into those that:

Promote the occurrence of the particular activity—DRIVING FORCES, and those

that **inhibit or oppose the occurrence of the same activity—RESTRAINING FORCES.**

He called this model **FORCE FIELD ANALYSIS:** A framework for identifying critical elements in a problem situation and implementing appropriate change. Although these **FORCES** are not static, they will be in equilibrium at any point in time. That is, the level of activity will move to the point where the totality of the **DRIVING FORCES** is equal to the totality of the **RESTRAINING FORCES.** Clearly, the individual **FORCES** will be of different magnitudes but their totals must be equal.

EXPERIENCE EVERY DAY   We experience this phenomenon every day . . . although we might not think of our experience in Force Field analysis terms. For example, a boat will sink into water until the weight of the displaced water is equal to the weight of the boat and its contents.

Another example: a person will stay with an organization as long as he perceives that the total benefits he receives outweigh the dissatisfactions that accrue from such association. When the resultant level of activity is not that which is desired, we have a problem, but if we can identify the **DRIVING FORCES** and the **RESTRAINING FORCES** we also have a framework for identifying a solution—especially if we have some idea of their relative magnitudes.

In our boat example, if the boat is too deep in the water, we can either increase its displacement or decrease the load in the boat—generally we will reduce the load—at least as a short-run solution.

Let's look at a more complex situation—the level of effectiveness of a manager in an organization:

CURRENT LEVEL
OF EFFECTIVENESS

LOW EFFECTIVENESS	HIGH EFFECTIVENESS
DRIVING FORCES	RESTRAINING FORCES
CRITICISM OR SUPPORT FROM SUPERIOR	NOT WELL ORGANIZED
MANAGEMENT SKILL TRAINING	UNWILLING TO DELEGATE
DESIRE TO SUCCEED	HEAVY WORK PRESSURES
LIKES WORK	LACK OF CONFIDENCE IN SUBORDINATE'S ABILITY
DESIRE FOR STATUS IN COMPANY & COMMUNITY	INCOMPETENCE OF SUBORDINATES
	CAN ONLY WORK AT DETAIL LEVEL
	POOR COMMUNICATOR
CLEAR CUT GOALS	CONFUSED GOALS

The above-listed **FORCES** are used for illustration, and are not intended to serve as a model for analyzing the effectiveness of any particular manager.

IDENTIFY CHANGE

After a **FORCE FIELD** diagram has been prepared, it can serve as a basis for identifying changes to achieve the desired level of activity. There are two ways to change the situation. We can apply pressure by increasing the strengths of the **DRIVING FORCES** or we can decrease the strength of the **RESTRAINING FORCES**.

In our example, if we increase the "criticism by the manager's superior," it will probably cause an increase in the manager's effectiveness, at least in the short run. But this increase may also be accompanied by increased tension, conflict defensiveness, fighting back, and retaliatory actions by the manager towards his own subordinates. This in turn, generates new **RESTRAINING FORCES** that will tend to reduce the level of effectiveness.

RESOLVE CONFLICTS

On the other hand, if we decrease one or more of the **RESTRAINING FORCES**, we might be able to reduce the amount of conflict and tensions, and, at the same time, move the equilibrium point in the desired direction.

Instead of asking, "What can be done to raise the manager's level of effectiveness?" we might ask, "What keeps his level of effectiveness from being higher?"

It may be a better strategy to reduce **RESTRAINING FORCES** than to try to increase **DRIVING FORCES**.

Oftentimes when a number of people are involved in a problem or its solution, communication becomes critical. Force Field analysis is a tool that can help reduce the communication conflicts by identifying the critical elements in the problem, and provide some insight regarding what changes might be appropriate.

GENERAL APPLICATION

This technique is applicable to a number of business problems: financial performance levels, employee turnover rates, management effectiveness levels, morale levels, production costs, expenses, relationships with customers, and many more. Generally, we will not be able to qualify the magnitude of the various forces, but we can learn a lot by just being able to identify them.

Force-field analysis: a case history

An application that improved organizational effectiveness

Dr. T. F. Gautschi, P.E.

Recently we discussed the concept of force-field analysis. It has proven to be a very useful technique for identifying the factors relating to problems such as employee turnover rates, production costs and organizational effectiveness. In this issue we will present the results of a force-field analysis to improve the effectiveness of a large growing corporation, along with the strategy that was adopted to improve the situation.

CURRENT SITUATION

DRIVING FORCES

- Current organization is profitable and healthy
- Recognition of symptoms of potential difficulty
- Recognition of the need for improved profit opportunities
- Good products
- Strong, dedicated top management that is determined to make corporation succeed
- Highly intelligent and motivated middle management anxious to help make the corporation successful
- A determination to minimize internal politics—no empire builders
- Reasonably clear charters for each major function: marketing, technical service & development, manufacturing, research and controller

RESTRAINING FORCES

- Preoccupation with problems; insufficient emphasis on opportunities for profit
- Cumbersome communication channels between key functions—especially between marketing and manufacturing
- Organization too inward oriented and not sufficiently oriented to the customer
- Top management too occupied with running day-to-day operations—not enough time for long-range planning
- Decision-making process slow and cumbersome
- Long-range planning sporadic and superficial
- Accountability not closely related to responsibility
- Overstaffing and inefficiency
- Executives do not have good control of their operations
- An environment that does not encourage total participation and involvement
- Executives do not have adequate financial information
- Market managers do not know what it costs to produce a product
- Profits should be higher—especially for some product lines
- Results are not easily measurable or visible
- Resources are not allocated in proportion to expected results
- Limited competitive ability relating to technological innovations

ORGANIZATION CHANGE

ANALYSIS

The strategy is to improve organizational effectiveness by decreasing Restraining Forces (RFs) and increasing Driving Forces (DFs).

An examination of the various RFs indicated that the functional organization of a certain company was limiting organizational effectiveness. The functional structure was appropriate when the company had a limited product line, served a single industry, operated mostly in the U.S., and had a limited number of customers.

But it now had a number of product lines, it served several industries, it operated worldwide and it had many customers. Although the company was currently profitable and healthy, management feared that the problems, identified as RFs, could only get worse with time in the functional type organization. So it was decided that a matrix form of organization should be adopted.

However, it would be risky because it would be a major departure from the traditional functional organization. It was believed that the matrix would provide the framework for the future growth and the increased organizational effectiveness that was desired.

For example, many of the professional staff would be working in dual authority relationships. The decision-making process would be flattened out or spread across the organization and there would be emphasis upon decision-making by consensus. These were new and drastically different concepts and might not be readily understood or accepted. This significant change required communicating the purpose and nature of the change to all employees, and the adoption of a new way of thinking about jobs.

The total transition would also require several years of hard work and a great amount of management commitment and involvement.

ADOPTED MATRIX

The matrix organization that was adopted has two major dimensions—cost-centers and profit-centers. Other dimensions, such as geographical area and space-time can be added later when the complexity of the business requires it. The cost-centers cover the functional responsibilities of marketing, field service, manufacturing, engineering and controller. The profit-centers are organized by product line and define the businesses the company is in.

The cost-center managers have the responsibility for technical performance, quality, reliability and cost and have the administrative responsibility for all human resources except for the staff reporting directly to the profit-center managers.

The profit-center manager's primary responsibility is to assure that the product line is generating the required profit. He carries out this responsibility through a team that is made up of representatives from each of the cost-centers. These representatives report directly to the cost-center manager (e.g. V-P of marketing, manufacturing, etc.) and work in a consensus mode with the profit-center manager. These teams make the business decisions to assure that the required profitability is maintained, that resources are properly allocated, that the product meets the customer's needs and that it is responsive to the business environment in terms of functionality, schedule and price. This team also acts as a focal point for all product line related information.

The profit-center managers report directly to upper management, as do the cost-center managers, and they are chosen primarily on the basis of their business knowledge, experience and leadership abilities.

SUPPORT SYSTEMS

To assure a smooth-running organization, several support systems were also used:

- **Management by Objectives** and the appropriate information systems
- **Personnel performance reviews** by both bosses
- **Planning process** carried out by cost-center and profit-center managers in accordance with established corporate ground rules. This involves both one and five-year plans
- **Profit reporting** where all sales and expenditures are assigned to a product line. This allows the company's total profit before tax to be clearly identified by each product line manager and the product line team.

CONCLUSION

The above described matrix organization has been in operation for about five years. It has reduced the restraining forces and has increased the driving forces—and as a result has proven very successful in improving organizational effectiveness in terms of growth and profitability.

FOOD FOR THOUGHT

"We must recognize that organizational development is not the solution to all of the problems facing industrial firms or other organizations in this country. I do believe, however, that it will be applied increasingly in the future as different types of social institutions—governmental, commercial, educational, military, etc.—learn that they often cannot cope with internal and external problems by using the traditional bureaucratic management structure and process . . . The hierarchical, bureaucratic model of management can no longer keep up with change . . . The solution to the problem is to loosen up our organizations, make them more flexible. In some cases, the traditional organization will be modified only slightly. In other instances completely new organizations, modeled along organic lines, will evolve. The critical need is to make it possible for organizations to adapt readily to their changing environments. And that is what organization development is all about."

—Dr. Michael Beer, Corning Glass Works

Dr. T.F. Gautschi, P.E.

Zero-base budgeting: what it is

Since there has been quite a bit of recent discussion regarding the zero-base budgeting (or planning) concept, it seems appropriate to devote an article to the discussion of: why it is important, how it works, its strengths and its weaknesses.

Why it is important

ITS IMPETUS

The zero-base philosophy has received impetus from four major sources:

(1) In the early 1970's Peter Pyhrr first applied it at Texas Instruments Incorporated with some apparent success.

(2) Gov. Jimmy Carter introduced it in the state government of Georgia for the fiscal year 1972-1973, and he credits much of his managerial success (in terms of reorganization and the better utilization of funds) to the ZBB technique. In fact, in his State of the State address to the General Assembly of Georgia on Jan. 11, 1972 he said that, "The zero-base budgeting procedure is almost certain to be copied throughout the Nation."

(3) Currently some 300 businesses and a dozen state governments are using some form of the ZBB concept.

(4) In the January 1977 issue of *Nation's Business*, President-elect Jimmy Carter stated that, "Immediately after my inauguration I will require zero-base budgeting for all federal departments, bureaus, and boards by executive order." In his first "fireside chat", President Carter reiterated his faith in zero-base budgeting. If the ZBB process is adopted by the federal government it will undoubtedly have an effect upon the planning and budgeting activities of the private sector as well.

PRESIDENTS' PLANS

It is interesting to note that Carter's five predecessors also initiated new budgeting and planning concepts of various sorts, and that they have had some impact upon organizational theory and practice.

—EISENHOWER: The program budgeting concept—this helped solve the problem of identifying the various budget line items with specific programs.

—KENNEDY: Cost-effectiveness analysis in DOD—this provided a way to compare the practices of the various programs in terms of their cost effectiveness.

—JOHNSON: The long-range planning concept—this required planning, programming, budgeting and analysis on a five-year basis even though funding was approved annually.

—NIXON: Tended to push the Management by Objectives approach to help establish priorities and improve program management.

—FORD: Required that the various programs be analyzed in terms of their economic impact, and priorities were established through cost-benefit analysis.

However, all of the above approaches were modifications to the traditional budgeting (planning) approach of incrementing the new on the old, whereas, in theory at least, the zero-base concept requires a major change in management philosophy to be successful.

What it is

Peter Phyrr defines zero-base budgeting as:

"An operating planning and budgeting process which requires each manager to justify his entire budget request in detail, and shifts the burden of proof to each manager to justify why he should spend any money. This procedure requires that all activities and operations be identified in decision packages which will be evaluated and ranked in order of importance by systematic analysis."

START FROM SCRATCH

Basically, zero-base budgeting (planning) requires that every element of the organization identify each function that it performs, its priority, the required personnel, and the cost for performing that function; and then having management approve those functions that have the highest priority within the funding, personnel, facilities and equipment constraints that have been established for the organization.

This is in contrast to the traditional incremented approach of accepting the prior year's budget level as a starting point and then examining the changes or marginal differences requested to implement the new budget or plan.

Generally, ZBB is *not* used for budgeting or controlling the direct labor and material costs associated with the manufacturing process. These direct costs are usually budgeted and controlled in terms of profits.

ZBB can be applied to all governmental functions, and to those industrial overhead functions that cannot be easily related to a profit figure. It is especially adaptable to discretionary cost areas in which service or support are the primary outputs, as is the case with most overhead and governmental functions.

Its strengths

ADVANTAGES

1. ZBB provides a basis for setting and controlling discretionary budgets on a rational basis.

2. It provides a basis for reducing suboptimization by implementing consistent priority levels throughout the organization.

3. It often provides the basis for combining and reducing the cost of service functions (such as publications or computer service) that have been scattered throughout the organization.

4. It may provide the basis for better utilization of people and other scarce resources by using them where they are needed the most.

5. The approval of an overall set of decision packages before the detailed budgets are prepared can save time and money and reduce confusion.

6. It provides a rational basis for cost reduction, when it is required, compared to the "meat-ax" approach of an arbitrary cut of 10 or 15% across the board.

7. In addition to the traditional comparison of budgeted and actual financial results, ZBB provides management with output and performance measurements that can be monitored periodically.

8. It can provide managers with a better understanding of what is going on in their organizations in terms of tasks, priorities, progress and resources allocated and utilized.

9. Changes in funding can be evaluated by considering the effect of moving the cut-off line that divides the approved decision packages from those not approved.

10. It provides a common data base and some basis for comparison between organizational units.

11. It increases the involvement of personnel at all levels in the budgeting-planning process which, in turn, generally increases understanding and commitment.

12. It decreases the possibility of maintaining separate fiefdoms that owe their existence to organizational complexity, and the misuse of power.

13. It forces decision making.

Its weaknesses

DISADVANTAGES

1. Because ZBB can be threatening, its participants may be reluctant to provide realistic budgets.

2. A large volume of decision packages can place a real burden on the people who must process them. This can be reduced somewhat by codification and computer analysis and storage.

3. The establishment of consistent measurement and priority criteria is difficult. In fact, this is probably the weakest aspect of the whole process.

4. The development of the decision packages is time consuming, at least for the first several submittals.

5. Since ZBB is such a major change in management approach, it must be carefully planned and much time and effort at all management levels must be devoted to assuring that it is implemented properly. It *cannot* be forced upon an organization. Each organizational element should have some time to work with the system and test it before implementation.

6. It is often difficult to prepare packages representing a minimum level of effort. Also, incremental resource requirements may vary, depending upon which increments are approved.

Dr. T.F. Gautschi, P.E.

Zero-base budgeting: how it works

Last issue (4-4-77) we said that zero-base budgeting requires that every element of the organization identify each function that it performs, its priority, the required personnel, and the cost for performing that function; and then having management approve the highest priority functions within the funding, personnel, facilities and equipment constraints that have been established for the organization. This issue will show how to do that.

DECISION PACKAGES

(1) The first step is to break the entire operation down into units called decision packages. These packages should be prepared by the responsible manager at each level. The packages should cover all activities of each organizational element—whether they be new or continuing. In many situations the decision package will correspond with the traditional cost-center or budget-unit. Decision packages may also include special programs or other activities that apply across the organization.

In all cases they should cover activities that can be analyzed and controlled by management and involve discretionary decisions.

(2) The decision packages should be assembled incrementally on a zero-base. Each increment should specify its priority, performance level, benefits and costs. To provide management with some flexibility, more than one increment should be required to provide the current (or recommended) level of service.

For example, the amount of system testing for a particular production prototype might be discretionary as shown in Fig. 1.

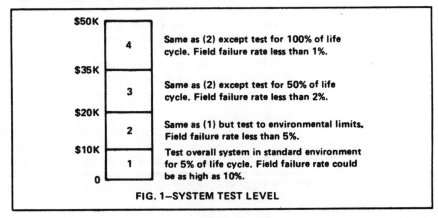

$50K	
	4 — Same as (2) except test for 100% of life cycle. Field failure rate less than 1%.
$35K	
	3 — Same as (2) except test for 50% of life cycle. Field failure rate less than 2%.
$20K	
	2 — Same as (1) but test to environmental limits. Field failure rate less than 5%.
$10K	
	1 — Test overall system in standard environment for 5% of life cycle. Field failure rate could be as high as 10%.
0	

FIG. 1—SYSTEM TEST LEVEL

Each additional test increment (1-4) has an additional cost and additional benefit (less risk of failure in the field) associated with it. With such a presentation, management can determine which level of testing would be most appropriate from an overall organizational point of view.

(3) The decision packages provide the basic input that will enable higher-level management to make the necessary resource allocation decisions.

AN EXAMPLE

For example, let's assume that the quality assurance function in a particular corporate division is divided into three major areas—(I) inspection, (A) failure-analysis, and (T) system-testing—and that each of these functions can be expressed in incremental decision packages that include cost, benefits, performance and priority. The quality assurance manager can then assemble the highest priority package that meets his funding constraints.

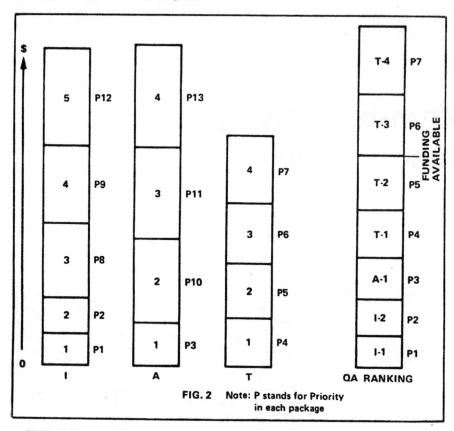

FIG. 2   Note: P stands for Priority in each package

This ranking process on a priority basis can then be extended up through, and across, the entire organization until a total package is developed.

(4) After the basic allocations are made by decision package for the entire organization, the preparation of the detailed budget then becomes more or less a clerical task.

The zero-base budget-planning concept has potential—especially for those activities that involve discretionary costs—and it is bound to receive further impetus from President Carter at the federal level.

In theory, it appears to have a number of strengths; however, the establishment of realistic measurement and priority criteria may be its Achilles' heel. In any case, it is a relatively new concept with which every manager should be familiar.

Further reading:

1. Peter A. Pyhrr, *ZERO-BASE BUDGETING: A Practical Management Tool for Evaluating Expenses*, ed. John Wiley & Sons, 1973.

2. R. H. Hermanson and G.S. Minimier, "A Look at Zero-Base Budgeting—The Georgia Experience", *Atlantic Economic Review*, July/August 1976.

3. P. J. Stonich, "Zero-Base Planning—A Management Tool", *Managerial Planning*, July/August 1976.

14

Technological Obsolescence and a manager's education

Dr. T. F. Gautschi, P.E.

By the mid-eighteenth century, mankind's total fund of knowledge had doubled from what it was at the birth of Christ. It doubled again by 1900 and again by 1950.

That's 1750 years for the first doubling to take place, 150 years for the next and only 50 for the next. But what's really mind-boggling is that the next two doublings of mankind's knowledge took place in 1960 and 1968.

TIMES ARE CHANGING

Technological obsolescence is thus becoming a serious problem for engineers and managers in our advanced technological environment. Not too long ago a person could expect that the knowledge and skills he built up in school and during early job training would be adequate (perhaps with some minimal additional education) to carry him through his working life to retirement. This is no longer possible in many positions, especially those that are at the forefront of technological change.

MEAGER DATA

For example, even though the computer has been a major force in our society for nearly two decades, many engineering managers have only the vaguest understanding of its basic principles.

It would help if we could develop statistics on the number of people confronted by the obsolescence problem. It would also be useful to assess the costs to society, the organization and the individual, resulting from a manager's professional obsolescence. Clearly our technical and managerial manpower are assets that should not be allowed to deteriorate. We do not have much in the way of statistics and data on the problem; in fact, we don't even have a consensus on just what constitutes obsolescence—its definition, characteristics or symptoms.

However, we do know that the "half-life" of an engineering education is about ten years. That is, for the engineer graduating today, half of what he has learned will be obsolete in ten years, and more than half of what he will need to know in ten years will not have been taught to him in college.

A study was recently made of management's evaluation of the performance of design and development engineers vs. age. The average percentile ranking increased with age until the early thirties, dropped slightly in the late thirties, and then fell steadily thereafter until retirement. Twenty years ago, performance peaked about ten years later. But that was before computers, television, space travel, supersonic aircraft, large scale integrated circuits, micropackaging, advanced communications and much more. In short, the problem of technological obsolescence is becoming progressively more critical.

AVERAGE PERCENTILE RANKING

1950's

1970's

25 30 40 50 60
AGE

OBSOLESCENCE IS SUBTLE

The sad thing is that an individual can be totally unaware that his skills are obsolete. For example, an engineer who is using discrete components to develop electronic control devices may be completely unaware that he could obtain standard LSI circuits that would do the entire job more reliably and cheaply. Or an engineer might be using a slide rule and a handbook to work out complex structural or thermal problems when he could get a more precise solution much faster by using a computer program available through a time-share terminal.

If we suspect that our skills are becoming obsolete, our psychological defense mechanisms may prevent us from admitting it to ourselves, much less to anyone else. Or we may recognize the symptoms, but simply not know what to do about them.

There are no easy solutions to this problem. However, I believe that there are some things we as managers and engineers must do.

FIRST RECOGNIZE THE PROBLEM

First, recognize that the obsolescence process begins early in our careers—long before we are aware of it. It's almost like the new car that starts to depreciate the moment we take delivery.

I am reminded of the mice that lived and played in a beautiful corn field. They had plenty of food, water, shelter and lived very happily. They thought nothing about tomorrow, because they couldn't conceive that things might change drastically even though each day the corn grew a little more mature. Then one day the corn was picked and the corn stalks were plowed under ... and so were the mice.

RESOLVE TO SOLVE THE PROBLEM

Then we must resolve to do something about slowing down or eliminating the obsolescence process. For the individual this means keeping up with the state-of-the-art in his chosen field and perhaps in related fields. For the manager it means the creation of an environment that will encourage subordinates to keep up with the developments in his field.

However, we must also assess the life expectancy of our chosen field—otherwise, we could end up being an expert in a no-longer-relevant field. For example, the conventional internal combustion engine could be made obsolete in the automobile by some other energy conversion system. If this happens, the engineer who has not kept up with structures, thermal design, materials, and mechanics might himself become obsolete.

THEN TAKE ACTION

After we recognize the problem and resolve to do something about it, we can easily identify a number of useful safeguards:
- Read periodicals and books
- Participate in various college courses
- Participate in special courses sponsored by your company, technical associations or college
- Teach classes in your field
- Take correspondence courses
- Share summaries or outlines of key articles/books
- Participate in discussion seminars

Discussion seminars worked very well for my colleagues and I while preparing for our written doctoral exams. Six of us met according to a fixed schedule and discussed agreed-upon topics in our field, a different man being assigned to present a report to the others at each meeting. When we felt reasonably confident in the field, we invited a recognized expert (in this case, one of our professors) to interact with us.

START NOW

The important thing is that whatever you plan to do, start now, and continue on a regular basis.

Let's be men, not mice.

Continuing education and professional vitality: management's role

Donald D. French, Northeastern University

A significant challenge facing management is the continued vitality of their organization and its professional staff. Often, individuals within organizations are held solely responsible for the maintenance of their professional skills. This rationalization has been conveniently used as a cop-out by many organizations whose management policies and practices are sorely out-dated and ineffective. Although the responsibility for maintaining professional competence and career development rests ultimately with the individual, the principal determinant of success in this endeavor lies within the practices of the work organization.

COMPETITIVE PRESSURES

Increasing competitive pressures facing organizations may jeopardize their survival unless they learn to better utilize the human resources they possess. Their future may be further threatened if they are unable to respond to the shifting demands of the environment. A responsive organization requires versatility in its professional staff. This versatility is not only based on competent performance of a professional's current job, but also is dependent upon the professional competence of the individual. Far too many professionals are engaged in highly specialized, fractioned organizational roles in which they perform repetitive tasks that do not enable them to utilize their abilities. The sharp definition of their job assignments and responsiblities, together with the organization's reward system do not provide them with sufficient motivation to maintain their professional competence. Consequently, many professionals experience a rude awakening when their jobs change dramatically and they realize that their current skills are inadequate for effectively performing new assignments.

MANAGEMENT ACTION

Since the job is a principal factor in the professional's development, it is essential for management to understand how work can be best accomplished while concurrently optimizing opportunities for career development. Professor Harold Kaufman, of the Polytechnic Institute of New York, suggests the following management action to minimize obsolescence and encourage professional growth:

- Monitor the degree of obsolescence in the organization and establish controls for its detection among individuals.
- Provide for objective appraisals of an individual's future potential and career development.
- Establish a flexible retirement policy and provide for portable pensions.
- Redesign jobs to improve utilization of knowledge and skills and to increase individual responsibility and influence.
- Change job assignments to avoid narrow specialization.
- Allow obsolescent professionals to change careers.
- Encourage development through colleague interaction.
- Select supervisors on the basis of knowledge and skills relevant to the type of work carried out by their subordinates.
- Create a good organizational climate through management policies that encourage and reward growth and development.
- Plan continuing education programs and evaluate their effectiveness in updating professionals.

CLOSER EXAMINATION

In response to increasing competition and new demands for improved performance resulting from rapid advancements in technology, more companies are beginning to examine the vitality of their professional staff. An extensive study was conducted by the University of California's Lawrence Livermore Laboratory to determine what personnel practices and approaches to organizational development would keep engineers updated and productive in a creative sense, two qualities that are considered essential for organizational growth. After a thorough assessment by the Laboratory's directors of personnel practices in a number of other major R&D

labs, they concluded that even in a no-growth condition management could take the following action to improve productivity of its existing staff:

- encourage continuing education
- rotate assignments including offering leave programs and personnel exchanges with other organizations
- improve salary management by orienting it to reward performance

In addition, management can take action to insure adequate turnover, including the early identification and termination of unsuitable employees by enforcing rigorous performance standards, and stimulated early retirement of aging marginal performers.

EXPANDED TRAINING

As more work organizations realize that continuing education can play an important role in increasing vitality, training budgets are being expanded. However, most training departments tend to shy away from dealing with the sophisticated technical training needs of practicing scientists and engineers. Even in companies with competent and aggressive training departments, professionals with highly specialized talents, or skills peripheral to the mainstream of their organization's business activity, are rarely given the attention they require in meeting their training needs. Yet, meeting these needs would enhance productivity and contribution from the experienced professional.

In order for a staff development program to proceed effectively, training needs must be assessed by both the practitioners and management. In this way, associated problems such as poor organizational climate, can surface and receive management attention, while training needs can get management concurrence and overall organizational support.

OPTIONS

Once the scope of training needs is assessed, the work organization has a number of options in providing the required training. Organizations can often choose between in-house or outside training. The subject or area of training is a major factor to be considered in this choice. Training that deals with proprietary information should be handled in-house. If existing staff members or outside consultants are available to act as resource persons, it is often less expensive to conduct programs internally.

Internal programs have numerous drawbacks, however. They promote "inbreeding" and further isolate participants from people and ideas in other companies. Opportunities to question accepted practices are reduced. These factors lessen the effectiveness of internal programs in combatting obsolescence and stimulating creativity. Over the short run, the symptoms of decreasing individual and organizational vitality are hard to detect, since work appears to go well, harmony is improved, and everyone seems to agree with one another. The insidious nature of obsolescence does not readily signal the failure of poorly designed training programs. Although cost per trainee may be lower, quality is rarely given sufficient consideration; that is, the cost-quality ratio is frequently neglected in making "in house—out-house" decisions.

OUTSIDE TRAINING

The prestige and stimulation from association with an outside training institution can enhance the overall quality of a training program. Employee loyalty and commitment improve from the realization that the organization is sincerely trying to help them progress. Emotional factors improving employee attitudes are difficult to measure and again are often neglected in choosing the approach to training.

Occasionally, non-competing companies in the same locale form a consortium to meet their common training needs. Employees from a cooperating work organization attend internally-developed training programs at other companies. Each organization pays for its share of the expenses. The additional trainees help reduce the cost of internal training for all concerned. This practice avails more programs to each organization and promotes improved opportunities for cross-fertilization among the participants.

Lastly, there is the affiliation with a training institution. Outside organizations are generally in a good position to survey and objectively advise management. They ususally have extensive resources available and excellent supporting services. They can offer a neutral ground for learning and bring together people with varying backgrounds and experiences. The institution should be able to set a good climate for learning and provide experiences beyond those possible with internal programs. They are also able to custom design programs and to supply appropriate resource people for the work organization. Generally, a balanced approach to the utilization of training resources works to an organization's best advantage. Cost effectiveness often points to in-house programs, but the value of stimulation from outside exposure should not be underestimated.

References

1. Kaufman, H.G., *Obsolescence and Professional Career Development*, (New York: AMACOM, 1974)

2. Decker, W.D. and Van Atta, C.M., "Maintaining Vitality and Productivity in R&D - Steps to Maintain High Level Staff Performance" in *Research Management*, Vol. 16, No. 3, March 1973.

Dr. T.F. Gautschi, P.E.
Mr. J.P. Greaney
Dr. R.L. Bjorklund

Career paths:
a preliminary report

Background

A joint effort to investigate career paths was initiated by Professor R. L. Bjorklund and John P. Greaney of Worcester Polytechnic Institute (WPI) and myself about six months ago. An early step in this investigation was the development of the Career Path Survey that was published in the April 19, 1976 issue of *Design News*. Nearly one thousand of you were interested enough to devote somewhere between thirty minutes and an hour completing the questionnaire and sending your answers to us. This fine response is really appreciated. It has provided a significant bank of data (about 250,000 data points) from which we expect to be able to draw a number of useful observations.

PROCESSING THE SURVEY

Progress

As you can imagine, the process of just entering the data into the computer is a big task. So far, we have input about one-third of the data at WPI where the analysis is being performed. We expect to complete this data input activity in the next few weeks, and are using the SPSS[1] system to process the data. Over the next several months, we plan to develop and present a series of glimpses into your career and job attitudes.

Who Responded?

Most of those who responded were engineers (two-thirds) listing Mechanical (one-half) or Electrical (one-fifth) as their field with product design, development engineering and production engineering as their job. Readers listing management as their current field (one-third) do technical management almost to the exclusion of all other areas (such as finance, personnel administration, or production management). We were not surprised that most of you work for large private sector organizations.

SOME RESULTS

People do change jobs!

Of our preliminary data, 35% had *five or more* jobs to date. More than 60% have had three or more jobs since they began their profession.

People who change jobs also change employers far more frequently than not.

We've concluded that, rather than finding their promotions or job changes where they work, they often find them in other organizations.

The average job changer has been on the job about three years.

Thus, over a person's lifetime of three or more jobs the previous employers will have lost (and the final employer gained) about 10 years of experience. This *is* considerable. If a company could decipher the cause of the job change, it could save a considerable amount of lost experience due to turnover.

The most important positive factors about companies were generally those related to the job and, therefore, controllable by the company or the direct supervisor!

With the exception of pay, the most important positive factors were opportunity for challenging work, personal enjoyment from work, opportunity for promotion and the opportunity for creative work experiences.

BEING IN ON INFO

The causes of aggravation and dissatisfaction are primarily related to information.

Dissatisfaction with the amount of information on careers and promotion opportunities, the affairs of the company and the opportunity to have significant input to the company decision making process were most frequently cited by readers as problems. This is reinforced by the results of our earlier Employee Loyalty Survey (*Design News* 4-7-75) where we concluded, "There is dissatisfaction with all of the job climate factors that were listed: the knowledge of career paths, recognition for work performed, the sense of accomplishment and the challenges received from work and other factors. Most dissatisfaction was expressed regarding the amount of information the respondents receive about what is going on in their companies."

From this we must conclude that professional technical employees feel that information is important and that they do not receive enough.

Of the career ambitions listed, the most important was "to make a contribution to my employer."

In the past some have thought that engineers had stronger ties to their profession than to their employers (they were thought to be "cosmopolitans" rather than "locals"). However, these data indicate that the respondents feel that "making a contribution to my employer outweighs the importance of "making a contribution to my profession". This possible change in attitude may be the result of the economic and technological environment that exists today. That is, even good engineers are finding it progressively difficult to change employers, and the technology is moving so rapidly that it is difficult to deep up with it on a broad front.

"Inventing something new" was seen as an important ambition.

This response was expected since most engineers characteristically see themselves as being innovative and creative.

Another important ambition was, "Working on projects that fulfill basic human needs."

Some have characterized the engineer as being primarily concerned with the technological aspects of a problem and trying to advance the state of the technological art regardless of how the results were used.

The response from this survey refutes this characterization. Engineers want most to work on projects that fulfill basic human needs. They could be driven by altruistic motives, or simply by the recognition that a firm can only stay in business as long as it meets its customers' needs.

---

1. SPSS is the Statistical Package for the Social Sciences, and is described in detail in *SPSS* by N. Nie, D. H. Bent and C. Hadlai Hill, McGraw Hill, New York, 1970. SPSS is an integrated system of computer programs for the analysis of social science data. In addition to the usual descriptive statistics, such as sample frequency distributions and cross-tabulations, SPSS contains procedures for simple correlations, partial correlations, multiple regressions and factor analysis.

Dr. T.F. Gautschi, P.E.
Mr. J.P. Greaney
Dr. R.L. Bjorklund

Career Path Survey results

Reporting strategy & temporal needs

In the December 6, 1976 issue of *Design News*, the Career Path research team reported progress in data entry and analysis of the large career data base that you have provided. We can now report that we have processed over 900 usable questionnaires.

REPORTING STRATEGY

Over 40,000 relationships exist between the 200 plus variables included in the Career Path Survey. We have considered several hundred so far, and we have selected a strategy for reporting the various important relationships. In this issue we will discuss your responses to the temporal questions—those that relate to everyday work and existence.

The next career path article will concentrate on topics that compare distinct groups with each other. That is, the differences in the responses between the mechanical engineers and the electrical engineers and so on. We will be considering differences between the various career choices as illustrated in Fig. 1. The emphasis in the second article will be on your answers to the longer-range transcendent questions.

Then, we will discuss the changes that you can expect in your career as it progresses in terms of maturity, with such comparisons as: different amounts of time since graduation, the promotions you've received, the number of pay raises and so forth. These points are illustrated as career progress points in Fig. 1.

Following the article on career maturity, we will devote an article to the important topic of shifting from engineering into management. We will show some interesting trends in terms of when one can be expected to make a move into management, and how differing needs can have an impact upon the decision.

INPUT FROM YOU

Finally, to assure that we meet your needs, we plan to devote one (or more) articles to your specific questions. This is suggested because we will be investigating only a fraction of the 40,000 relationships that exist between the 200-plus variables, and there may be others that are important to you. Table 1 is a listing of the various types of information that we have collected from your questionnaire responses. For ease of review we have listed the variables in three major categories. *If you are interested in having a particular relationship, or combination of relationships, analyzed, just send your request to Dr. T. Gautschi, Design News, 221 Columbus Ave., Boston, MA 02116.*

TEMPORAL NEEDS

As you may recall, "Human Needs & Motivation" (Management Forum 1-6-75) described the contributions of Abraham Maslow and Frederick Herzberg to the theory of motivation. Herzberg modified the Maslow hierarchy of needs (see Fig 2.) by postulating that some of our needs are motivators while others are potential dissatisfiers. The lower level needs—basic, safety and some belongingness are

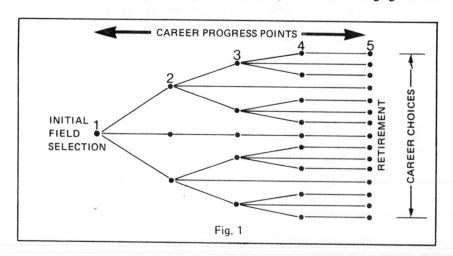

Fig. 1

MASLOW'S HIERARCHY OF NEEDS

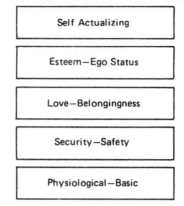

Fig. 2

potential dissatisfiers. That is, improving or increasing them cannot be used to motivate behavior, but their absence can become a source of dissatisfaction. Both sets of needs may be termed temporal because they are related to everyday work and existence.

Table 2 lists the questions that are related to temporal needs and reports the number of respondents that listed each item as their most important job factor. As we would expect, earnings (item 9) was ranked most important more times than any other factor. While "high earnings" is not the same as "wealth" in the higher-level ambitions, it is certainly related to the way engineers think.

The next most important factors were "personal enjoyment in your work", and the "opportunity to do challenging work". The "opportunity for promotion" was ranked in fifth place just after the "opportunity to do creative, innovative work". All of the other factors were indicated by less than 10% of you—even job security was mentioned as being most important by only 6.35%.

In terms of the Herzberg model the most important factors were over 50% heavier weighted towards the motivational factors. Maintenance factors—pay, promotion & job security—36%, and the motivational factors—enjoyable, challenging and creative work, and opportunity for professional development—almost 51%.

It is also interesting to note the factors that were *not* selected (less than 1%) as most important needs:

- Company prestige
- Physical working conditions
- Job prestige
- Amount of stress & strain
- Chance to work on socially relevant projects

Table 1
RESEARCH VARIABLES

EDUCATIONAL INFORMATION:

1. Type of degree
2. Year of degree
3. Field of degree

PERSONAL ATTITUDE INFORMATION:

1. Your overall career ambitions
2. Job factors that are important to you
3. Level of satisfaction in important job factors
4. The factors that precipitated your job changes

JOB INFORMATION:

1. Number of jobs
2. Number of promotions
3. Type of terminations
4. Number and type of salary changes
5. Years on each job
6. Job function
7. Number of employees supervised
8. Size of organization
9. Type of industry
10. Engineer or Manager
11. Professional field or specialization
12. Self employed

- Fringe benefits
- Opportunity for retirement
- The amount of information available on career paths & promotional opportunities
- Your opportunity to influence decisions at higher levels
- The amount of information you receive about what's going on in the company

In our next issue we will discuss your answers to the life-long ambitions questions—that is, your transcendent responses, those that are most important to you in the overall.

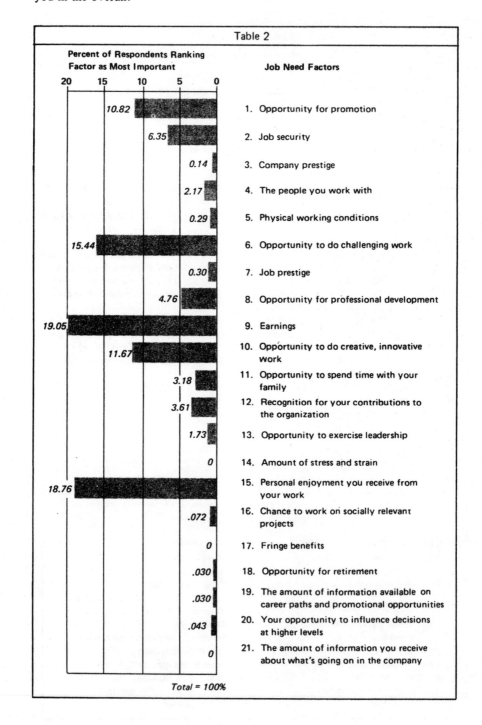

Table 2		
Percent of Respondents Ranking Factor as Most Important		**Job Need Factors**
10.82		1. Opportunity for promotion
6.35		2. Job security
0.14		3. Company prestige
2.17		4. The people you work with
0.29		5. Physical working conditions
15.44		6. Opportunity to do challenging work
0.30		7. Job prestige
4.76		8. Opportunity for professional development
19.05		9. Earnings
11.67		10. Opportunity to do creative, innovative work
3.18		11. Opportunity to spend time with your family
3.61		12. Recognition for your contributions to the organization
1.73		13. Opportunity to exercise leadership
0		14. Amount of stress and strain
18.76		15. Personal enjoyment you receive from your work
.072		16. Chance to work on socially relevant projects
0		17. Fringe benefits
.030		18. Opportunity for retirement
.030		19. The amount of information available on career paths and promotional opportunities
.043		20. Your opportunity to influence decisions at higher levels
0		21. The amount of information you receive about what's going on in the company

Total = 100%

Dr. T.F. Gautschi, P.E.
Mr. J.P. Greaney
Dr. R.L. Bjorklund

Technical careers: transcendent needs

TEMPORAL/ TRANSCENDENT NEEDS

As we mentioned in the last article in this series, Maslow and Herzberg have greatly influenced thinking about motivation for all levels of people in different walks of life. Their concepts of human needs and job satisfaction have led to revisions of management philosophy on a rather broad scale. You may recall that we categorized Herzberg's formulation of maintenance (intrinsic) factors as well as motivational (extrinsic) factors as *temporal needs*. Maslow's first four needs: Physiological, Security, Belongingness (Social) and Esteem were also grouped as temporal needs. This in no way diminishes their importance in shaping a person's actions and goals.

However, these needs—whether they are directly or indirectly related to the job, or whether they are deeply planted in one's psyche—are primarily felt on a present or now-based time orientation. Thus, while one's earnings, job challenge, or other important temporal considerations may be related to the satisfying of lifestyle expectations, personal success in life is more frequently thought of, and evaluated in terms of, the mark that one makes on the environment. It is these goals in our environment, and our ability to achieve these that fits into Maslow's highest rated human need: self-actualization. We have labeled these lifetime goals as *transcendent needs,* because their satisfaction is a requirement for self-actualization.

LIFE SCRIPTS

Why are the transcendent needs of people so often unfulfilled? Like it or not, the signals we receive from our parents, peers and society as a whole (TV, educators, religious spokesmen, etc.) shape each and every one of us significantly. The earlier these signals are received and interpreted by us, the more they become entrenched. Eric Berne's (originator of Trans-sectional Analysis) *Life Scripts* framework helps to explain the fact that the rewards and punishment we receive in pre-adolescent years significantly shape our transcendent needs. Berne realized the importance of Life Scripts only after years of research in more temporal areas of human communications and interaction. The concept of the Life Script emerged in his final work, (published posthumously : *What Do You Say After You Say Hello?*) and is much like our transcendent needs listed in Table 1.

Achievement of the transcendent need becomes the "spoils which go to the victor" in a winning Career Script. The successful engineer or manager must research his character with extreme candor by asking the questions "Why am I here?" and "Why am I doing this particular thing?" at an early stage in his career. Answers that fall into the category of "other people's expectations for me" suggest that self-actualization to fulfill transcendent needs will not materialize. Self-actualization and the fulfillment of the transcendent needs are focused clearly and sharply on one's self. While the road to success unquestionably includes other people (the Belongingness and Ego Status levels of Maslow's hierarchy) actually experiencing success is totally personal.

LIFETIME AMBITIONS

With the concept of overall transcendent needs in mind, we included a question in our Career Path Survey that addressed lifetime goals. Table 1 lists the career ambitions that were included and compares the responses of Mechanical and Electrical Engineers. (Mechanical and Electrical Engineers were chosen for this comparison because they made up the bulk of the respondents.) The ambitions listed were fairly generic and did not refer to specific ambitions (such as "inventing a way of transmitting solar power from the moon's surface") but did include general ("inventing something new") goals. While the ME and EE rankings differed slightly, there were only two major differences between the responses of the two groups. But all the responses were enlightening and interesting, both when considering the ranking of the total group and the comparative overall ranking of the two major groups within the population of responses.

"Make a Great Contribution to My Employer"

Both the Electrical Engineers & the Mechanical Engineers, and the sample in general, rated this as "somewhat" or "very important" more frequently than any other statement. We believe that this characteristic of engineers is significant, especially with regard to communications and the recognition of their accomplishments. Engineers in this survey are desirous of returning significant contributions to their employers. Interestingly, compared to the least frequently mentioned goals, the engineers in this sample are less than half as interested in either becoming presidents of their companies or being powerful and influential as primary lifetime ambitions.

INVENTION

"Invent something new"

This career ambition was second most frequently cited as important by Mechanical Engineers and fourth by Electrical Engineers. While the difference in response is 13%, it is clear that these ME readers thought invention was very high on their list while to EE readers, invention was a somewhat lower ambition.

"Make a great contribution to my profession"

For MEs, the desire to make a general contribution to the profession was the third most frequently mentioned career goal while it was fifth for EEs. Perhaps a new invention is viewed by MEs as an important contribution to the profession or maybe they simply have a higher level of need in both areas. Clearly, all three of the top mentioned ambitions are related directly to the work of our readers. This is consistent with Herzberg's concept that intrinsic job-related factors are the most important in motivating people.

"Work on projects that fulfill basic human needs"

At first, it might seem inconsistent that so many MEs would rate this as an important career ambition for them because engineers are often considered to be more interested in things than people. Yet they rated this higher than "invention of something new". One explanation may be that while they prefer to consider the rather impersonal technical side of problems, they also have a strong realization that the human aspects of engineering decisions are the fundamental basis of their importance.

GETTING TO THE TOP

"Become wealthy"

Second on the list for EEs and fifth on the list for MEs is the desire to become wealthy. This contrasts with our observation in the last article that all respondents felt that their earnings were most frequently responsible for their changing jobs. This contrast supports our overall distinction between *temporal* and *transcendent* needs. As a lifetime ambition, wealth clearly takes a back seat to other considerations. However, it is still in the top five and, as such, is something to be contended with.

Regular earnings are a matter where comparisons between colleagues and friends, and justice (see Edgar Schein, *Organizational Psychology*) are the important issues. Our concern with our regular paycheck (assuming it is sufficient for most expenses) is generally whether we are well paid given our contribution and effort. However, becoming wealthy is a rather abstract goal, and one that few employees accomplish in their lives. For instance, working for pay will only allow a few to enter the six-figure annual income bracket and to accumulate more than a relatively small fortune. Wealth is achieved in other ways, such as inheritance, entrepreneurial fortune, invention (royalties) or grand larceny. Therefore, it is a source for what psychologists call "cognitive dissonance"; on one hand knowing something to be true (that we can never be wealthy) and on the other, behaving, existing, or feeling in a way that is inconsistent with that knowledge. Usually some coping mechanism will resolve the feeling or we will rationalize the conflict by saying that it really isn't important.

"Start a business of my own"

Examination of your responses to this question presents one answer to the previous area (wealth), and also suggests a picture of the anti-bureaucracy tendency of engineers. Nearly twice as many engineers would like to start their own business than become the president of the one in which they work! In order to reach the top of an organization, the engineers in our sample would prefer to go out on their own rather than scramble to the top of an existing company (most worked in large private firms) just to deal with the administrative jumble if and when they got there. The assumption that most engineers are more interested in things than people comes to light here. An engineer who becomes president of a large corporation would spend more time with administrative and management duties than design, invention, or other engineering function. On the other hand, an engineer starting a small business would spend more time on technical problems than would the president of a large company.

TOTAL SAMPLE

The listing of the responses of the total sample in Table 1 shows that it is skewed slightly towards Mechanical Engineers. This is to be expected since there are more than twice as many MEs than EEs in the sample. In cases in which EEs show response differences greater than either MEs or the total sample (as in "Become powerful and influential" and "Become president of my company") we can say that these differences are significant. Also note the relationship between becoming powerful and influential and becoming president of a company. One way to achieve power and influence would be to assume the presidency of a corporation. The results present in this case fit that mold.

YOUR INTERPRETATIONS

The rest of the career ambitions that are shown in Table 1 are more than halfway down the list of your transcendent needs. This does not mean that none of you felt they were important. Many of the 927 responses were unique. What we have shown is a description of the general tendencies of the readers who responded. Your own interpretation here is more important. You can observe how *your own* ordering of your values and priorities compares with that of the others.

PONDER THIS

The important issue is that we *consider* our transcendent needs, that is, these overall ambitions, the consumation of which will perhaps be the most important thing in our professional lives.

An interesting thought—what would I like to have written about me after I die?

TABLE 1
CAREER AMBITIONS

		0	10	20	30	40	50	60	70	80	90	
A. Invent something new	M.E.	MMMMMMMMMMMMMMMMM										(77)2
	E.E.	EEEEEEEEEEEEEEEEEEE										(64)4
	Total	TTTTTTTTTTTTTTTTTTTTTTT										(72)3
B. Become president of my company	M.E.	MMMMMMM										(27)10
	E.E.	EEEEEEEEEEEE										(35)10
	Total	TTTTTTTTTTT										(29)10
C. Work on projects that fulfill basic human needs	M.E.	MMMMMMMMMMMMMMMMM										(73)3
	E.E.	EEEEEEEEEEEEEEEEEEEEE										(70)3
	Total	TTTTTTTTTTTTTTTTTTTTTTTT										(73)2
D. Make a contribution to my profession	M.E.	MMMMMMMMMMMMMMMMM										(73)3
	E.E.	EEEEEEEEEEEEEEEEEE										(61)5
	Total	TTTTTTTTTTTTTTTTTTTTTTT										(69)4
E. Make a contribution to my employer	M.E.	MMMMMMMMMMMMMMMMMMMM										(84)1
	E.E.	EEEEEEEEEEEEEEEEEEEEEEEE										(81)1
	Total	TTTTTTTTTTTTTTTTTTTTTTTTTTT										(84)1
F. Become wealthy	M.E.	MMMMMMMMMMMMMMM										(63)5
	E.E.	EEEEEEEEEEEEEEEEEEEEEE										(71)2
	Total	TTTTTTTTTTTTTTTTTTTTTT										(66)5
G. Start a business of my own	M.E.	MMMMMMMMMMM										(44)7
	E.E.	EEEEEEEEEEEEEEEE										(51)6
	Total	TTTTTTTTTTTTTTTT										(47)7
H. Publish my work	M.E.	MMMMMMMM										(33)9
	E.E.	EEEEEEEEEEEEE										(37)9
	Total	TTTTTTTTTTTTT										(36)9
I. Teach my profession	M.E.	MMMMMMMMMMMM										(50)6
	E.E.	EEEEEEEEEEEEEEEE										(49)7
	Total	TTTTTTTTTTTTTTTTTT										(53)6
J. Become powerful and influential	M.E.	MMMMMMMM										(37)8
	E.E.	EEEEEEEEEEEEE										(43)8
	Total	TTTTTTTTTTTTT										(38)8
		0	10	20	30	40	50	60	70	80	90	

Percent of respondents rating this somewhat important or very important.

LEGEND:
Mechanical Engineers MMMMMMMMMMMMMMM
Electrical Engineers EEEEEEEEEEEEEEEEEEE
Total Sample   TTTTTTTTTTTTTTTTTT

Note: Numbers in parentheses at right are accurate percentage values.
The rank for each item for each group appears at right in bold.

Dr. T.F. Gautschi, P.E.
Mr. J.P. Greaney
Dr. R.L. Bjorklund

Company size and careers: is biggest best (for you)?

This is the fourth article in our series analyzing your responses to the Career Path survey. We turn our focus here to a matter of BUREAUCRACY. Size of firms is often viewed as an important aspect that causes us to have positive or negative views toward the firm. Some feel that big firms are usually better than small firms. They have more resources, provide more opportunity for advancement, high pay and challenge. Others feel that large firms don't have the personal climate that they find and appreciate in small firms. Further, they sometimes feel that small firms provide better opportunities for making an individual contribution and reaping a direct reward through promotion or profit.

EEs VS. MEs

We have considered some questions about size relationships. One general question had to do with the kind of people that frequent large and small firms. Are they at all different? We also wondered if their short-term values differed and if their long-term career interests showed any interesting patterns. Another question we considered was what happens differently on the job—for instance, pay raises and promotions. Are they better in small firms or large? And when you change jobs, how and why do you do it?

Who is most likely to be found where?

We compared the two major engineering types on this matter of company size and were surprised to find some interesting differences. EEs are more frequently found in the largest firms than MEs. We grouped firms five ways from under 100 employees to over five thousand. The trend is fairly clear. As an EE, you are more likely to work in a larger firm than your ME friends. Recalling our last article, EEs indicated more interest in climbing to the top in their present firms. It now looks as if their path to that executive suite may be long and more competitive.

Of interest to us was the marked contrast in the kind of firm that draws the Product Design Engineers and the R & D Engineers. About 70% of the R & D Engineers work in firms with 1000 or more employees while about 50% of the Product Design Engineers work in those firms. This is related to the ability of large firms to support both research and development to a larger degree than smaller firms. The meaning to you is that if you like R & D, you are more likely to find work in a large firm. Or, put another way, if you don't like large firms, you'd probably do well to be in Production or Product Design, because there is a better chance to find a career in smaller firms doing that work. As both Figs. 1 and 2 indicate, most engineers work in large or very large organizations. However, of the different specialties, Product Design Engineers reported most frequently that they were

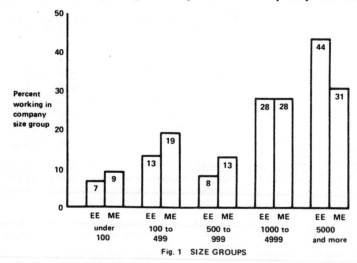

Fig. 1 SIZE GROUPS

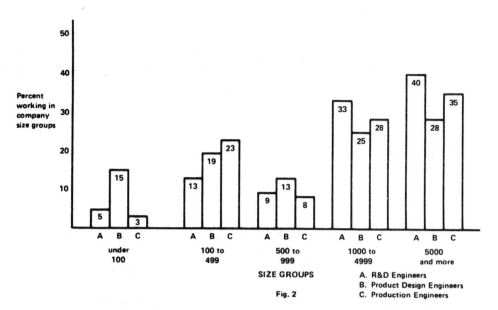

Fig. 2

SIZE GROUPS

A. R&D Engineers
B. Product Design Engineers
C. Production Engineers

PROMOTIONS & PAY

employed by small to medium-sized firms (47%). Therefore, if you are interested in changing to a larger or smaller firm, you may want to consider changing your work specialty. This may, of course, be more difficult for some than for others.

How does firm size affect the job?

For one thing, we found that readers who are presently working in very large firms have had, on the average, almost one less job during their career (to date) than those in the very small firms. This may be attributed to the somewhat greater ability of the large firms to provide promotion opportunity and stability. We found that 48% of the readers in very small firms had no promotions in their current job while 31% of the readers in the very large firms had no promotions. This trend held true only to a point. About the same number in the small and large firms had three or more promotions in their current jobs. However, we found that people who have had more jobs are less frequently employed in large firms. This was a steady trend. The percentage of readers who said they worked in very small firms increased with the number of jobs they had held (up from 5% to 14%) and the number in the very large firms decreased with the number of jobs held (down from 42% to 28%). One might interpret this by suggesting that the large firms in this country are subsidizing

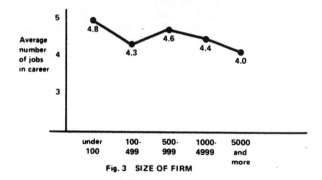

Fig. 3 SIZE OF FIRM

smaller firms by training new employees and giving them the experience so that they are more valuable to their next employers. One might also argue that people simply leave the large firms because they find them unsatisfying. There is some indication that both points have some truth to them, however, we did find an alternative answer. That is, the readers who responded indicated that they stayed almost twice as many years on their jobs when they worked in the very large firms than in the very small firms (7.2 years vs. 3.7 years), which may be the most persuasive argument about the ultimate attraction of large firms.

Pay raises are another factor that we considered. Although employers of all sizes must compete in the same employment market, the very large and the very small firms gave more large pay raises (15% or more) than the rest. The medium and the large firms gave more raises on the order of 5 to 15%. Interestingly, 20% of the respondents in very small firms reported pay decreases.

How does a firm's size affect the satisfaction of your needs?
Referring back to our two previous reports, you will recall that we identified two different types of needs and then described how you ranked them and how you felt about them. Regarding of the TEMPORAL needs, (everyday aspects of life in your job) the survey indicated that you felt the most important were the opportunities: for promotion, to do creative/innovative work, to do challenging work, to receive personal enjoyment from work and to receive fair pay for your efforts.

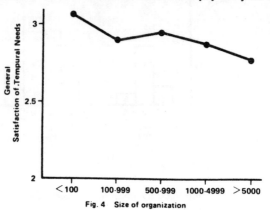

Fig. 4   Size of organization

JOB SATISFACTION

The satisfaction of those temporal needs was found to vary somewhat with company size. In general, people in smaller companies were slightly more satisfied than people in larger organizations. Looking into these differences further, we divided them into the five most important temporal needs found in the survey, shown in Fig. 5. Those employed by the smallest organizations reported the need to do challenging, creative and innovative work as being the most satisfying along with the personal enjoyment they receive from their work. Medium-sized companies (500 to 999 employees) were perceived as having the best opportunity for promotion while both medium-sized and larger organizations satisfied their employees most with regards to earnings.

Individuals working for enjoyment and the fulfillment of their creative needs gravitate towards the smaller firms, where they presumably find more freedom to pursue these goals. Medium-sized companies apparently offer the mobile, promotion conscious person the appropriate environment for advancement while the largest companies are the most adept at satisfying the number one temporal need—earnings.

One would think that the larger the firm, the greater the opportunity for promotion, but results show a rapid decrease in the satisfaction with promotional opportunities as organizational size increases. We believe the important point here is understanding what you have, contrasted to what you think you have. In the case of promotions, large firms do offer more, but job satisfaction is less.

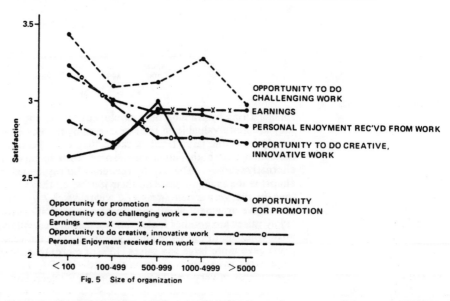

Fig. 5   Size of organization

Table 1   Percentages of Unimportance and Importance of
10 transcendent needs by size of company

Size of organization	Invent Something New		Become President of my Company		Work on Projects that fulfill Basic Human needs		Make a great Contribution to my Profession		Make a great Contribution to my Employer		Become Wealthy		Start a Business of my own		Publish my work so that it will be read		Teach my Profession to Others		Become Powerful and Influential	
	U	I	U	I	U	I	U	I	U	I	U	I	U	I	U	I	U	I	U	I
<100	24	76	63	37	35	65	40	60	12	88	27	73	49	51	61	39	32	68	62	38
100-499	24	76	66	34	21	79	39	61	11	89	30	70	45	55	79	21	53	47	68	32
500-999	21	79	77	23	29	71	25	75	14	86	32	68	60	40	62	38	52	48	64	36
1000-4999	24	76	71	29	23	77	29	71	16	84	36	64	52	48	62	38	47	53	59	41
⟩5000	26	74	63	37	26	74	28	72	19	81	39	61	54	46	60	40	46	54	68	32

U = UNIMPORTANT
I = IMPORTANT

Importance of transcendent needs

The other type of needs that we discussed in the last article are the TRANSCENDENT needs. These are the dreams that you would like to fulfill some time during your lifetime and that ultimately stay with you for long periods of time. Table 1 shows how people in different sized firms described their own TRANSCENDENT needs. There are some interesting differences shown here. For instance, people in larger firms have a relatively higher interest in participating in projects that fulfill a basic human need. One might view this as a luxury that larger firms can afford and do promote. As a result the larger firm will be somewhat more attractive to the person who feels that this is of high importance. This is also true of the question of making a great contribution to the profession.

WEALTH VS. SECURITY

However, the difference is the reverse on the question of wealth. People who feel that to "become wealthy" is important are found more frequently in very small firms and somewhat less so in the very large firms. While there may be more security in a large firm, there may be a better chance to get rich in a small firm. As technical professionals in a small firm, they may well have more opportunity for wealth through the possibility of obtaining a share in the ownership.

There is a higher percentage of readers in the very small firms that feel that to "teach my profession to others" is important as a lifetime goal. Perhaps they feel a more intimate relationship to the profession, or perhaps they perceive a more significant need in the people around them for professional development.

On leaving your jobs

The bottom line on the impact of the size of firms on your life is the matter of "Why did you leave your last job for your present job?", "How did you leave" and "Where did you go?"

Interestingly, the most frequent reason for leaving your job was lack of satisfaction with your opportunity for promotion. This was true for all sizes *except* in the very small firms. People were most frequently attracted to these jobs because of a desire for more challenging work. Challenging work was in third or fourth place as a reason for coming to the other sized firms. Across the board, people expressed their second highest sense of dissatisfaction with their earning power.

CHANGING JOBS

When asked to indicate where they went for a new job, whether it was within the present firm or to a new firm, the most frequent answer was to a new firm. But the percentage staying in their present firm increased directly with its size. The conclusion is that large firms not only keep people on the job longer, promote them more frequently, but they also have the ability to offer significant job changes within the firm more frequently than the smaller firms. Similarly, when changing jobs, people most frequently stay in their own company's size range. But this is mostly true in the case of the very large firm. People who work in the very large firms almost always move to other very large firms. That tendency diminishes as the size of the present firm decreases until in the medium and small firms only 29% stay in that size range.

This report is fairly optimistic about very large firms. It seems that all size firms have advantages. But we have concluded that the American folklore about large firms being unpleasant, stifling and generally irritating places, is not the view you portray.

Which function for you?

Dr. T. F. Gautschi, P.E.
Mr. J.P. Greaney
Dr. R. L. Bjorklund

In our last article we called attention to some factors you should consider when choosing what size company to work for. If you recall, we learned that the size of company affected what job functions would most likely be available to you. Looking into this further, we investigated the differences between a number of variables related to four engineering job functions: Research, Development, Product Design and Production Engineering.

Engineering Field Affects Job Function

Your engineering field (ME or EE) affects your opportunity to pursue a certain job function. Fig. 1 shows that, if an EE, you will be twice as likely to be involved in Development Engineering as your ME colleagues. Mechanical Engineers are far more likely to work in production and significantly more likely to be involved in product design. Research is performed by an approximately equal percentage of both MEs and EEs.

Engineering Function and Job Change

Engineers in Development and Product Design changed jobs by assuming positions with a different company to a higher degree. This was to be expected, since it was the trend established in our earliest work with the Career Path Survey. However, as shown in Table 1, a startling difference is seen in the case of Production Engineers. By a ratio of 4:3, Production Engineers take their job changes within the same company. This may mean that Production people are more frequently moved from plant to plant in large manufacturing concerns as the need for their skills arises, thus changing location rather than company.

Table 1

Engineering Function	Same Company	Different Company	Laid Off	Fired	Other
		Type of job change			
Development	27%	54%	13%	0%	6%
Product Design	15%	50%	22%	3%	10%
Production	41%	29%	24%	0%	6%

Table 2

Engineering Function	More than 15%	5-15%	Same	Decreased
	Salary change			
Research	17%	30%	33%	20%
Development	33%	35%	24%	8%
Product Design	38%	28%	23%	11%
Production	28%	32%	23%	17%

Promotion and Engineering Job Function

You are almost twice as likely to receive two or more promotions in your job as a Research or Development Engineer and Product Designer than as a Production Engineer. Only 15% of the Production Engineers reported two or more promotions, while Development Engineers topped the list with 34% receiving two or more promotions. Researchers reported 32% while 29% of the Product Designers had two or more promotions.

Salary Change

As Table 2 shows, Development and Product Design is where the big pay raises lie. A third or more of the respondents in each of these two functional areas reported greater than a 15% pay raise when changing jobs. Table 1 shows that *at least half* of the Development and Product Design Engineers also changed companies when changing jobs, thus one might say that the best road to a big pay raise is to leave for greener pastures (i.e., another organization), especially in Development and Product Design. It is of particular interest to note that Research Engineers reported only half as many large pay raises (more than 15%) and more than twice as many pay *decreases* than either Development or Product Design Engineers.

Job Function and Type of Industry

One-fifth of the Research Engineers in the sample worked in either government or education while only 8% of Development Engineers and even fewer Product Design or Production Engineers held jobs in those two industries. In contrast, over 90% of the Development, Product Design and Production Engineers worked in business or industry while less than 80% of the researchers were so employed. From this we can say that if you don't want to work in business or industry, a job in research may well be the only sure way out. There is little opportunity for the other three functional areas (Development, Product Design and Production) outside of private industry, hence you can expect to work in such an organization if one of those three areas is your field.

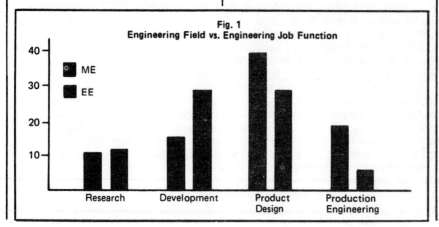

Fig. 1
Engineering Field vs. Engineering Job Function

Which function for you? (Part 2)

Dr. T.F. Gautschi, P.E.
Mr. J.P. Greaney
Dr. R.L. Bjorklund

Last issue (6-20-77) we discussed how your engineering field affects your opportunity to pursue certain job functions. This issue will focus on causes of job change and importance of transcendent needs.

Causes of Job Change

There was a real difference in the most important job factor that precipitated change among the four engineering job functions (see Table 1). Research Engineers left their job most frequently because they were dissatisfied with opportunity for promotion, while Development Engineers were most likely to leave if there was a lack of challenging work for them to do. Both Product Designers and Production Engineers tended to most frequently look elsewhere when dissatisfied with earnings.

Satisfaction of Temporal Needs

General satisfaction with temporal needs varied with Engineering Job Function as shown in Fig. 1. Research Engineers were by far the most satisfied, registering a 2.93 on this index. Production Engineers averaged somewhat lower at 2.54 with Development Engineers and Product Designers, assuming positions in the middle of the scale with 2.69 and 2.79, respectively. As you will recall from the second article in this series, Temporal Needs are those at the lower levels of Maslow's hierarchy of needs and are those associated with everyday work and existence.

Transcendent Needs

In our third article we presented the concept of transcendent needs. Tran-

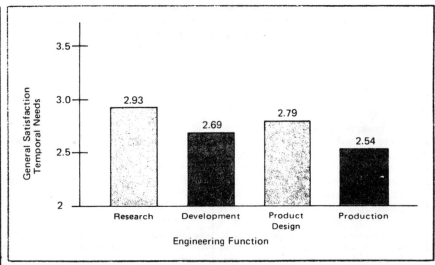

Fig. 1   Satisfaction of Temporal Needs by Engineering Function

scendent needs are those lifetime goals intrinsic to one's career, the satisfaction of which leads to self-actualization as defined by Maslow. Table 1 shows how the importance of ten transcendent needs varies with engineering job function. Research Engineers see publishing their work and teaching their profession to others as being important to a far greater extent than do those involved in the other three functions. Production Engineers place a great deal of emphasis on becoming wealthy and starting a business of their own than to others. Perhaps the Production Engineers are the most entrepreneurial type in the sample. The Development and Product Design Engineers in the sample exhibited no outstanding departures from the average values we presented, however, this was to be expected since the general sample contains such a large percentage of Product Designers.

In considering the Transcendent Needs as they related to your career it is most important that you first evaluate yourself and decide what you want most out of your career. Only those who take the time for periodic assessments of their need satisfaction will have any chance of realizing their lifetime goals. We believe that occupational satisfaction can be achieved by any reasonable person, as long as he or she develops a strategy for realizing those goals felt most important.

Transcendent Needs	Invent something new		Become president of my company		Work on projects that fulfill basic human needs		Make a great contribution to my profession		Make a great contribution to my employer		Become wealthy		Start a business of my own		Publish my work so that it will be widely read		Teach my profession to others		Become powerful and influential	
Engineer Function	U	I	U	I	U	I	U	I	U	I	U	I	U	I	U	I	U	I	U	I
Research	21	79	68	32	21	79	25	75	18	82	46	54	50	50	25	75	32	68	68	32
Development	18	82	84	16	22	78	35	65	17	83	37	63	64	36	58	42	46	54	56	44
Product Design	21	79	76	24	24	76	30	70	15	85	36	64	51	49	68	32	48	52	63	37
Production	35	65	67	33	23	77	26	74	16	84	23	77	37	63	68	32	59	41	65	35

Key: U=Unimportant
       I=Important

Engineering Job Function and Importance of Transcendent Needs

TABLE 1

Should you move into management? (Part 1)

Dr. T.F. Gautschi, P.E.
Mr. J.P. Greaney
Dr. R.L. Bjorklund

In this, our final two-part article in the Career Path Series, we will discuss the differences between managers and engineers. In general, there seems to be ample opportunity for engineers to make the switch to management. Is it worth it, and are those who change satisfied? How do their needs differ from those who remain engineers? We will answer these questions and others in this report.

Trend towards management

There is evidence of a definite and consistent trend towards management in our results. Table 1 shows how the percentage of respondents in management increases with the number of jobs one has. Only 5% of those respondents presently in their first job had a management position, while 42% of those with more than five jobs listed their present job function as management. In every response group, there is a perceptible trend towards management. This holds true whether an individual has had only two jobs or more than five.

Transcendent needs

Engineers and managers differed significantly in only four of the ten transcendent needs. As one would expect, managers were much more interested in becoming president of their company than engineers. Managers were less interested in "working on projects that fulfill basic human needs" and more concerned with "becoming wealthy". More engineers were concerned with "publishing their work so that it would be widely read", reflect-ing the somewhat more "professional" attitudes of engineers when compared to managers. Table 2 lists the results for the ten transcendent needs.

Temporal needs

By a large amount, *"the opportunity to do challenging work"* seems most important to managers while it places a distant third for engineers. *Earnings* and *"the personal enjoyment received from work"* were of approximately equal importance to both managers and engineers. This difference of importance attached to temporal needs is significant. It may well be that those engineers who readily accept challenge and are willing to take risks are the ones who move to management.

Table 3 lists the average levels of satisfaction of engineers and managers for the five most important temporal needs. On a scale of 1 to 4, managers reported significantly higher levels of satisfaction than did engineers. As table 3 indicates, managers exhibit a higher level of satisfaction than do engineers on all five important variables.

Of special importance here is the fact that 10.6% of the managers left their jobs because of a lack of opportunity to exercise leadership, while that complaint didn't even rate with engineers. (Only 4.2% of the engineers left for lack of opportunity to exercise leadership.) It seems clear that the biggest difference between engineers and managers is "leadership".

Table 1

Percentage of Respondents in Management

# of jobs	Present Job	First Previous Job	Second Previous Job	Third Previous Job	Fourth Previous Job
1	51%				
2	27%	12%			
3	44%	15%	7%		
4	38%	17%	12%	6%	
5	40%	38%	20%	10%	6%
6 or more	42%	40%	30%	19%	15%

Percentages in blocks indicate the percentage of managers as opposed to engineers in sample.

Table Three
Satisfaction of Five Most Important Needs

	Engineers	Managers
1. promotion	2.39	2.85
2. challenge	2.97	3.31
3. earnings	2.82	3.01
4. creative work	2.71	3.03
5. personal enjoyment	2.84	3.08

(on a scale of 1-4)

Table 2--Transcendent Needs

		1 Invent something new		2 Become president of my company		3 Work on projects that fulfill basic human needs		4 Make a great contribution to my profession		5 Make a great contribution to my employer		6 Become wealthy		7 Start a business of my own		8 Publish my work so that it will be widely read		9 Teach my profession to others		10 Become powerful and influential	
		U	I	U	I	U	I	U	I	U	I	U	I	U	I	U	I	U	I	U	I
N=548 Engineers		26	74	26	74	23	77	28	72	18	82	37	63	53	47	61	39	47	53	63	37
N=262 Managers		30	70	58	42	35	65	36	64	14	86	28	72	51	49	72	28	48	52	60	40

U=Unimportant
I=Important

Should you move into management? (Part 2)

Dr. T.F. Gautschi, P.E.
Mr. J.P. Greaney
Dr. R.L. Bjorklund

In this final article of our Career Path Series, we conclude our discussion of engineers and managers.

The temporal needs that precipitate job change yielded some interesting results. While managers were most satisfied with their opportunity for promotion, more often than not, they had left their present job in search of promotion. If one compares the percentages for promotion (managers 18.8%, engineers 13.7%) and job security (managers 7.9%, engineers 11.0%) a significant trend appears. Apparently managers are more mobile, more ambitious and will readily change jobs if they believe that a better opportunity for promotion exists elsewhere. Engineers, on the other hand, put more emphasis on job security and don't appear to be willing to take the risks that managers are willing to accept to get ahead.

Promotion

Managers received significantly more promotions than did engineers. Table 5 illustrates these findings. Managers are much more satisfied with promotions than are engineers and they change jobs more frequently because of opportunity for promotion. The managers' success in their search for promotion is well documented in table 5.

Salary change

Managers get more big raises than do engineers. This may be why managers change jobs less frequently because of pay than engineers. Also, managers were shown to be more satisfied with their earnings than engineers. Again, this difference in salary change may be behind this greater satisfaction with earnings. Table 6 tabulates these results for engineers and managers.

Size of company

Engineers worked in larger companies than did managers. While two-thirds of the engineers responding worked in firms with 1000 employees or more, little more than one-half of the managers were so employed. Apparently there is more opportunity for working in a smaller firm for managers than engineers. Table 7 shows the distribution of engineers and managers according to size of company.

Summary

Throughout the Career Path Series we have been considering the differences between people in several careers. These differences are important because they allow for choice in one's career. As people progress through their careers, they should periodically take stock of what path they're following and which direction they're heading. The fact that managers were more satisfied than engineers brings out an important point—*you must be willing to take some risk and explore new areas if you want to increase your occupational happiness.* Those who persevere in jobs not totally to their liking will never find happiness and satisfaction. We encourage you to look critically at what you do and at the options available to you. We hope that the Career Path Series has given you some insight and at least a starting point for your own consideration and analysis of your career.

Table Four
Temporal Needs Precipitating Job Change

Engineers	Managers
14.6% Earnings	18.8 Promotion
13.7% Promotion	13.6 Challenge
11.0% Job Security	12.3 Earnings
10.1% Challenge	10.6 opportunity to exercise leadership
8.0% Opportunity for professional development	7.9 Job Security

Table Five
Promotions of Managers and Engineers

Number of Promotions	None	One	Two	Three or More
Engineers	41%	30%	17%	12%
Managers	26%	41%	17%	26%

Table Six
Salary changes for Engineers and Managers

Salary Change	more than 15% increase	5 to 15% increase	remained the same	decreased
Engineers	31%	35%	23%	11%
Managers	41%	36%	15%	8%

Table Seven
Size of Company

Size of company	<100	100-499	500-999	1000-4999	>5000
Engineers	7%	15%	12%	29%	37%
Managers	12%	18%	14%	27%	28%

The story of Richard West

The making of an engineer

GRADUATION

This is a true story about a friend of mine—Richard West. I wanted to tell it because it might be helpful to those of you who manage others, and also offer a certain amount of hope to the college graduate who is trying to make the transition from the world of academia to the 'real' world of profits, schedules and limited resources.

Six years ago Richard graduated with a B.S. in engineering. He had selected a small, but relatively expensive school, because he wanted a good education. Richard was not from a wealthy family so he had to work part-time during the school year, work each summer and borrow the maximum allowable amount of money to get through school.

After graduation Richard accepted a commission in the Army to fulfill his military obligation. Fortunately, he was assigned to the engineering corps and was able to get some practical experience in his field of engineering.

FIRST JOB

After discharge from the service, Richard took an engineering trainee position with the U.S. Government. It was an interesting job, but after two years Richard realized that the opportunities in his particular specialty were limited without an advanced degree. However, he was reluctant to try to go back to school because he now had a wife, and they were expecting their first baby. Should he be content doing something less than he knew he was capable of doing? Or should he plunge further into debt and return to school for a master's degree in his specialty?

BIG DECISION

After considerable thought and discussion he and his wife decided that he should go back to school and get the advanced degree. Fortunately, he was able to get an assistantship and some financial aid through the federal G.I. bill. So the amount they had to borrow was not great, but they did have to "scrape along" for 18 months. Richard did well in graduate school. He received the best grades in his class, and received fine recommendations from the faculty.

The next problem was to find another job. Richard was graduating at the depth of the worst recession since the 1930's. He now had a wife and a baby and considerable debt, and there were no openings with the government agency that he had left to go to school.

HOPE

Through an unusual circumstance he learned that a fine company had an opening requiring his specialty, and that it was even located in the area of the country where Richard and his wife wanted to live. He sent in his resume, visited their offices and interviewed with their key managers. Then, after what seemed an eternity, but was really only three weeks, he was offered a position doing just what he wanted to do in a location just where he wanted to do it! He quickly accepted, and started to work.

The challenges of working out new relationships and learning the business and the prospect of finally doing useful, important work were especially significant after having spent so many years in preparation. Richard was happy. He was a husband, a father and a working engineer.

DESPAIR

But after a few months, when the newness began to wear off, Richard perceived that he wasn't being given much discretion in his work activities. In fact, his supervisor was really making all of the decisions and Richard and the other "engineers" were operating more or less at the technician level in support of the supervisor. Richard wasn't being given any projects of his own, and oftentimes when asked a question about some aspect of a design, the answer was, "You don't need to know about that." He did receive a lot of communication. However, it was all in the form of detailed directions and criticism—the supervisor was even concerned about the grammatical construction of Richard's engineering reports. But the supervisor never had time to discuss any alternatives, or even his own design approach—he was just too busy getting the work out.

There was always a large backlog of work because the supervisor and his "helpers" just couldn't grind out the designs fast enough to satisfy their customers. Also, they didn't have time to make valid estimates, so they were usually facing cost and schedule overruns as well.

DOUBT

Needless to say, Richard was not happy! Was this the payoff for all of those years of study and the accumulation of a significant debt, and those years of "scraping by" while in graduate school?

It got to the point where Richard just put in his eight hours at work each day and no more. He never discussed his work with his wife, or anyone. His job was becoming something to be endured rather than to be enjoyed. He often seemed tired and listless. In a sense he probably felt that he had been "ripped off" by the system. There were times when he even daydreamed about opening a restaurant or becoming an artist.

RENEWED HOPE

FULFILLMENT

In the midst of all this despair, Richard's supervisor left the company, and a new supervisor was brought in to take his place. That was over six months ago.

The new supervisor is a complete contrast to the old one. He treats Richard, and the others, as professionals and now *they* are responsible for the various tasks. The new supervisor perceives his job as one of coaching Richard and the others, one of helping them to perform at a higher professional level, one of interfacing with customers to work out more realistic cost estimates and task schedules. The whole environment has changed. Now Richard is involved, he talks about his work, he often works a little late to complete some aspect that he is interested in, he is full of energy and life is exciting! He is even thinking about taking some additional courses at night school.

The future is still unknown—but now it at least offers Richard the possibility of accomplishing the things that he had hoped to do.

RETROSPECT

As for the team, schedules are now being met, their technical quality has improved and there is even some talk about applying some advanced techniques to improve their quality and productivity even further.

Now a few questions for *you* managers.

- Do I sometimes forget the importance and significance of each person on the team and operate in a theory X mode like the first supervisor?
- Do I view my job basically as "a one-person operation with helpers", or do I view it as an opportunity to maximize the contributions of each member to the organizational objectives?
- Am I concerned about the individual growth of the various team members, or am I too busy with production activities?
- Do I give too much detailed direction and do I not delegate enough discretion to my subordinates?
- Are the people working with me concerned and involved—or are they simply enduring the job?

"When the administrator feels himself to be the sole driving agency, and finds himself chiefly engaged in arousing those who are apathetic and coercing those who are antagonistic, there is something vitally wrong with the administration. An executive should find himself engaged chiefly in directing the energies which create themselves naturally in all parts of the business, and in finding the proper outlet for the eager upward striving of the ranks below."

E. D. Jones, 1925

Dr. T.F. Gautschi, P.E.

The engineering career path

The choice is yours; make it wisely

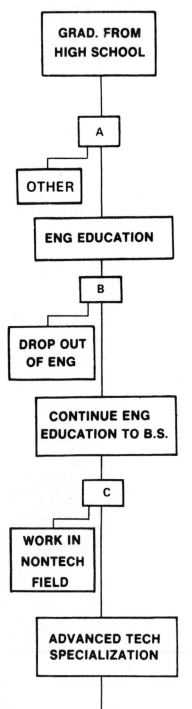

The choice of the career that we intend to follow through our working lives is one of the most important decisions with which we are ever faced. Yet most of us make this choice on the basis of limited input, and usually at a young age. Consequently, many people end up locked-in, and devoting much of their lives to a field that does not really interest them, or in which they are not particularly proficient. The purpose of this article is to propose a descriptive model to enhance our thinking and communication on this very important subject.

Unlike some fields, the serious student must make a decision to enter the engineering field while in high school, or at least during the first year in college in order to prepare for and obtain all of the technical training that is required. (See decision point A). This decision is usually made upon the basis of some combination of: (1) an aptitude for mathematics and the physical sciences, (2) the glamour of technical achievement such as the computer, space exploration and jet aircraft, (3) the perceived prestige and security, (4) the influence of parents, teachers or friends (5) the ready availability of information about engineering oportunities, and (6) the relatively high starting salaries.

When this decision is made little is usually known about the real career opportunities or what is expected of the undergraduate or graduate engineer.

Decision point B usually occurs during the first or second year of undergraduate training. It involves an assessment of whether or not to continue to pursue the rigorous course of technical study that is laid out—some drop out at this point, and turn to a different field of study.

In a sense, the first year or two becomes an extension of the initial decision process. In fact, as we shall see, the entire career process should involve periodic reassessment based upon actual experience and demonstrated aptitudes. This process could be accelerated if we had valid testing techniques, but to date the only valid basis for making career decisions seems to be actual work experience.

Unfortunately, some continue to pursue an engineering education when they shouldn't. When a person is in college a significant switch in his major field of study often looks too formidable, especially when weighed against the time and resources already expended. However, in the big picture this should only be a small consideration. Because the farther one goes, the more locked in they become. Life is too short, and too precious, to be devoted to a field where a person's intrinsic needs for self-fulfillment cannot be met, or to a field where the job is endured in order to meet material needs.

Decision point C occurs at the completion of an undergraduate degree. This involves one of three alternatives: (1) continue education for an advanced technical degree, (2) take a job in a technical field or (3) take a job in a nontechnical field. For those choosing a technical field, the decision must be further defined through the choice of technical specialty and at what place along the R & D spectrum they want to work. This decision is largely influenced by the graduate's knowledge of what opportunities are available, and limited work/education experiences.

The timing of decision point D will vary, but will usually occur about five years after graduation. According to Edgar Schien of M.I.T.:

"We've begun to think of the individual's involvement in his career in terms of the concept of career anchors. A career anchor is a syndrome of ability, skills, motives, and values which guide and constrain the person's career. Career anchors are probably formed fairly early in life, but neither the individual nor the employing organization can really determine the anchor until the person has had a variety of career experiences and has been able to observe what he is good at and what he is bad at, what he likes and what he doesn't like."

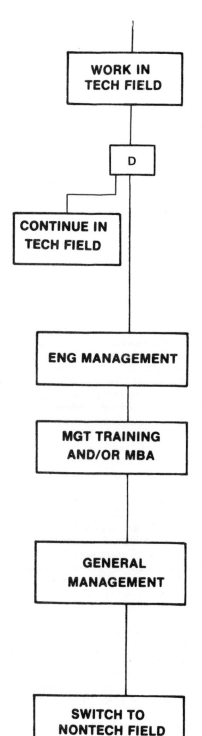

WORK IN TECH FIELD

D

CONTINUE IN TECH FIELD

ENG MANAGEMENT

MGT TRAINING AND/OR MBA

GENERAL MANAGEMENT

SWITCH TO NONTECH FIELD

So, as stated above, the entire career process continues to involve reassessment based upon actual experiences and demonstrated aptitudes.

Decision point D involves the pursuit of one of the following alternatives: (1) continue in the technical field as a specialist. This has been termed as being a "cosmopolitan" orientation, That is, professional colleagues, rather than employers, are the primary reference group—these are the true professional engineers and scientists. They are "turned on" by the technical aspects of their work. They don't aspire to management positions. They are more interested in working with things than in working with people. Generally those who are most successful on this track had the higher undergraduate grade point average (A or B) and have acquired one or more advanced technical degrees, and continue to be involved in state-of-the-art educational activities as either a student or as a teacher. (Some organizations provide paths for technical specialists to acquire the same salary levels and status symbols as those who go into management. However, I believe that the existence of this parallel path is more fiction than fact.)

If this is true, most cosmopolitans will reach their ultimate organizational level fairly soon, and then have to make a decision to go to another employer who will provide greater financial and status remuneration for technical contribution or be satisfied with the level that they have achieved.

Alternative (2) Move into engineering management as a project engineer or as a functional manager. This decision requires a dual commitment:

(a) to become more of a technical generalist and (b) to devote time and energy to management tasks like planning, staffing, directing, controlling, reviewing and budgeting.

Once they enter this track, many engineers find that they enjoy working with people and that their engineering training provides an excellent background for performing most engineering management tasks. However, at this point the need for some management training is usually recognized. Some organizations provide this training internally, and most will reimburse tuition charges for the new or prospective manager to take evening courses at a local college or university. This track can eventually lead to a position like chief engineer or director of engineering—a very responsible position requiring both good technical and good management capability.

During this process, some will find that their real interests and capabilities lean more to general management than they do to engineering management. These people will often complete the requirements for an MBA and/or seek other special courses and experiences in the general management field. When this occurs, and the person demonstrates real capability, and with a certain amount of good fortune, he or she can enter the general management field as a vice-president for a major function or group of functions, and eventually achieve the top position in the organization.

Alternative (3) At decision point D a third alternative sometimes should be chosen—to leave the engineering field and enter some new field or take a shot at going directly into general management—usually via some administrative staff position. Since an engineering background is a good foundation for management responsibility, this alternative often works out very well for those who choose it, and have the requisite interest and capability or working with people, and performing management type functions.

There have been two major threads in this discussion. (1) The choice of career path can *not* be a one-time decision; a person should periodically assess his or her capabilities and interests as revealed by career experiences and make modifications or changes to their career paths accordingly. This can occur quite early or quite late in one's career.

(2) Since everyone has different capabilities and interests, no one career path is intrinsically better than any other. In other words, not all of us will make good managers. Neither will all make good technical specialists. True success should be the recognition and acceptance of what we want to do and can do; and then to do it to the best of our ability. Life is too short and too precious to accept any other alternative.

Joe and his career path

Sometimes it is difficult to be objective
when we are too close to a situation

XYZ COMPANY

The following is a true story about one of my former graduate students, and his current struggle to establish a viable career path.

Joe has a B.S. in electrical engineering from M.I.T., and he is in his late thirties. Up until 18 months ago he held the position of chief engineer for the relatively small XYZ company that specializes in the development and manufacture of miniature electric motors and relays. He had been very satisfied with XYZ until the firm was purchased by a mini-conglomerate. At first, he was optimistic about the acquisition, but after a few months new policies were instituted that Joe strongly opposed—especially some in the marketing area requiring price cutting and a reduction in quality standards. This bothered Joe because he felt that the new management was being very short-sighted in taking a quick profit and not being particularly concerned about the company's image or future sales. So he resigned.

ABC COMPANY

He then accepted a position with ABC. It is a larger company (sales $20 million/year) engaged in the development and manufacture of computer peripheral devices. In ABC Joe reports directly to the president and is responsible for quality assurance of all of the firm's products.

When Joe first arrived at ABC, it was experiencing significant quality problems, and a number of customers were threatening to go to other vendors if ABC didn't "shape up". During the last 18 months Joe has straightened out the entire quality area, and ABC is now developing, manufacturing and delivering reliable products.

FUTURE CHALLENGE?

These 18 months have been exciting and challenging for Joe—there were few dull moments, and lots of decisions to be made. But now that things are running smoothly Joe is beginning to wonder about his future career path. Also, he is a little bored with managing a more or less "routine" operation—especially after he brought in a very competent manager for quality assurance who reports directly to Joe, and who now makes most of the day-to-day decisions.

At the time he brought in the manager for quality assurance, Joe expected to be promoted to chief engineer. However, there has been a recent change that set up the organization into three product divisions, each with its own vice president and general manager, and with its own chief engineer. Manufacturing, marketing and quality assurance are handled on a corporate basis, but there are no immediate plans for a VP of engineering at the corporate level. Nor is there likely to be one in the foreseeable future.

In reaction to the organization change, and the previously mentioned reduction in excitement and challenge in the quality area, Joe decided that it was probably time to move on to another organization. So he prepared a resume, and asked me if I would go over it with him and help him think through his career path situation. We met for lunch and to talk.

After some preliminary chit chat, we got down to the business at hand.

By the way, although such preliminaries might seem like a waste of time, they are not. Some sort of ritual is necessary to get tuned to each other's "wave lengths" and to establish a common bond as a basis for more serious discussion. This is also true when a person—such as a speaker, chairman or professor—plans to interact with a group.

LONG-RANGE OBJECTIVES

My first question was, "Joe, what are your long-range objectives?" Not surprisingly, Joe hadn't really thought too much about the long range. He had been much more concerned about the near future.

So, my next question was, "Joe, are you primarily interested in being a technical expert in a particular field or do you see your future in a management position?"

AN IMPORTANT DIFFERENTIATION

In terms of a previous article, I was asking Joe if he wanted to be a *cosmopolitan*—a specialist whose primary interest is in his technical specialty and who would be willing to change his organization affiliation if necessary in order to advance his knowledge and experience. Or if he wanted to be a *local*—someone who would be willing to depart from his technical specialty in order to remain and advance in a particular organization. For as a person advances in a management hierarchy, his job usually has decreasing technical content and more conceptual content.

After a little reflection, Joe, appreciating the importance of this question, responded that he really pictures his future more in the management field than as a technical specialist, and in a medium-sized company.

ABC ORGANIZATION

Then I asked Joe to describe his present company and his relationships with the people in it.

As mentioned earlier, the company has three divisions, each headed by a VP and general manager. These people, along with the VP for manufacturing, report to an executive VP. The executive VP and the directors of quality assurance, marketing

and finance report to the president.

THE PRESIDENT

Joe thinks that the president is an unusual person—extremely talented, and with a primary interest in the technical aspects of the firm's activities. In fact, the president is currently heading a special ad-hoc group in the investigation and application of some state-of-the-art technology to a new product area for the company—an area in which ABC may well be the most competent of any firm in the industry. The president has an appreciation for the management activities of planning, organizing, staffing, controlling and budgeting, but doesn't really want to spend his time on such tasks. In a sense, he seems to want to operate primarily as the VP of engineering, and as the overall policy maker.

As we talked, Joe mentioned that in recent months the president has asked him to assume the responsibility for certain administrative support activities. He also had discussions with Joe regarding the need for plans beyond the current-year operational plan, the need for some sort of project approval procedures and for scheduling and control mechanisms. He even stated that he wished that he had a button that he could push that would indicate which projects were behind schedule, and for what reason.

This sounded to me like an excellent opportunity for Joe to assume quite a bit of challenge and responsibility in the management area, so I wondered to myself why he was considering leaving the firm.

RELATIONSHIP WITH THE COMPANY

So my next question was, "Do you have any negative vibrations regarding your relationships with the people in the organization—especially the president, the VP's or the other directors?"

Joe's response was a strong affirmation of having very good relationships with all of these people.

So our conversation continued...

"How is your relationship with the exec VP?"

"It is really very good, in fact he has kind of taken a fatherly interest in me."

"How old is he?"

"Oh, he will be retiring in a few years."

"How about your financial remuneration?"

"That's fine. In fact, in addition to a good salary, I also participate in the executive profit-sharing plan."

"How about your perception of the company's future?"

"We develop and manufacture interface components that are used in every communication and computer system. We are *not* in competition with the conventional computer peripheral manufacturers, nor with the systems suppliers. Rather, we are a vendor to such firms. Our product line is based upon some very sophisticated technical concepts, but at the same time our products are designed and packaged so that they can be treated as "black boxes" by our customers. Our product line will continue to grow as the computer is applied to more and more situations. Currently, our sales are increasing at a healthy rate, and I expect them to continue to do so at least for the next several years before they level off at perhaps $50 million per year."

"Something must be bugging you, what do you think it is?" "Well, I don't feel very much at home with the technology that we use in this business. I have a good understanding of it in general, but I would have difficulty developing new concepts. I feel much more comfortable in the electric motor and relay field than I do in the digital electronics ares."

"Would you feel comfortable developing a three-year plan for the company and working out project approval procedures, and establishing a process for project control?"

"Yes, I would like that!"

WHY LEAVE?

So then I asked him, "Why are you thinking about leaving ABC, especially when it is so difficult to break into a new company at the upper management levels?"

He responded, "Now that we have had this discussion, I am beginning to think that my future might well be right here with ABC. At least I should thoroughly investigate the possibility before doing anything rash. It is strange how I couldn't see my situation very objectively before we had this discussion. ABC may just be the kind of company I was looking for without realizing it. There are several steps that I plan to take in the immediate future:

ACTIONS TO TAKE

1. Think more about ABC, and how I could help make it a continuing and viable organization. This is a critical period in its growth and I now believe that I can make a real contribution to its success.
2. Discuss my ideas and career path with the president to determine what he thinks about my future with ABC.
3. Take positive action to learn more about the technology used by ABC. I can do this through discussion, reading and taking a few graduate or special courses in the field. I don't intend to become a technical expert, but I would like to feel more at home with the technology.

"I am glad that we had this discussion, I didn't really recognize the possible potential for me right here with ABC. In a month or so I would like to get together with you again to discuss my progress and perhaps set up a further plan of action."

Continuing education is not enough

Dr. T. F. Gautschi, P. E.

Why do some professionals remain high performers throughout their careers—even into their 50's and 60's—while others do not? How do the high performers do it? Undoubtedly continuing education is a prerequisite for maintaining a high level of performance, but there is evidence that many low performers take just as many courses as do the high performers. So continuing education does not appear to be the entire answer. It is necessary but not sufficient.

In searching for an answer to this question I came across a recent study which proposes an interesting approach to this subject. The authors identified four successive career stages—apprentice, colleague, mentor and influencer—each of which involves different tasks, different types of relationships and different psychological adjustments. In a sample of 550 professionally trained employees, they found that those who performed well in each successive role were the ones who were able to maintain high performance throughout their entire careers—whether 40, 50 or 60 years of age. They also found that those who did *not* move into the next appropriate stage within a reasonable time period were judged as being the lower performers in the stage where they were. Those that did not continue to progress to the next appropriate stage would eventually have their performance judged as below average in their present stage.

This all seems so reasonable that we wonder why it isn't commonly used. Undoubtedly, the major problem has been the identification and acceptance by industry of the multi-stage character of a professional career. In contrast, the University has formalized a four-step approach for the professional career. Typically, the professional path proceeds from Instructor to Assistant Professor, to Associate Professor and then finally to Professor. Each step has time-in-step requirements and specified levels of competence.

The various professional steps (or ranks) are recognized, sought after and considered as indications of one's professional achievement. Administrative duties and responsibilities are assigned without direct regard to rank. For example, an assistant professor can be the chairman of a department that has both associate and full professors in it.

Quite likely we all use some sort of mental model to help us think about careers in industrial organizations. Unfortunately, most of our models are inaccurate and misleading. If the high performing professional's career can be divided into a number of identifiable stages, this approach could greatly improve the mental models that we apply in such key areas as: job assignments, career planning, career counseling, performance evaluation and the design of organizational structures and environments. Such applications could not only enhance the career paths for the individual professional on terms of job satisfaction and motivation, but it could also result in higher productivity for the organization.

Once the various stages are identified, the key variable would then be job assignment. Jobs should be sought after, assigned, and accepted, to assure a natural and reasonable growth through the successive stages, i.e., the time spent at the apprentice stage should be utilized to become proficient in the "apprentice" tasks and for preparing to enter the "colleague" stage, and so on, into the "influencer" stage.

Four-stage career model

This model proposes that the professional who *maintains* a high level of performance goes through four stages in his career. Each stage is described as unique with its own tasks, relationships and psychological adjustment demands. However, they are really four points on a continuum.

Stage I

This stage can be best characterized as an *apprentice* or *intern* relationship. The central tasks involve helping, learning and following directions. It is a continuation of the dependent role that the young professional played throughout his educational period. At the same time it must also prepare him for assuming greater independence in the next stage.

In a sense this is a transition stage where the young professional learns such skills as how to get things done through both formal and informal communication channels, how to utilize his technical skills in real life problems involving real people in real organizations. He also learns that most professional tasks involve a small amount of high level challenging analysis and a large amount of routine work. This can be very frustrating for the bright, eager young professional who has devoted so many years to preparing to do something "really important". This is a critical stage and the young professional should not despair and feel that he has been ripped off by the system.

The important thing to recognize is that this stage is one of preparation and transition, and that the young professional should try to do the best possible job of learning the appropriate skills. From my experience I would suggest that Stage I should be perhaps one to two years in duration.

Stage II

As the professional completes his internship and begins to develop a reputation as being a technically competent individual who can work somewhat independently and produce significant results, he is ready for Stage II. He now becomes a *colleague* and should be given the opportunity to work more and more independently on progressively more difficult tasks. At this stage he should recognize that real organizational power is often a function of his expertise. So he should try to acquire a unique competence in some area of specialization. This can be a difficult decision because the technological field is so dynamic. He would have to be careful to assure that his chosen specialty would have a reasonable life expectancy. The specialized area could be a content area such as underwater vehicle structures; or it could be a set of specialized skills such as those associated with systems analysis.

During this phase a colleague relationship must be worked out between him and his supervisor. This requires a change in the professional's self-concept and it also requires that the supervisor be able to accept the new relationship. Some supervisors cannot handle this, and to fully enter Stage II and prepare for III the professional might have to change supervisors.

During this stage the professional colleague should learn to be self-reliant and develop his own ideas and standards of performance. This can be quite a contrast to his earlier experience of having others do such things for him.

I would guess that it should take a person between seven and eight years to become a totally qualified Stage II professional ready to move on to Stage III.

Stage III

In this stage the professional should be taking greater responsibility for influencing, guiding, directing and developing other people. He becomes an informal mentor helping others to move through Stage I. This does not require management responsibility—only about one-third of the Stage III professionals are managers. Rather, he accomplishes this function through the power which is gained through his expertise. During this stage he also broadens his area of interests and capabilities. He also interfaces with people outside of the organization as a representative or linking pin for those inside. He obtains contracts, gets budgets approved, secures scarce resources, etc. In Stage III the professional can play any or all of three roles—manager, idea person, and informal mentor. In each of these roles his power is determined by how others perceive his level of influence and expertise. He must also develop confidence in his own ability to influence others and to produce significant results.

In Stage III the professional may well begin to move away from detailed technical knowledge and towards a more conceptual view of things. He starts to move from a nearly total concern about doing things right to a broader concern about doing the right things.

Many professionals *never* move beyond Stage III and its attractive package of counseling opportunities, technical involvement, recognition and status rewards. However, to continue to play a vital role at this stage, the professional can *not* rest on his laurels. Unfortunately, if he slacks off at this stage he could become prey to younger, more eager competitors.

Stage IV

Some professionals go on to a fourth stage where they can significantly influence the direction which the organization takes. These *influencers* gain their power through a demonstrated capability to read the environment and to make the appropriate organizational responses. About three-fourths of the Stage IV professionals are middle to upper level managers; the others play the roles of entrepreneur or idea innovator in some sort of staff position.

The Stage IV professional is almost entirely involved with doing the right things, whereas in the earlier stages, he was concerned with doing things right. To do this he must have a reasonable tolerance for ambiguity and recognize that there are acceptable ways of doing things other than his own. He should be more concerned with results and not so much with the details. He should be more concerned about the long range than about the immediate day to day problems.

Again, this is only a framework, not an infallible procedure that one must follow. However, it should help refine your mental model and thus provide guidelines for your thinking and acting in the areas of career counseling, career guidance, career decisions and job assignments.

1. "The Four Stages of Professional Careers" by G. W. Dalton, P. H. Thompson and R. L. Price. *Organizational Dynamics*, Summer 1977, published by AMACOM.

15

Time management and life goals

Dr. T. F. Gautschi, P.E.

Many professionals spend more time working than is really necessary. This is true especially for managers. It is not uncommon for their average work week to be close to 60 hours, including the time they spend going through their briefcases of material brought home from the office.

Naturally, everyone's work habits are not the same. At one end of the spectrum are the "workaholics". These people seem to be driven to spend every possible minute doing something related to their jobs, regardless of the actual amount of time required. At the other end of the spectrum are the "workavoiders." These are people whose challenge seems to be to do the minimum amount of work required in order to be retained by the organization. In between these two extremes is the "workaccomplisher," a person who keeps his time expenditure at a level compatible both with his short range and long range goals, and accomplishes a great deal through effective and efficient use of his time.

Time management is a very individualistic activity, and the best managers are those who manage their time best. We must keep in mind that each of us is allocated the same 1,440 minutes per day (168 hours per week) regardless of the level of our position or our responsibilities. Time is a finite resource which is depleted one tick at a time

whether it is used wisely or not. It is far more important to budget the time we have to spend than it is to budget the money we have to spend—lost money can somehow be replaced, but lost time is lost forever.

There are two basic interrelated but often confused approaches to time management. One is concerned with *effectiveness* (doing the right things) and the other is concerned with *efficiency* (doing things right). Both are important, but is should be clear that "doing the right things" takes precedence. One's approach should be to implement the right activities efficiently. This generally involves a four-step process:

1. Set goals. Decide what you want to do with your life, both on and off the job.
2. Establish priorities for the goals you set.
3. Determine those tasks and activities that are required to achieve your goals.
4. Follow a procedure that will use the least amount of time to implement your tasks and activities.

Thus, the keys to effectiveness are setting goals, establishing priorities and conceptual planning. The keys to efficiency are detailed planning and scheduling. All of this must be undergirded with a personal concern for managing

time and a commitment to exercise perseverance and self-discipline.

Setting goals is perhaps the most difficult task. Most of us tend to drift through life simply reacting to whatever opportunities seem to surface, with few, if any, specific goals to guide us. I am sure that many of you can identify with the man who said, "Here I am 50 years old, and what have I really accomplished with my life? All I seem to do is get up in the morning, rush off to work, work against an impossible time schedule, return home, eat, try to do what I couldn't get to at work, go to bed, get up and start all over again."

A long-range perspective with appropriate goals and priorities can keep life from becoming monotonous and can provide you with a real sense of accomplishment.

At a recent time management seminar that I conducted for engineers and scientists, the following goal areas were explored:

1. Further education for self, spouse and/or children
2. Wealth
3. Organizational position
4. Change in vocation
5. New hobbies
6. Relationship with family (children or parents)
7. Health
8. Doing something important
9. Religion

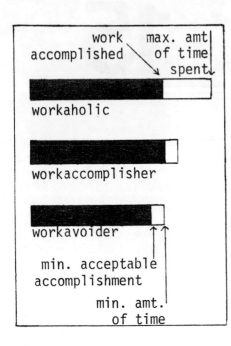

10. Vocational advancement
11. Preparation for retirement
12. Learning to enjoy life as it is

Three questions that will help you gain perspective on goal setting are:

1. What would I do if I were independently wealthy?
2. How would I like to spend my next three to five years?
3. What would I do if I knew that I would die six months from today?

A good plan is to list your top three or so goals along with priority tasks and a schedule for their achievement on a 5 by 8 card. Review and modify your schedule, if necessary, every 30 days and try to complete at least one priority task each week.

Remember, this list of goals and tasks is not carved in stone, so review and change it whenever necessary. Place your goals and tasks list someplace where you will see it often. The important thing is that this list should represent your life goals.

Too many managers work more than is necessary, not because they are indispensable (no one is!) but because (a) they feel comfortable being busy (they confuse activities with results); (b) they fear failure; (c) they lack other interests (this can be corrected by preparing and implementing a life-goals list); or (d) they really don't know how they spend their time. Remember—it is not how much we do that counts, but how much we get done.

Time Management: the to-do list and time-log

Dr. T. F. Gautschi, P. E.

Now that you have a life goals list (*Design News*, 10-23-78) you should take a look at the other end of the spectrum—what you should be doing *today*.

The To-Do List

The best technique I have found for accomplishing this is to prepare a daily *to-do list*. This list should be prepared at the same time each day—the last thing before you leave work or the first thing in the morning when you get to work. Prepare one list for each day. Once you have a form that suits you, use it regularly. I use 3 by 5 cards. This form is easy to handle, and the cards can be filed for future reference.

Your to-do list should contain all the activities or tasks that you plan to do that day. It should be coordinated with your life goals list and your overall schedule/commitment calendar.

Most important, your to-do list must be *prioritized*. This is a key to *effective* time management. Always prioritize and then work on the highest priority item first, leaving the low priority items until last. Often you will not be able to get to some of your lower priority items, which is all the more reason for prioritizing!

Try to schedule blocks of time for your first-priority activities—preferably during the time when you work best. Don't start doing low-priority items because they are short and easy to do. Simply divide your high-priority task into several smaller tasks that you can do in shorter periods of time. Remember, you can always find time for what you really *want* to do.

Don't fall into the trap of simply allowing the work to expand to fill the time available. Your objective is to manage your time more effectively, not necessarily to cross off items from your to-do list. Try to accomplish at least one task from your life goals list each week. This way, you won't get caught in the "endless treadmill syndrome," where each day, and each week, and each month seems like the previous one.

Every two weeks or so, look over your accumulated lists. What are your main activities? How do they compare with what you believe should be your principal job activities? How do they look on balance? Have you been overscheduling? Or underscheduling? Does your supervisor agree with the tasks you have been concentrating on and their priorities? Do you exhibit habit-patterns that you would prefer not to have?

If you have a secretary, it might be a good idea to compare your respective to-do lists to ensure that you are working together on what's important. Your to-do list can be a good communication tool.

The Time Log

To help you get off on the right path in your time management endeavors, you should keep a log of your activities for a month or so. The form below has been found useful. Use a separate page for each day. Entries should be for not less than 15 minutes and not more than four hours. An analysis of the entries in your time log should help you manage your time better.

Four questions that should be answered from an analysis of your time log are:

1. What have I been doing that does not need to be done at all?
2. What have I been doing that could be done by someone else?
3. Have I been concentrating on the high-priority tasks?
4. Have I allowed the work to expand to fill the time available?

The following are excerpts from material written by three of my students describing some of their experiences with keeping a time log.

Student #1, an instrumentation designer, writes: "For some weeks I kept track of the time that I spent at my various tasks. I also recorded the content of "grass fires". A careful review of this record showed that regardless of priority, I would run off to all "fires" with equal willingness and speed. Often a far more important task that I was working on suffered.

Since this realization, I have become somewhat selfish with my time. Often, I now continue with the task at hand until a better time to set it aside occurs, or the higher-priority job is completed. Surprisingly, many of the problems (grass fires) that I previously would have dropped everything for seem to disappear by themselves."

Student #2, an engineering manager, writes: "As a result of keeping a time log for the past several months, I have become much more aware of the need to eliminate or reduce my personal follow-up or constant involvement."

Student #3, a mechanical engineering manager, writes: "An analysis of how I invested my time over the past several months was quite informative. It highlighted that I was spending an inordinate percentage of my time on the technical contribution function. I was involved in too much minute detail. This meant that I was neglecting important managerial functions, and my subordinates were not being encouraged to grow through the assumption of increased responsibility."

The time-log should be viewed as a source of data for analysis and, as such, it should be kept for at least a month. A new series of time-logs should be prepared about every six months and whenever your job changes. Remember, the key time-management tool that you should use on a regular basis is your to-do list, tied in with your appointment/commitment calendar and your life goals list.

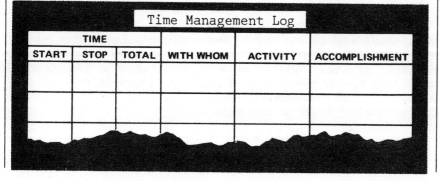

Time Management Log					
TIME					
START	STOP	TOTAL	WITH WHOM	ACTIVITY	ACCOMPLISHMENT

Time-robbers in communications

Dr. T. F. Gautschi, P. E.

Our previous two articles on time management (*Design News*, 10-23-78 and 11-6-78) dealt with the importance of time management and the establishment of life goals, and the prioritized to-do list and time-management log. The purpose of this and our next several articles is to identify some of the more common time-robbers and to explore some possible solutions.

We can define time-robbers as those things that interfere with the effective or efficient use of our time. They are like weeds in a garden. They will continue to grow and flourish and eventually will take over the garden unless actions are taken to eliminate them. And they keep coming back, although perhaps in a slightly different form, unless the gardener is constantly on the alert. To eliminate the time-robbers, we must first accept the fact that although they exist in our lives, they can be reduced or eliminated by the person who becomes a better time-manager, just as you can have a weed-free garden if you work at it.

Most time-robbers can be classified in one of two categories: *communications* or *operations*. Under communications-related time-robbers we find: the telephone, meetings, reports and other paperwork, visitors, inadequate delegation, and prolonged bull sessions. The operations-related time-robbers include: indecision, lack of priorities, fire fighting, unplanned assignments and special requests, delays, reading, overcommitment and conflict. This and the following article will discuss the *communications-related time-robbers*.

Most managers will agree that they are in the communications business. Sure, they plan, organize, staff, make decisions, control and budget; but the whole thing is tied together with communications. Yet, few managers receive any kind of formal communications training or even give it much thought. I suppose this is true because, since we learn to talk and write and interact with others at an early age, we feel we can handle all our communications activities intuitively. However, as indicated by the above list of time-robbers, communications is a consistent management weakness.

The telephone

Problems with the telephone center around the frequency and length of calls that are considered interruptions. Since 20% of your calls will cover about 80% of your important business (according to Pareto's rule), some sort of filtering and temporary storage of your incoming calls could be instituted.

For example, you could ask your subordinates to call you only during the last 15 minutes of each hour. Few emergencies cannot wait 45 minutes. If you think this is impractical, what do the callers do when you are away at a meeting, on vacation, or on a business trip? Also, a short daily staff meeting could reduce the number of calls.

. If you receive a lot of outside calls, you could ask your secretary to screen each call and hold all but the most urgent until you pick up the list at a time more convenient for you. Here again, Pareto's 80-20 rule applies.

Instead of telephoning whenever the urge strikes you, you could prepare a list of calls that you would like to make, along with a note regarding their purpose. Then place several calls one after another. When you are interrupted, don't get upset. Think to yourself, "Answering the phone is part of my job." This should make it easier to pick up your train of thought when the call is completed.

Meetings

Meetings are a fact of organizational life. When they are properly conducted, they are a most effective tool for sharing information, giving instructions, or for solving problems where the relevant inputs are distributed among several people. But often they are too frequent, too long, ineffective and indecisive. The "tool" is okay, it's the manner in which we use it that causes the problem. Condemning all meetings would be like my throwing out my tennis racket because it doesn't volley well—it's not the racket's problem, it's my problem.

Since a meeting can involve a considerable investment of time, it should be approached in a professional manner. First, the meeting caller (MC) must establish the *specific purpose* for the meeting, preferably in writing.

The MC should determine if there is a more time-effective alternative to holding the meeting. The MC should approach this task from the viewpoint that he should be able to justify the time expenditure if called upon to do so. There are three general purposes for meetings: sharing information, giving instructions and solving problems. The MC should plan the details of the meeting including an agenda, a time schedule, who should attend and any required prework.

The purpose, agenda, schedule and required prework should be sent to the attendees in time for them to prepare for the meeting. The MC is then obligated to assure that the meeting goes according to plan, and to prepare and distribute any decisions or actions that are agreed upon.

More communications time-robbers

Dr. T. F. Gautschi, P. E.

In our previous article (*Design News,* 11-20-78), we discussed the telephone and meetings. In this article, we will continue our discussion of communications-related time-robbers.

Reports and other paperwork

Most managers believe that any kind of paperwork is a time-robber, especially reports. Unfortunately, once an organization is established, paperwork routines tend to become fixed and are often difficult to change. As the organization grows, the paperwork also tends to grow, and eventually it gets out of hand. Somehow paperwork gives people good feelings about doing things—seemingly important things. Paperwork is tangible and easy to prepare, and it does have the appearance of productivity.

Employees pursue self-protective activities, including excess production of paper, to prove that they are doing their jobs, either when they feel that their jobs are in jeopardy due to a poor economic climate, or when the organization stresses rigid controls, detailed procedures and motivation by fear of punishment.

Modern technology has not yet provided an answer to the excess paperwork problem—in fact, it has tended to increase paperwork. High-speed printing machines and photocopiers now give even the middle-level employee the ability to churn out great piles of paper at a prodigious rate.

Too many reports have masses of trivia, with a little essential data sandwiched somewhere in between. Because it is difficult to wade through a report, important information is often neglected, or obtained in some other manner. Too often, reports become the *end* rather than the *means* to an end.

As mission operations manager for the Surveyor Project (first unmanned lunar landing spacecraft), I was led to investigate the operation's data requirements because we were exceeding the reproduction capability of the entire flight operations facility! What we found was that nearly every analyst was requesting a complete printout of all data on the chance that he might need some part of it.

Trucks would bring paper in three- to six-ft stacks to the analysts, where it would sit on the floor until a new batch of data was "brewed." Then the old stacks of paper would be removed and a new stack would be brought in. Once this process got started, no one questioned its validity. Needless to say, the paper requirements were drastically reduced by providing each analyst with only what he needed, and usually on specific request.

The need for every report should be questioned. There should be no "sacred cows." If you are requesting a report, state your requirements in clear and specific terms. If you are providing a report to someone else, be sure to agree on what is required. If you receive or provide useless information, it is your own fault. Too many reports are historical records being sent to people who never use them.

Keep your reports brief; try using exception reporting. Remember, 80% of the information usually can be communicated with 20% of the verbiage. Lee Grossman[1] has prepared a useful "report checklist," summarized as follows:

1. *Do I need this report?* If not, tell the writer to remove your name from the distribution list.
2. *Is the data relevant to your job?* What is the worst that would happen if you didn't get it?
3. *What decisions depend on the data?* If you don't use it for decision-making, you don't need it. You can do without "nice-to-know" reports.
4. *Does it come on time?* Either get information on time or cut it out altogether.
5. *Does it come often enough or too often?*
6. *Is it too accurate?* Use value analysis on data to determine lowest degree of accuracy you require.
7. *Is the format conducive to action?*
8. *Is there too much information?* Reports and memos should be trimmed so only pertinent data is included.

Visitors

The uninvited or unplanned-for visitor is another form of time-robber. Clearly, visitors are a form of communication, and periodic face-to-face interaction will enhance other forms of communication. Visits become time-robbers if they are not planned or when the degenerate into prolonged bull-sessions or are with someone you really don't need to talk to.

Visits by people from the home office should be scheduled. There are a few ways to get that point across, like not being available, or simply telling the visitor that you could spend more time with him and be better prepared if you could plan for his next visit.

People referred to you by your superior can be a problem. Why not ask your superior what his intentions are? He may just be trying to get rid of the person, or he may really feel it would be worth your time to meet him.

Then there is the vendor. He wants to sell you something or obtain some information, and sometimes he is not easily put off. A good technique is to see if you can get your purchasing agent to handle such visitors as part of his duty.

There are a few techniques that you can try on the unscheduled visitor. Meet in a waiting room or hall. Never sit down. Tell him that you don't have the time now, and suggest that he return at a more convenient time. Have your secretary openly announce another commitment, or simply have her call you on the phone after 15 minutes. Perhaps you can pass the visitor on to someone else who has more knowledge or interest in his problem.

Inadequate delegation

Delegation is entrusting part of the work, or its management, to others. It is an important time-management tool. The more you use it, the more effective it becomes. First, because the subordinate grows with added responsibility, and second, because you become more proficient in the delegation process.

Successful delegation has three basic requirements:

1. Identify and assign duties or objectives to be accomplished. Don't be fuzzy or ambiguous.
2. Assign the necessary authority to carry out the duties.
3. The subordinate must accept the obligation to accomplish the assigned duties.

15

Prolonged bull sessions

A certain amount of informal interaction is important for maintaining good rapport among those who work together. However, if such sessions are too frequent and too long, it is usually a symptom of a more fundamental problem. It probably means the participants are not committed to the accomplishment of significant and measurable results. Overstaffing, poor planning or poor delegation could be the real culprits. So the solution is not to legislate against prolonged bull sessions, but to determine the underlying problems and take action to correct them.

Conflict

Conflict is found in every organization.[2] Whenever people work together there will be differences in perspective, information and opinions. When conflict is properly dealt with, it can produce better results and encourage creativity through the interaction of different points of view. On the other hand, when conflict is poorly handled, it becomes a time-robber by reducing communication and developing a climate of distrust, and by wasting the time and energy of a lot of people.

There are three basic strategies for dealing with conflict:

1. *Domination.* Here the conflict is resolved by someone in authority making a unilateral decision. This strategy is quick (at least in the short run), but it generally does not involve a very deep commitment to the solution by those involved in the conflict.

2. *Compromise* involves bargaining, and a solution where each party "gains a little and gives up a little." This takes a little longer, but it does increase the commitment of those involved. The goal is to reach agreement, not to develop the best solution.

3. *Integration* establishes a common definition of the problem and formulation of a solution which meets everyone's criteria. It can provide the highest-quality solution and the greatest commitment by those involved. However, sometimes the results do not justify the amount of time required.

Footnotes

[1]*Fat Paper,* Lee Grossman, McGraw-Hill, 1976, p. 146-48.

[2]Warren H. Schmidt, in "Conflict: A Powerful Process for (Good or Bad) Change," *Management Review,* Dec. 1974, reported that the typical manager spends about 20% of his time dealing with some sort of conflict.

Time-robbers in operations

Dr. T. F. Gautschi, P. E.

This is a continuation of our time management series. The previous two articles discussed the communications-related time-robbers. This article and the next will take a look at some *operations-related time-robbers.*

Operations has to do with how the manager approaches and implements the managerial functions of planning, organizing, decision-making, controlling and budgeting. Time-robbers are those things which keep the manager from implementing these functions effectively and/or efficiently.

Indecision

Indecision can result from at least eight different factors:

1. *Lack of confidence in the facts.* This is often the result of inadequate fact-finding or validating procedures.

2. *Insistence on having all the facts*—"paralysis of analysis." Managers should satisfice, not maximize. That is, they should establish the necessary constraints, then search sequentially for the *first* solution that satisfies the constraints. (The maximizer would continue to search until he found the solution that exceeds the established constraints by the greatest margin. This could prove to be costly in terms of time and emotional energy.)

3. *Fear of making a mistake.* Accepting risk is an integral part of the manager's job. Depending upon the importance of the decision, the manager may want to prepare a sensitivity analysis before making the decision.

4. *Lack of a rational decision-making process.* The decision maker should:
   a. identify the problem.
   b. get the facts.
   c. investigate alternatives and their consequences.
   d. make the decision.
   e. communicate the decision.
   f. use feedback as appropriate to improve the decision.

Under pressure we may tend to skip some of these steps, which can result in wasted time.

5. *Lack of well-defined constraints* in schedule, performance and cost.

6. *Not recognizing that a decision must be made.* This can occur when responsibility is not clearly specified, or when the importance of a particular decision is not recognized.

7. *Procrastination.* This strategy involves hoping that the problem will disappear, that the decision will be more obvious over time, or that someone else will take the necessary action.

8. *Consultation.* The decision-maker may delay the decision to:
   a. assure that all valid inputs are considered.
   b. increase the acceptance of the decision by those involved.
   c. diffuse the responsibility for the decision.

(a) and (b) can produce a better decision; (c) is a cop-out and wastes time.

Lack of priorities

Priority involves the combination of two perspectives:

1. *Urgency* relates to meeting established schedules.

2. *Importance* is determined by the impact that the satisfactory completion (or non-completion) of the activity has in the general scheme of things. According to Pareto's rule, 80% of the value is probably covered by 20% of the activities. The trick is to focus on the high-value activities.

Although it may be difficult to assign priorities on an absolute basis, relative priorities are not that difficult to assign. Everyone agrees that to properly control our time we must approach our various activities on the basis of priority. However, there are often "lack of priority" problems. They exist for at least two reasons:

1. *The goals and objectives for the organization are not clearly stated.* Thus, the first step towards assuring that valid priorities are specified is to clearly state the goals and objectives in operationally relevant terms.

2. *The supervisor and his subordinate may each assume a different priority* for a particular task, and act accordingly. To eliminate this problem, specific agreement regarding the priorities for each current task should

be made by the people involved. The supervisor should not assign a task without indicating its priority, and a subordinate should try to get a statement of priority for every task that he accepts.

(To-do lists and time-logs are tools which can help assure that priorities are assigned.)

Firefighting

Firefighting is the response to an unexpected problem that seems to demand immediate attention. This malady is especially prevalent among key people in small companies who do not have regular firefighting forces. When a company's R&D organization is located physically close to its production activities, the R&D personnel tend to be involved in an inordinate amount of firefighting to the detriment of the longer range, and often higher priority, development activities.

Firefighting activities can result from several things:

1. *Inadequate planning*
   a. unrealistic time estimates
   b. neglecting to initiate some long lead-time procurement
   c. lack of knowledge regarding what is being planned

2. *Some significant change* in the total system
   a. forecasts grossly incorrect
   b. more difficulty than expected

3. *A physical failure* in some part of the system

4. *Inadequate delegation* and over-dependence on the firefighter.

5. *The feeling of accomplishment* that the firefighter has after he has extinguished a fire tends to cloud the priority that he assigns to them.

6. *A subordinate's reluctance to present bad news* often allows a small fire to become large before any action is taken.

The obvious solution to these problems is to schedule some part of each day to firefighting activities, and to devote the balance of the day to regular work.

More operations time-robbers

Dr. T. F. Gautschi, P.E.

This is the sixth and final article in the Time Management series. It continues a discussion of operations-related time-robbers.

Unplanned assignments and special requests

The number of items in this category can be reduced by good planning and by anticipation of changes in the planning assumptions.

Good planning involves the establishment of valid objectives, and the identification and assignment of the tasks required to achieve the objectives, along with the appropriate priorities, schedules and resource allocations. Generally, the planning process is most effective when those involved in its implementation are involved in its generation.

If one is alert and aware of what is going on in his area, he can often anticipate an unplanned assignment or special request. For example, if a competitor announces an unanticipated technical feature or price change in your area of responsibility, you can be reasonably sure that you should evaluate its impact on your plans.

At times, this category of time-robber can be worse than "fires", especially when special requests come down to you from "up above." These requests have a way of expanding in uncertainty on their downward path, so that by the time they reach the doer they often are significantly larger in scope than originally intended.

A good strategy for handling unplanned assignments and special requests is to try to obtain an agreement with the requestor on the objectives, scope and particularly the relative priority of the task prior to the expenditure of any significant effort.

When the requestor is faced with the relative priority issue, he has two basic courses of action: (1) He can provide some schedule relief regarding your current tasks so that the special task can be fit into your schedule; or (2) he can conclude that the special task is not as important as other activities on your to-do list, and either delay or cancel it.

To reduce the number of requests that are made by people at your own level, it's usually a good idea to have them filtered through your supervisor to confirm their scope and priority.

There will always be some special requests even when there is good planning, good anticipation and properly established priorities. In this case, try to fit the special task in to the normal work flow with the least amount of disruption.

Delays

Webster says that to delay is "to cause to be late or behind in movement or progress." Most delays are the result of some sort of failure in planning, coordination or control.

Many development programs can be thought of as a race in which each participant wants to finish next to last. No one wants to finish his aspect of the program first or last. Everyone tends to utilize any slack that may exist between the path for which he is responsible and the critical-path in order to make his part as good as possible. (This is an example of Parkinson's Law which states, "work expands to fill the time for its completion.") So when an unexpected problem occurs in some aspect of the project, an overall delay is usually the result.

Different perceptions of priority among the groups involved in a project can cause delay problems too. This often can be remedied by discussing with support groups the importance of the program and of their particular actions.

Reading

The ever-increasing volume of management and technical literature, along with operational correspondence, has made reading a serious time-management problem.

As with the other time-robbers, there are a few guidelines which should help a person manage his time better.

The 80/20 rule should be a guiding philosophy—80% of the value can be gained in 20% of the time. Books should be read more like we read the newspaper—scan and pick out the important information. Read with a purpose. Often a yellow felt pen is useful for highlighting the important material for future reference. Write notes in the margin when appropriate.

Memos should be prepared with the reader in mind. They should contain an objective, a summary, and designated action, followed by any appropriate background or discussion material.

Try to handle each piece of correspondence only once. Do something about it before putting it down. Handwritten notes on the letter or memo usually save time.

Carry reading material with you and use waiting or travel time to catch up. Some excellent material has been put into tape cassette form and can be listened to while you are driving or even when you are mowing your lawn.

Some sort of cooperative technique could be used to gather and distribute key information more efficiently. A group of people could meet during lunch a couple of times a week and each member could report on some area that he is interested in. Or technical and management summary papers could be prepared and exchanged. The company librarian could conduct literature searches in specific areas of interest.

Over-commitment

This time-robber seems to be most prevalent when the due date for an interesting or pleasurable task is somewhere in the future and we do not follow any kind of time management plan. In this situation we might tend to commit most of our time and attention to the pleasurable task and then try to squeeze in those activities in which we feel less secure, ineffective or in which we have little interest.

An excellent question to ask yourself is, "What is the best use of my time right now?" Learn to say no. Make tradeoffs between the various activities that place demands on your time; work on the items which have the highest priority. Learn to delegate.

The management of time

"Lost time is never found again" B. Franklin

Dr. T. F. Gautschi, P.E.

DON'T WASTE TIME

The science of management boils down to how we allocate our time. Our supply of time is totally perishable. The only variable available to us is the use that we make of this finite resource. It is even more important to budget our time than it is to budget our money.

Too often we just drift from one situation to the next without giving much thought to where we are heading or what we are actually accomplishing—much like the ball in the pinball machine that bounces from bumper to bumper while wending its way down the board. When we do not set goals and plan our time, we tend to drift into the following types of activities:

1. **Interesting Activities:** It's easy to spend our time on things we are interested in.
2. **Comfortable Activities:** This tendency is especially prevalent when we move to a new job or are promoted. We tend to persist in our old work habits and resist adopting new ones.
3. **Short-term Activities:** Generally it is easier to respond to the situation, or crisis, than it is to think about, and plan for, future activity.
4. **Pleasurable Activities:** It's more pleasurable to tell someone that he is doing a good job than it is to go through the "agony" or preparing and discussing a comprehensive performance appraisal.
5. **Those Activities That We Are Forced To Do:** These usually involve an outside threat or control. Progress reporting can be an example of this—especially if we don't really understand the need for the report.
6. **Overcommittment:** This is particularly true when the due date for the needed task is somewhere in the future, and it is something that we would like to do.
7. **Lack Of End Product Definition:** This permits us to spend more time on the things we like to do and less on the things we are reluctant to do.

The squirrel in the revolving cage can be extremely busy, but all he is doing is pushing the wheel round and round. Sometimes I think many of us do the same thing, but on a grander scale.

PUT SPICE IN YOUR LIFE

We have all heard of the person who has had one year's experience ten times. These people have no particular challenges, risks, excitement or defeats. They just plod along day by day—and year by year. I believe that life can be, and is intended to be, more exciting than that. I agree with Adlai Stevenson when he said, "It's not the days of your life, but the life in your days that counts."

SET GOALS

Our first step should be to determine our goals—what we want to achieve now, and also with the passing years. Hopefully, we can partially achieve these goals through our participation in the organization in which we work.

The organizational goals, represented by the responsibilities assigned and accepted, are fulfilled to the extent that we are contributing as expected. Thus it is essential that we understand what these responsibilities are and the criteria by which we are judged. Nothing can be more frustrating than spending a lot of our energy and time trying to meet the wrong goals.

FAMILY IS IMPORTANT

In setting our goals let's not forget our families. It is easy to get into the situation, regarding our work and outside activities, where we rationalize that we are doing it for the family, and yet spend little or no time with them. Then one day we wake up to the realization that our family is all grown and we begin to wonder what could have been done if only we had . . .

Now is the time to change this pattern, because 'today is the first day of the rest of our lives'—there is still time to think through our goals and priorities so that we can fulfill our reason for being.

This challenge applies to all aspects of our lives including our work, our families, our church, our social activities, our recreation and anything else that is important to us. When we manage our time properly we should be able to look back at the end of a day, or a week, or a year, and feel a genuine sense of accomplishment and not one of frustration and futility.

HEALTH IS IMPORTANT

Also let's not forget our physical and mental health. Too often we will go years without being concerned about our bodies, then when they have deteriorated through abuse to the point where we can no longer do our thing, we would do almost anything to get our health back. Having a healthy body is like a savings plan. Regular consistent attention to it doesn't take much time, yet it will pay great dividends in the long run.

GATHER DATA

Our next step should be one of gathering data. At first this may be difficult because we don't like to admit that we have been wasting time, or spending time on activities that do not contribute significantly to our job responsibilities or our overall goals. We must recognize and overcome this problem by being completely honest with ourselves.

Depending upon circumstances, any one of the following techniques can be used for data gathering: (1) the log—this should list time, activity, with whom and what was accomplished; (2) the work sample—a statistical technique where we record our activities during selected time intervals that are varied from day to day; (3) the 'guestimate'—this is the easiest but it is also the least accurate. I prefer the log.

This data gathering activity should be pursued to the point where the data collected is in fact a representative sample of the work situation—usually a month is adequate.

ANALYZE THE DATA

Then we should analyze our work tasks in an effort to bring them in line with our goals. Such questions as *can this activity be eliminated? delegated? can it be combined with other activities?* or *can the time be reduced?* are appropriate. We should also question if we are devoting enough time to certain critical activities such as planning or evaluation. Also look for "time robbers and time savers" (See *DN* 12-3-73).

TAKE CORRECTIVE ACTION

Once we know how we have been spending our time, we should plan to improve our time spending in the future. Then take corrective action by preparing a list of changes and activities to be accomplished. A 12-month calendar will help assure that we don't forget something important, as well as put things in perspective. This should include non-work-related activities as well as those related to our work. We can implement this plan by reviewing the accomplishments each day at the close of the day and preparing a list of activities for the next day. I use 3 by 5 cards to describe each task along with its priority. This makes it easy for me to shuffle the tasks, as necessary, to assure that I am working on the highest priority activities. Also, with the appropriate notations, the cards can serve as record of my activities.

SUMMARY

1. Don't waste time, it's our most precious asset.
2. Set goals and priorities.
3. Gather data—keep a log
4. Analyze the data vs. goals.
5. Plan corrective action to meet goals.
6. Implement your plan.

Remember, our mental attitude regarding our use of time is most important. If we don't want to do something, we can find a thousand reasons for not doing it. But if we want to do something, nothing will stop us. Let's stop wasting time.

TIME: A management resource

Dr. T. F. Gautschi, P.E.

Hints on how to preserve that precious commodity

Webster says that time is a period (or interval) between two events, a period of history, a period of existence.

Time is infinite in duration, and is without doubt the most valuable commodity that we have. Yet, in spite of its preciousness and vast potentialities, there is hardly anything that we squander quite so thoughtlessly.

We cannot speed time up, slow it down or store it up—it ticks away endlessly and relentlessly—with each of us being given the same allotment of 1,440 minutes each day. However, we must admit that time seems to pass at different rates. A week at tennis camp passes quickly, while the week before some special event (like vacation or Christmas) moves slowly. It also appears that time speeds up when we are busy and as we grow older.

We cannot buy or sell time.

We cannot control time. We can stop the clock on a football field—but we cannot stop the clock in the game of life.

For all of us time is short in supply and high in demand.

Have you often wondered, "Where has the time gone?" Obviously no one had increased the rate of time expenditure, the clock continued to tick off 60 seconds in every minute. The real question should have been, "How could I have planned so poorly and left so much to be done in so little time?"

The science of management seems to boil down to how we allocate our time. We must recognize the fact that time ticks away whether we plan for its use or not. Therefore, to accomplish the most with the time we are allocated, we should set goals with appropriate priorities and work out plans and schedules for their accomplishment.

The real key lies in how we use what we have.

In a recent seminar I asked the participants to list what they thought were the principal **time robbers** and **time savers** in their work situation. The list is impressive, and I think it may help you. The various items are not listed in any priority. Also, the opposite of a time robber is usually a time saver (e.g., indecision is a time robber and timely decision-making a time saver.) Some of these pairs are listed primarily for emphasis.

TIME ROBBERS

- General bull sessions
- Extensive coffee breaks
- Personal telephone calls
- Unsolicited visits and phone calls from vendors
- Junk mail
- Indecision
- Tension
- Over-communication
- Self-protection activities
- Overdependent subordinates
- Geographical dispersion
- Cultural dispersion
- Inadequate delegation
- Inadequate screening of interviews
- Poorly planned meetings
- Late arrivals to meetings
- Inefficient filing
- Unplanned assignments
- Lunch with vendors
- Duplication of designs
- Waiting for long-distance telephone line
- Farewell parties
- Unnecessary travel
- Phone call interruptions during a business discussion
- Poor work organization and assignments

TIME SAVERS
- Dictation vs. writing in long hand
- Efficient secretary
- Well-planned meetings
- Recording meeting reports and action items
- Efficient filing system
- Written speed-memos and telecons
- Use of calculators and other business equipment
- Effective delegation
- Good library and research service
- Local coffee pots vs. coffee break
- Cultivating friends in organization
- Effective staff meetings
- Use of FAX & TWX
- Correspondence
  - Short memos & letters
  - Fast answers
  - Form letters
  - Handle only once
  - Follow-up file
  - Reader-oriented
- Speed reading
- Liberal use of "circular file" (trash basket)
- Ready access to important reference material
- Common information and data-base
- Conference calls and telephone squawk box
- Skills inventory
- Timely decision-making
- Anticipation—prepare alternative "what if" plans

The list could go on, almost endlessly.

Clearly, the time robbers and time savers depend on our individual styles and techniques. We should use whatever works best for us.

Remember that our success and ultimate effectiveness depend primarily upon how we use our time.

The great dividing line between success and failure can be expressed in five words: **I did not have time.**

Survey report: Ethics in engineering management

Dr. T. F. Gautschi, P. E.

Our survey shows we all want to be ethical—as long as it doesn't cost us too much.

Case 1: Final Results

Imagine that you are the president of a company in a highly competitive industry. You learn that a competitor has made an important scientific discovery that is not patentable and which will give him an advantage that will substantially reduce the profits of your company for about a year. There is some hope of hiring one of the competitor's employees who knows the details of the discovery.

	You	Others
a) Probably would try to hire him.	67%	80%
b) Probably would not try to hire him.	33%	20%

Case 2: Final Results

Should corporation executives act solely in the interest of the stockholders without regard to the interest of employees and consumers?

	You	Others
a) Yes, because maximizing profit is management's responsibility.	1%	23%
b) No, some consideration should be given to the employees and customers	64%	44%
c) As much as possible without creating employee or customer problems.	35%	33%

These seem to be times when many leaders—not just engineering managers—are questioning their own beliefs and ethical standards, and many long-held attitudes are being viewed with a fresh skepticism. Your response to the Aug. 20 survey was an attempt to determine how you view these kinds of issues. The following is what I think you were saying in your nearly 600 responses.

We can certainly conclude that complicated issues such as the conflict between profits and ethics will always cause debate, and there are no easy formulas for determining what is right or wrong in most situations. However, when the morality (or perhaps legality) of a situation is clear we tend to make our choice on the basis of what is ethical—especially if the stakes are not too high. In case three, 84% felt that it would be unacceptable to pad an expense account under any circumstances: *theft is theft; the cheating might not stop here;* and *thou shalt not steal* were typical comments.

No matter how highly principled a man may be, he may be forced to function in a gray area of ethics simply because no black-and-white alternatives are available to him. When expense account padding is discovered it is easy enough to say *I have been in this situation and it's disgusting,* but when you were asked to comment on what others might do in the same situation, your feelings were divided among the three choices. Perhaps you feel there are situations where padding would be ok.

Sometimes, managers choose a less-than-ethical course in order to attain the ultimate good. Although most traditionalists deplore the idea of so-called situation ethics, this is in fact the law of the profit jungle in which most managers are compelled to operate. Case one gives us a good example of this, where 67% would try to hire the employee from the competitor to maintain company profits. This position was justified by statements like *right or wrong it's done every day* or *this is no time to be idealistic. When ethics vs. profits, profits win out.* As one respondent summed up, *it's called survival.*

Every person in a position of responsibility employs guidelines of some sort, whether or not he recognizes them. What are some of these guidelines?

Case 3: Final Results

An engineering manager earning $20,000 a year has been padding his expense account about $1,000 a year.

	You	Others
a) Acceptable if other executives in the company do the same thing.	4%	35%
b) Acceptable if the executive's superior knows about it and says nothing.	10%	32%
c) Unacceptable regardless of circumstances.	86%	33%

Case 4: Final Results

Sam works for you. He is technically capable and a good worker, but he does not get along well with the others in your group. So when Sam has an opportunity for a transfer, you encourage him to take it. What would you say to Sam's potential supervisor when he inquires about Sam?

	You	Others
a) Stress Sam's strong points and avoid his personality problem.	10%	26%
b) Stress Sam's strong and weak points.	80%	47%
c) Try to be neutral.	10%	27%

Case 5: Final Results

When it becomes necessary to reduce the work force.

	You	Others
a) Separate older, less efficient employees.	47%	43%
b) Separate the younger, lower-paid employees.	18%	15%
c) Separate solely on seniority.	35%	42%

One is simply expedience. Here we consider the consequences of alternative decisions and then choose the one that will maximize profits without any special regard for ethical aspects. We make the most "cost effective" decision. In case one, for example, some respondents said they would not hire a competitor simply because it wasn't good business. *One year's profit may not be worth hiring someone so disloyal* or *plan would probably backfire.* Others cited potential legal problems: *It's illegal to capitalize on the trade secrets of a competitor.*

Another guideline is precedence. Here we adopt a certain decision because others have made the same decision under similar circumstances, or have handed down a set of rules or procedures that can be followed without worrying about the ethics. In case five, for instance, 35% said they would separate solely on seniority when work force reductions became necessary. Precedence guides these managers: *it is neutral; keeps personalities out; seniority is best measure of overall performance.* The 47% who favored separating the older, less efficient employees also cited precedence, such as the manager who said it was *a good time to get rid of deadwood.*

Many respondents objected to the limited choices of case five, but when layoffs become necessary, we sometimes have a limited choice of options. We cannot always say *separate solely on value to work force* or *keep the best workers, young or old.* As respondents noted, *union rules* may dictate policy. In difficult situations like these, precedence can save us from thinking through—and living with—the ethics of a particular choice.

Some try to follow Christian principles in decision making, using Biblical standards with particular emphasis on the golden rule. In case four, for example, 80% said they would stress Sam's strong and weak points, because *I would expect the same* or *this is fair to all.* In case eight, when asked whether you would carry an older employee whose work has been inefficient, only 9% favored layoff; the majority (55%) favored a cut in pay, with the rest carrying the man until retirement. Profits come first when it came to hiring an employee from a competitor, but here the golden rule seemed to apply for most: *They gave their best for years, inefficiency may be partly your fault....Treat a man with some dignity, he may be too old to find a job....Give him a chance to improve....It's repulsive to treat a human like a pressed-out lemon.* Even managers who favored a pay cut tempered their decision: *Temporary reduction may induce better performance....most fair, it tells employee his value has decreased....Layoff is too drastic.*

Many managers rely on superiors or experts. They follow the same pattern as those millions of Americans whose morning devotional is not the Bible but the syndicated column of Ann Landers or other widely-admired advisors. Sometimes this results in what seems to be an ethical decision, such as the manager in case one who refused to hire from the competitor because he may be subject to nondisclosure—the opinion of an expert. In case two, 64% thought some consideration should be given to employees and customers as well as stockholders. Many relied on the opinions of experts to justify their position: *long-range planning requires that consideration be given the employees and customers....Maximize overall company profits.*

Many rely on personal values. Everyone has convictions concerning what he knows or feels is right. These personal values, implicit or explicit, are inherent in everybody's behavior, but they vary from one person to another and from one situation to another for the same person. Consider case two, in which many said that employees and customers deserve consideration along with the stockholders: *employees are human resources....they are just as important as*

Case 6: Final Results

You are an engineer, but you are not directly associated with the DOT project. The other day you overheard a conversation in the cafeteria between the program manager and the project engineer that makes you reasonably sure that a large contract will soon be given to the ABC Company to develop and manufacture a key DOT subsystem. ABC is a smaller firm and its stock is traded over the counter. You feel sure that the stock will rise from its present $2.25 per share as soon as the DOT contract is let.

		You	Others
a)	Do nothing.	35%	13%
b)	Buy stock.	61%	66%
c)	Tell friends.	2%	17%
d)	Tell broker.	2%	4%

Case 7: Final Results

You are the project engineer working on the development of a small liquid rocket engine. You know that if you could achieve a throttling ratio greater than eight to one, your system would be considered a success and continue to receive funding support. To date, the best you have achieved is a four to one ratio. You have an unproved idea that you feel has a 50% chance of being successful. Your project is currently being reviewed to determine if it should be continued. You would like to continue it. How optimistically should the results and the new ideas be presented?

		You	Others
a)	Realistically, even if funding is cut off.	74%	36%
b)	Optimistic enough to assure obtaining funding.	26%	64%

Case 8: Final Results

What should one do about employees with long good records, whose work becomes inefficient?

		You	Others
a)	Carry until retirement.	36%	47%
b)	Lay off.	9%	37%
c)	Reduce Salary.	55%	16%

financial resources or *there is no company without customers and employees.* On the less ethical side are those 61% who would buy stock based on inside information. Their personal values say *there is nothing wrong with keeping alert....It's ok to use this information as long as you don't spread it around....Sounds wrong but I'd take advantage of the situation.*

Are business and ethics simply incompatible? Many think so. These people say only a dreamer tries to combine business and ethics. They say problems encountered in business should be dealt with purely as business problems and that ethics are simply irrelevant. In case one, for example, 68% said they would try to hire the competitor's employee because it looked like the course of action needed to maintain the company profits. *Profits vs. ethics, profits wins.* In case six, 61% would trade stock on inside information, an attitude summed up by the respondent who commented *Since I have no control I see no moral responsibility.* In case seven, although 74% said they would present the situation as honestly as possible, 64% said others would be falsely optimistic to win the contract. Does this indicate what you would do if pressed against the wall?

Can we draw any conclusions from the cases so far? In my opinion they show that when the chips are down—when financial stakes are high, or the competition is really severe—our professional image and pure survival often appear incompatible with ethical considerations.

I would guess that few people find that such a framework gives them much real satisfaction in their work. Most managers, particularly those who view religion as a deep and serious commitment, probably wish that business life could be different; but they believe business is amoral and have resigned themselves to accepting that belief. Many of these people find that participation in church activities, community affairs and charity work gives their lives some of the meaning that they feel is denied in their work. I fear though, that this kind of offhours ethics tends to add to frustration rather than reduce it.

In contrast, others claim that good ethics is just good business. In case three for example, one opinion is that expense account cheating *cuts into company profits.* In case four, some said Sam's strong and weak points should be stressed because *it's reality....why cover up, the other supervisor expects an honest assessment.* In case six, 35% wouldn't trade on the stock, some on principle, but others said good ethics is just good business: *The stock may also go down,* said one; *avoid possible conflict of interest* said another. This position is supported because a business that behaves ethically often induces others to behave ethically toward it.

Further, some feel that a "good" man who steadfastly tries to be ethical, i.e., to do the right thing, somehow always overtakes his immoral or amoral counterpart in the long run. Case seven brings this out. Here the manager could be realistic, and ethical, for a long-range benefit; or lie just a little for a short-term gain. Fully 74% chose to be realistic: *When in trouble don't lie....Ethics demands it,* and *any other way is compromising my personal self-esteem.* Advocates of this approach explain their attitude by saying that some divine force assures the ultimate triumph of right. Its operation cannot be understood or analyzed, just accepted.

Ethical behavior that is motivated solely by a belief that such action will bring prosperity to you or your organization is, of course, immoral. We certainly have the right to be glad when an unethical man fails and sad when an ethical man fails, but if we advocate ethical behavior on the ground that it will lead to success—even success in the long run—then we are talking expediency, not ethics. (The man who tells us to follow Jesus because he'll make us rich is simply ignorant of the fact that the devil might make us rich quicker.)

However, many find support of this good-ethics-is-good-business proposition to be a more gracious, more comfortable and a more human position than its rejection. Your response to many of the cases supports this point.

Conclusion. The notion that the manager can operate by simply ignoring ethics, or by applying so-called "situation ethics", overlooks the fact that ethics should force us to question our goals as managers, as well as our goals as citizens in society.

We cannot afford to do otherwise, for as Arnold Toynbee recently said, "No society has ever flourished without a spiritual mission; the quest for material progress alone is insufficient to spur men to the achievements that are required to create an enduring, dynamic, progressive nation." And as if to warn the ethics-be-damned manager, Toynbee goes on to say "all through history material progress as a national goal has led to stagnation, boredom, and moral decay."

Ethics in change-Part 1

R. L. Bjorklund, Ph.D. and Pat Hebert, Student, Worcester Polytechnic Institute,
Management Dept.

In a time when many institutions are operating in the harsh light of public scrutiny, managers are regularly reminded of the tragedies of the mid-seventies—Watergate, corporate political campaign contributions, insurance fraud, design misrepresentation, and corruption of, and by, public officials. The mid-seventies served to raise the consciousness of managers and engineers in a real way about the ethical dilemmas that they face. We believe that a substantial clarification of values has taken place. Many managers and engineers have been forced by circumstances to reevaluate their conduct and their professional standards. Yet, ethics remain a perplexing problem. Many actions that seem absolutely unethical in some instances paradoxically seem ethical in others.

Thus, business ethics appear to be situational, and for this reason it is very difficult to define a code of ethics for management. Many articles have been written in this area, focusing on the need for such a definition. In view of this need, and taking into account the situational dilemmas encountered by professionals, we have determined how some people view themselves, and others, in terms of ethical behavior, given various situations. For example, in dealing with a superior, how ethical can (or must) an engineer be while ensuring the continuation of funding for a project?

In 1973, 600 *Design News* readers responded to a survey conducted by Dr. Gautschi. The survey contained questions similar in content to the one just stated. The results of his work showed that we all want to be ethical, as long as it doesn't cost us too much! Four years later, following the Watergate and Lockheed scandals, we have repeated Gautschi's previous survey to determine if ethical standards have changed.

As you may recall, eight brief situations were described and a set of alternative responses were listed (Management Forum 8-23-73). These situations are now followed by a comparison of the 1973 and 1977 responses by the *Design News* readers.

IMPROVING YOUR COMPANY'S MARKET POSITION

Under consideration here are dilemmas that force one to choose between ethics and profits. A comparison of past and present figures shows that people are much more ethical in their opinions of themselves than in the past. This is a drastic turnaround in the respondents' attitudes. "One year's loss is not worth lowering my moral standards." "Progress is made through innovation, not copying." Opinions of others are constant; almost all readers in 1973 and 1977 feel that others would hire a competitor's employee if profit were endangered.

CORPORATE RESPONSIBILITY TO EMPLOYEES, CUSTOMERS AND STOCKHOLDERS

Case 2: Should corporation executives act solely in the interest of the stockholders without regard to the interest of employees and consumers?	1973		1977	
	YOU	OTHERS	YOU	OTHERS
a) Yes, because maximizing profit is management's responsibility.	0	28%	0	20%
b) No, some consideration should be given to the employees and customers	68%	42%	65%	28%
c) As much as possible without creating employee or customer problems.	32%	30%	35%	52%

Corporate executives are becoming increasingly aware of their social responsibilities due to government, public, and union demands. Case 2 reflects this pressure as indicated by both past and present figures; B is the most popular response, which gives consideration to both employees and customers. People's opinions of others have crystallized in this case in the last three years: 52% of the respondents chose C, which suggests more responsibility towards stockholders.

Case 5:
When it becomes necessary to reduce the work force.

	1973		1977	
	YOU	OTHERS	YOU	OTHERS
a) Separate older, less efficient employees.	28%	46%	20%	55%
b) Separate the younger, lower-paid employees.	28%	5%	38%	5%
c) Separate solely on seniority.	44%	49%	45%	40%

Case 8:
What should one do about employees with long good records, whose work becomes inefficient?

	1973		1977	
	YOU	OTHERS	YOU	OTHERS
a) Carry until retirement.	37%	28%	29%	10%
b) Lay off.	8%	54%	5%	75%
c) Reduce Salary.	55%	12%	66%	15%

Case 5 deals with employee problems. In cases 4 and 5 the majority of the respondents have chosen the solution that appears to be the most fair and honest. Majority opinions about others in these cases reflect the regard that people hold for the decision-making style of their colleagues in 1973 and 1977.

Case 8 illustrates the increased responsibility that employers have to employees who have been with their company for a long time and have good records. The majority of our respondents in 1973 chose C: an inefficient worker would be penalized, but if he has a long, good record he should not be laid off. In 1977, 66% of our respondents also chose C, which is a 10% increase from 1973. Opinions of others have crystallized around B, which favors a lay-off of an inefficient worker.

The last three years have affected people considerably in their opinions of themselves and of others. There has been a significant increase in the number of people who report themselves being more responsible to employees and customers. In regard to others, however, the majority of our respondents felt that their colleagues would elect to lay off the inefficient worker. Which is more ethical? We are uncertain.

Case 7:
You are the project engineer working on the development of a small liquid rocket engine. You know that if you could achieve a throttling ratio greater than eight to one, your system would be considered a success and continue to receive funding support. To date, the best you have achieved is a four to one ratio. You have an unproved idea that you feel has a 50% chance of being successful. Your project is currently being reviewed to determine if it should be continued. You would like to continue it. How optimistically should the results and the new ideas be presented?

	1973		1977	
	YOU	OTHERS	YOU	OTHERS
a) Realistically, even if funding is cut off.	74%	35%	78%	21%
b) Optimistic enough to assure obtaining funding.	26%	65%	22%	79%

HONESTY—THE BEST POLICY?

As we have already stated, business ethics are complicated and confusing because they fall into the category of situational ethics. For this reason many professionals do not always feel that honesty is applicable in all situations. Case 7 clarifies this point: 26% in 1973 and 22% in 1977 chose to shade the truth in this situation. The majority of responses, however, favored the ethical (honest) response, even if the results were fatal. This case also illustrates that people are less capable of trusting another person now than they were in 1973.

Ethics in change - Part 2

R. L. Bjorklund, Ph.D. and Pat Hebert, Student, Worcester Polytechnic Institute, Management Dept.

Case 4:

Sam works for you. He is technically capable and a good worker, but he does not get along well with the others in your group. So when Sam has an opprotunity for a transfer, you encourage him to take it. What would you say to Sam's potential supervisor when he inquires about Sam?

	1973		1977	
	YOU	OTHERS	YOU	OTHERS
a) Stress Sam's strong points and avoid his personality problem.	13%	26%	13%	39%
b) Stress Sam's strong and weak points.	78%	54%	65%	27%
c) Try to be neutral.	9%	20%	22%	34%

Case 3:

An engineering manager earning $20,000 a year has been padding his expense account about $1,000 a year.

	1973		1977	
	YOU	OTHERS	YOU	OTHERS
a) Acceptable if toher executives in the company do the same thing.	4%	32%	4%	40%
b) Acceptable if the executive's superior knows about it and says nothing.	23%	38%	4%	23%
c) Unacceptable regardless of the circumstances	73%	30%	90%	37%

The situational aspects of honesty are clarified by examining the results of Case 4. Here, 13% more of our respondents chose to be neutral rather than honest by stressing Sam's strong and weak points. There is also a 27% decrease from 1973 in those who had believed others would project Sam's qualities honestly.

When considering the padding of expense accounts in Case 3, we find that there is a 17% increase from 1973 in those who believe that such action is unacceptable regardless of circumstances. Also, 4% in 1977, as compared to 23% in 1973, believe that padding an expense account is acceptable if the executive's superior knows about it. People appear to be less willing to follow or condone the unethical actions of others.

ARE BUSINESS AND ETHICS COMPATIBLE?

Many people think that the answer to this question is no. In Case 6, 66% chose B, to buy the stock. This is a 12% increase from 1973. This could be due to the sagging economy when more people are out to make money quick. As one respondent commented, "To make money, why not?" It seems that trading on the basis of insider information is more acceptable in 1977 than it was in 1973.

Case 6:
You are an engineer, but you are not directly associated with the DOT project. The other day you overheard a conversation in the cafeteria between the program manager and the project engineer that makes you reasonably sure that a large contract will soon be given to the ABC Company to develop and manufacture a key DOT subsystem. ABC is a smaller firm and its stock is traded over the counter. You feel sure that the stock will rise from its present $2.25 per share as soon as the DOT contract is let.

	1973		1977	
	YOU	OTHERS	YOU	OTHERS
a) Do nothing.	36%	10%	32%	8%
b) Buy stock.	54%	74%	66%	80%
c) Tell friends.	4%	16%	0	12%
d) Tell broker.	6%	0	2%	0

Case 1 reveals that 55% in 1973, but only 39% in 1977 would hire a competitor's employee to avoid a financial loss. This decrease could be explained by the fact that more people fear the legal implications of such an act. However, even though more people are ethically guided in their decision making, there are still quite a few who rank profits ahead of ethics in their business dealings.

Case 1:
Imagine that you are the president of a company in a highly competitive industry. You learn that a competitor has made an important scientific discovery that is not patentable and which will give him an advantage that will substantially reduce the profits of your company for about a year. There is some hope of hiring one of the competitor's employees who knows the details of the discovery.

	1973		1977	
	YOU	OTHERS	YOU	OTHERS
a) Probably would try to hire him	55%	90%	39%	86%
b) Probably would not try to hire him.	45%	10%	61%	14%

In general, it appears that the readers are more conscious of the ethical problems they face and seem to take more ethically appealing positions themselves. Yet, they also seem to suspect the ethics others use in the decisions that they make. But the most important lesson we learned from the follow-up is that it is difficult to determine what *is* ethical. The dimensions of professional management ethics must be identified before one can decide whether or not to follow an ethical path.

As a step towards identifying some of these dimensions we have developed a list of behavior characteristics that may be considered unethical. They fall into five categories: (1) Dishonesty, (2) Illegal, (3) Manipulative, (4) Unfair, and (5) Wasteful

Dishonesty contains three potential elements. They are falsification, misrepresentation, and deceit. *Illegal* actions in management problems usually involve theft, conspiracy, corruption, extortion, and perjury. Coercion and exploitation are elements that could be involved in a *manipulative* scheme. If a subordinate is treated *unfairly*, it could be due to nepotism, inequitable or prejudicial treatment of others on the part of a superior. *Wasteful* contains two potential elements: activities that are economically wasteful and/or environmentally wasteful.

Some of these activities are considered more unethical than others. Furthermore, certain circumstances seem to justify one or another of these behaviors to some people.

QUESTIONNAIRE

Therefore, in an effort to clarify, we are asking that you complete the following questionnaire and send your responses to Dr. R. L. Bjorklund, Management Dept., Worcester Polytechnic Institute, Worcester, MA 01609. Your responses will be analyzed and the results will be reported in Management Forum as soon as possible.

BEHAVIOR

Part I: For each reason listed below, please indicate (with a check) those behaviors that may be justified.

		DISHONEST	ILLEGAL	MANIPULATIVE	UNFAIR	WASTEFUL
1.	There are no situations that justify this behavior.					
2.	This vehavior is almost always justifiable.					
3.	To improve your job security.					
4.	To avoid losing your job.					
5.	To maintain an advantageous personal status in the corporation; i.e. promotions, bugetary advantages, etc.					
6.	To improve a poor personal status in the corporation.					
7.	To obtain an extremely advantageous personal status in the corporation.					
8.	To obtain an advantageous interdepartmental status in the corporation.					
9.	To improve an extremely poor interdepartmental position in the corporation.					
10.	Under the direct orders of your superior.					
11.	At the implicit direction of your superior.					
12.	To make a critical sale.					
13.	To make a routine sale.					
14.	To avoid the loss of a critical customer.					
15.	To avoid the loss of an average customer.					
16.	To reduce the effectiveness of a key competitor.					
17.	To make a breakeven profit.					
18.	To avoid a serious financial loss.					
19.	To increase profits to meet a goal that has been established by your company.					
20.	To increase the price per share of your company's stock.					
21.	To increase the price per share of your company's stock because it is dangerously low.					
22.	To obtain an extremely high price per share of your company's stock.					
23.	To maintain a high credit rating.					
24.	To increase a dangerously low credit rating.					
25.	To gain an advantage with public officials.					
26.	To pirate a praticularly valuable employee from another company.					
27.	To screen out potentially disadvantageous employees.					

Part 3: How unethical are each of the following activities?

	TOTALLY UNETHICAL	VERY UNETHICAL	MILDLY UNETHICAL	NOT PARTICULARLY UNETHICAL
Dishonesty	1	2	3	4
Deceit	1	2	3	4
Falsification	1	2	3	4
Unfair treatment	1	2	3	4
Inequitable treatment	1	2	3	4
Nepotism	1	2	3	4
Prejudice	1	2	3	4
Manipulation	1	2	3	4
Coercion	1	2	3	4
Exploitation	1	2	3	4
Illegal activity	1	2	3	4
Conspiracy	1	2	3	4
Corruption	1	2	3	4
Extortion	1	2	3	4
Perjury	1	2	3	4
Theft	1	2	3	4
Wasteful activity	1	2	3	4
Wasteful economically	1	2	3	4
Wasteful environmentally	1	2	3	4

Part II: Please fill in this personal confidential information.

(1) Sex _____   (2) Age ____   (3) Marital Status:

Married   _____
Divorced   _____
Separated _____
Widow(er) _____
Single   _____

(4) No. of Children _____   (5) Age of Oldest Child _____

(6) Religion: (7) Graduation Date From:

Cahtolic   _____   High School   _____
Protestant   _____   College   _____
Jewish   _____   Graduate School _____
Other (write in) _____

(8) Professional Type: (9) Engineering Function:

Engineer   Production Engineering _____
ME   _____   Product Design   _____
EE   _____   R & D   _____
Industrial   _____   Other (write in) _____
Other (write in) _____
Other (write in) _____

(10) Management Function: (11) Approximate the number of employees
                                          under your supervision:

Technical Management _____   0-4   _____
Research   _____   5-8   _____
Purchasing   _____   9-12   _____
Marketing   _____   13-18   _____
Production   _____   19-25   _____
Other (write in) _____   25-50   _____
                                     51-100   _____
                                     101-150   _____
                                     151-200   _____
                                     201-250   _____
                                     More than 500 _____

(12) Present Annual Salary: (13) How many companies have you worked for as a professional? _____

Less than $10,000   _____
$10,000-$15,000   _____
$16,000-$20,000   _____
$21,000-$25,000   _____
$26,000-$30,000   _____
$31,000-$35,000   _____
$36,000-$40,000   _____
$41,000-$45,000   _____
$46,000-$50,000   _____
More than $50,000   _____

(14) How many years have you worked for your present employer? _____
      How many years did you work for your past employer? _____

(15) In regard to your present job, how would you describe your
      satisfaction with the following:

Level of Pay   High ( )   Medium ( )   Low ( )
No. of Promotions   High ( )   Medium ( )   Low ( )
Level of Challenge High ( )   Medium ( )   Low ( )

(16) Company Type: (17) Approximate the number of people who are employed by
                                   your company:

Commercial Manufacturing _____   Less than 100   _____
Industrial Manufacturing _____   100-499   _____
Service   _____   500-999   _____
Sales/Distribution   _____   1,000-1,999   _____
Public Service   _____   2,000-2,999   _____
Utilities   _____   3,000-3,999   _____
Transportation   _____   4,000-4,999   _____
                                        5,000-9,000   _____
                                        10,000-20,000   _____
                                        More than 20,000 _____

Ethical values of today's managers and engineers

A summary of your responses to the 5-16-77 Bjorklund-Hebert questionnaire on ethical values

Dr. T.F. Gautschi and Dr. R.L. Bjorklund

Sex: male
Average age: 41 years
Average no. of children: 2.6
Religious affiliation: 50% Protestant, 25% Roman Catholic, 4% Jewish, 21% Other
Management: one-half are technical managers with an average of 10 subordinates
Salary: 88% receive between $16,000 and $35,000 annually
Average no. of companies worked for: 3
Time with present employer: 9 years
Company type: Industrial or commercial manufacturing firms of diversified sizes
Engineering function: most respondents are mechanical or electrical engineers engaged in product design, R & D or product engineering

It can be stated that ethics, at least in part, are defined by the predominant attitude of the group of people who make up the society. You, as engineers/managers, represent a significant sample of society, so what *you* consider ethical is important. Biblical scholars might suggest the Ten Commandments as an absolute set of principles—your responses reflect a high degree of agreement with this position (to the extent that we asked relevant questions).

Differentiation between groups of values. In terms of your attitudes, you believe that items in Group A and D are almost *totally* unethical. These are items that relate to honest and legal conduct. You find extortion the most abhorrent of these and deceit the least. But in all cases of value issues in these groups you find them very distasteful. We could categorize this, in theoretical terms, to be a punishment oriented or a law-and-order attitude.[1].

The other three groups—B, C and E—represent unfairness, manipulation and wastefulness categories. Generally speaking, you do not seem to differentiate between them in any relative terms. You consider them distasteful, but little more. Manipulation is seen as mildly unethical and nepotism about the same.

A surprise and a paradox. The predominant category of respondents to the questionnaire classified themselves as design engineers or R & D engineers or product engineers. Yet, you indicate by your responses that waste is the second least offensive behavior on the list. One might have expected you to be more concerned with engineering economy, and for that matter, environmental waste. On a relative basis, you do not consider waste to be in the same league with issues of honesty or legality.

---

1. Lawrence Kohlberg developed a hierarchy of moral development in which he says that there are six stages: punishment and obedience, personal usefulness, conformity to the group will, law and order, social contract, and a total principle based on personal conscience.

		ACTIVITY	AVERAGE RESPONSE	TOTALLY UNETHICAL 1	VERY UNETHICAL 2	MILDLY UNETHICAL 3
A	(1)	Dishonesty	1.3			
	(2)	Deceit	1.6			
	(3)	Falsification	1.3			
B	(4)	Unfair treatment	2.3			
	(5)	Inequitable treatment	2.4			
	(6)	Nepotism	2.6			
	(7)	Prejudice	2.2			
C	(8)	Manipulation	2.8			
	(9)	Coercion	2.2			
	(10)	Exploitation	2.2			
D	(11)	Illegal activity	1.2			
	(12)	Conspiracy	1.4			
	(13)	Corruption	1.2			
	(14)	Extortion	1.1			
	(15)	Perjury	1.2			
	(16)	Theft	1.2			
E	(17)	Wasteful activity	2.7			
	(18)	Wasteful economically	2.6			
	(19)	Wasteful environmentally	2.5			

What makes you violate your values?

Dr. T. F. Gautschi and Dr. R. L. Bjorklund

The two questions that we will consider here are (1) Which (if any) of your values are you willing to violate, and (2) Under what circumstances would you be willing to violate them?

Manipulation. As indicated in the table, manipulation is the value that you are most frequently willing to violate. Last issue you also defined manipulation as the least unethical of 19 activities. So your response is consistent, but it is a little surprising that manipulative behavior is such an acceptable strategy.

Wastefulness. A relatively small proportion of you considered wasteful activity as justifiable, yet it was rated as the second least unethical activity on the list of 19. Operationally speaking, one might conclude that wastefulness is not instrumental in solving your kinds of problems and therefore you are less inclined to adopt it as a behavior except where it is useful. However, 55% said they would be wasteful under the direct orders of their superiors, and 39% said they would do so to avoid the loss of a critical customer.

Dishonesty and illegality are both very strongly held values, as indicated by the low percentages that believe such action is justified. However, where the stakes are high enough (as indicated by items 4, 10, 11, 18, 26 and 27), some of you feel that dishonesty is justified. In these cases (which we call "critical"), a significant (but small) number said they would be dishonest to save a job, or a critical customer, or a severe financial loss or for hiring/firing reasons. Interestingly, fewer said they would commit illegal actions, though frequently a falsification (which is part of dishonesty) is *also* illegal. Items 10, 12 and 18 were the most frequently cited wherein a respondent would consider illegal activity.

Conclusions. The respondents to the questionnaire are an ethical group for the most part. Over 25% of the respondents consider any of the listed activities as totally unethical. The others have a hierarchy of reasons for violating their standards when they feel that they must. (1) They will usually have to view an unethical activity as instrumental in a solution before they consider adopting it as their behavior. (2) Those items that they consider most unethical are the same values that they rarely would consider violating. (3) They will violate their own ethics more frequently for personal gain (save their jobs) than for corporate gain (save a customer, loss, raise price per share of stock). (4) They will conduct themselves unethically in "critical" situations more frequently than in routine situations.

Percent of Respondents who indicate that they believe the action below is justified by the situation described

	Dishonest	Illegal	Manipulative	Unfair	Wasteful
1. There are no situations that justify this behavior.	63	65	23	26	25
2. This behavior is almost always justifiable.	2	2	31	8	10
3. To improve your job security.	5	2	49	17	16
4. To avoid losing your job.	9	5	57	29	26
5. To maintain an advantageous personal status in the corporation, i.e. promotions, budgetary advantages, etc.	4	2	46	15	15
6. To improve a poor personal status in the corporation.	4	2	48	17	16
7. To obtain an extremely advantageous personal status in the corporation.	4	2	43	18	12
8. To obtain an advantageous interdepartmental status in the corporation.	3	2	43	15	12
9. To improve an extremely poor interdepartmental position in the corporation.	4	2	50	21	18
10. Under the direct order of your superior.	8	5	48	42	55
11. At the implicit direction of your superior.	6	3	43	30	42
12. To make a critical sale.	5	4	48	26	34
13. To make a routine sale.	3	3	34	11	16
14. To avoid the loss of a critical customer.	6	4	50	28	39
15. To avoid the loss of an average customer.	2	3	38	13	18
16. To reduce the effectiveness of a key competitor.	5	2	44	23	25
17. To make a breakeven profit.	5	3	40	19	25
18. To avoid a serious financial loss.	9	6	53	34	36
19. To increase profits to meet a goal that has been established by your company.	3	2	42	16	21
20. To increase the price per share of your company's stock.	3	3	34	13	13
21. To increase the price per share of your company's stock because it is dangerously low.	5	3	38	20	19
22. To obtain an extremely high price per share of your company's stock.	3	2	32	12	11
23. To maintain a high credit rating.	4	2	35	14	14
24. To increase a dangerously low credit rating.	7	2	40	20	23
25. To gain an advantage with public officials.	6	5	39	15	15
26. To pirate a particularly valuable employee from another company.	7	2	38	21	19
27. To screen out potentially disadvantageous employees.	6	4	51	29	23

Attitudes and values in engineering management

Dr. T. F. Gautschi

Your response to the Attitude and Value Survey has been excellent—we exceeded our goal of 1000 by 88. In this and the next two issues of Management Forum we will summarize the results. In the charts shown below, you can see that in comparison to the average *Design News* reader, the respondents to the survey are skewed towards those with more education, higher salaries, more years experience and more companies worked for. So, we have succeeded in reaching those engineers who have become—or are about to become—engineering managers. How do *your* survey answers compare to this management-oriented group?

As I mentioned in the questionnaire article, the art of managing involves the learning of theory, the learning of technical skills and, perhaps most important of all, the learning of the attitudes and values of the management profession. The trouble is that most formal education emphasizes the knowledge and skills and neglects the attitudes and values. This is not surprising because the former are reasonably well understood and documented, while the latter are not well defined and are subject to frequent change. But attitudes and values, as undefinable as they may be, are vitally important to our success as engineering managers. It is the naive manager indeed who thinks he can do his job without them.

Let us begin our survey report by dividing the questions into six major areas (how many of you were aware of the categories?) and discussing each area separately. A few words of explanation on the charts: the four bars on each chart represent the percentages of respondents who either strongly disagreed, disagreed, agreed or strongly agreed.

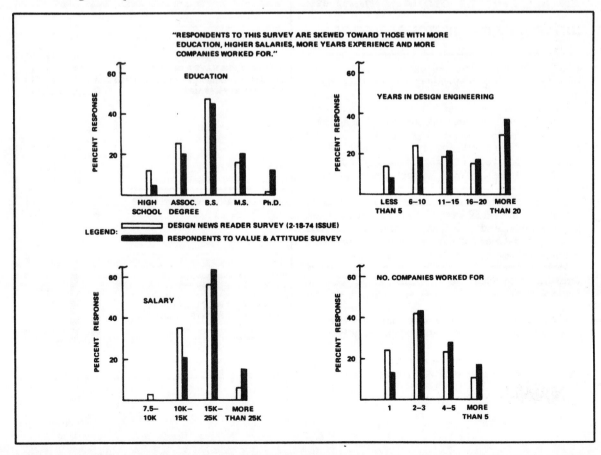

The conflict between business and society

Summary. The vast majority of respondents feel that the corporation has a definite obligation to be actively involved in community affairs, that a corporation can sell an inferior product as long as the corporation has a good public image, and that management will *not* do what is best for its employees, as a group, without outside pressure. However, only about 50% feel that the individual needs a union to protect him if he works hard.

The response in favor of corporation involvement in community affairs was 77% for all respondents. It would be interesting to investigate what forms such involvement is taking and what forms it should take. Also, many of the comments indicated that corporations *should* be involved, but that they are not.

About 70% of all respondents (regardless of salary level, years of experience or firm size) believe that pressure must be applied to management by unions, or by the government, to assure that management does what is best for their employees as a body. However, only 50% of those who have 20 or more subordinates feel this way. Quite likely the definition of "best" changes as one moves up the management ladder. The manager will tend to feel that "best" is that which

---

About 70% of all respondents . . . believe that pressure must be applied to management by unions, or by the government . . .

---

enables his firm to survive and grow and thereby provide continuing employment, whereas those not in management are more concerned about the individual. With a constant definition of best, I am sure that the difference between management and nonmanagement answers would have been even greater. This statement is supported by another study* where 67% of the executives believed that management would do what was best for the employee without outside pressure from unions.

In contrast, the answers were about split as to whether an individual who works hard needs a union to protect him. And a much larger percentage of those with higher salaries and more subordinates feel that a union is not needed to protect the individual.

Most managers believe that they do *not* need outside pressure to do what is best for their employees and that the individual does *not* need a union to protect him.

I wonder if managers become managers because they feel this way, or do they feel this way because they are managers?

*See Attitude Change During Management Education by E. H. Schein, *Administrative Science Quarterly,* 1967.

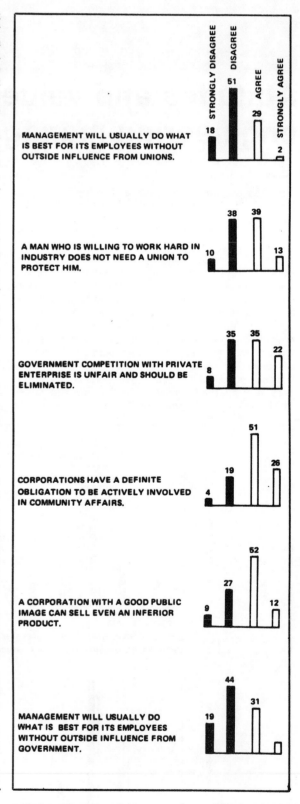

How we perceive management

Summary: Almost 90% of the respondents agreed that managers are not *always* sincere in their dealings with other people, and a little over 60% feel that most managerial jobs require a person to compromise his ethics or morals to some degree and that most corporations do not have clear objectives.

Nearly everyone feels that managers are not *always* sincere in their dealings with other people. This opinion did not vary with salary, religion, years experience, the number of subordinates, education or race. Many pointed out that probably no one, manager or not, is *always* sincere in his dealings with other people. This statement is also compatible with the results of our recent ethics survey.

Although 60% of the respondents feel that most managerial jobs require a person to compromise his ethics or morals to some degree, the percent of agreements decreases with increasing salary, the number of subordinates, and education. (Schein's survey in *Administration Science Quarterly*, 1967 found that only 18% of the executives agreed on this question).

Part of this large difference can be accounted for by the fact that Schein's survey was pre-Watergate. I

... people are more willing to admit non-ethical behavior.

---

believe that his percent agreement would be much larger today because people are more willing to admit non-ethical behavior. Again, this goes along with the finding of our ethics survey, where we concluded that "nearly everyone will be unethical if the stakes are high enough." We are probably no less ethical today—we are just more willing to admit it.

Nevertheless, we can conclude that management views their practices differently than their subordinates do.

About 60% of all respondents agreed that most corporations do not have clear objectives that can serve as guides to decisions. This opinion did *not* vary with salary level, the number of years experience, the number of subordinates, the level of education or the size of the firm. (Schein's study only shows 48% agreement among executives on this question.) This response certainly has implications regarding goals, strategic and long-range planning, as well as how most firms are managed. I am convinced that to be well managed, a firm must have clear-cut objectives and that a firm can be most effective when its objectives are communicated down to its lowest management levels. When the lowest management levels are not sure of what the corporate objectives are, they can hardly be expected to direct their efforts in an effective way to meet them.

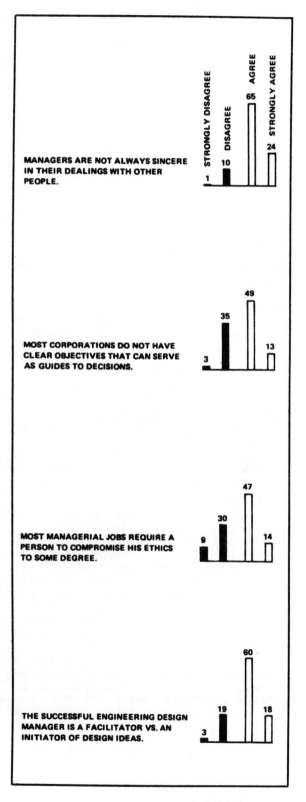

Rating some theories of management

Discussion. About 62% feel that there are sound principles of business that should *not* be changed even if economic and technological conditions change. This percentage holds true regardless of salary level, number of subordinates, years experience, or education; *except* for those making more than $28K and having more than 20 subordinates. Two principles are suggested by this survey. (1) A firm should have a clear-cut hierarchy of authority and responsibility, (2) a firm should have clear objectives and these should be communicated through all levels of management.

Another emerging principle is that people can and will be more effective in an environment that is characterized by acceptance, candor, meaningful work and open communication. Two other important principles are that a firm exists primarily to provide a reasonable financial return on the owner's investment, and that consistent personnel practices and equitable financial remuneration to all employees is important.

77% of the respondents feel that most industrial management problems can be attributed to a few causes. This percent holds regardless of salary level, years of experience, the number of subordinates or firm size.

Some attitudes toward people

41% of the respondents feel that the average employee in industry prefers to avoid responsibility, has little ambition, and wants security above all. 60% believe that managers usually do *not* deal with people in a democratic manner.

64% feel that individual decisions are superior to group decisions. (This *disagrees* with current group dynamic theory and will be discussed in a later Forum article.)

27% agree that the human factor is more important than the economic factor in business decisions.

Discussion. McGregor identified two contrasting theories about people. Theory X says that people want to avoid responsibility, have little ambition, and want security above all. Theory Y takes the opposite view of people. (These theories will be discussed under Leadership in a later Forum article.) 59% of the respondents in this survey seem to hold a Theory Y view of man and 41% have a Theory X view. This percent holds true for the various levels of experience and number of subordinates supervised. However, the Theory Y view increases with salary level and firm size to about 70% at salaries above $28K and firms with more than 5,000 employees.

In contrast, only 40% feel that managers usually deal with people in a democratic manner (i.e. as if they are Theory Y).

I was surprised at the response where only 27% feel that human factor is more important than the economic factor in business decisions. More than likely this is in response to how you feel that it is and *not* how you feel it should be. Perhaps this is why so many feel that management will *not* do what is best for the employee without outside pressure. This response is typical for all salary levels, years of experience, and number of subordinates.

How an organization views individuals

The vast majority feel that the private life of the employee is *not* a direct concern of his company. Almost 30% of all respondents strongly feel this way. About 65% of all respondents believe that the man who gets ahead in industry has someone sponsoring him, and that most large corporations place more emphasis on the corporate loyalty of the employee than on his individual growth.

Discussion. The responses to question 17 were about 30% in agreement for all salary levels, years of experience, and number of subordinates, except for those making more than $28K. This group was about 40% in agreement. Many of those that agreed qualified their answers by stating that the company should only be involved in an employee's private life when it affects the employee's work.

The sponsor concept was agreed to by 65% of all respondents and held constant for all salary, education, experience and firm size levels. So, if you don't have a sponsor, and you want to get ahead in industry, you had better find one. Many feel that this is not an ideal situation, but that it is the way that life in industry really is. This doesn't negate the requirement for competence and hard work, but simply stresses that a person had better find a sponsor as well. I guess that this factor is what we often term politics in an organization. "It's not only what you know, but also who you know that makes the difference."

60% agreed that most corporations place more stress on loyalty to the corporation than on an employee's individual growth. This percent held true in all categories of salary, years of experience and number of subordinates *except* for those above $28K and who have more than 20 subordinates. These groups were only about 55% in agreement.

This area could be a source of concern for the engineer, since many feel more closely associated with their profession and their professional growth than they do to the firm that employs them.

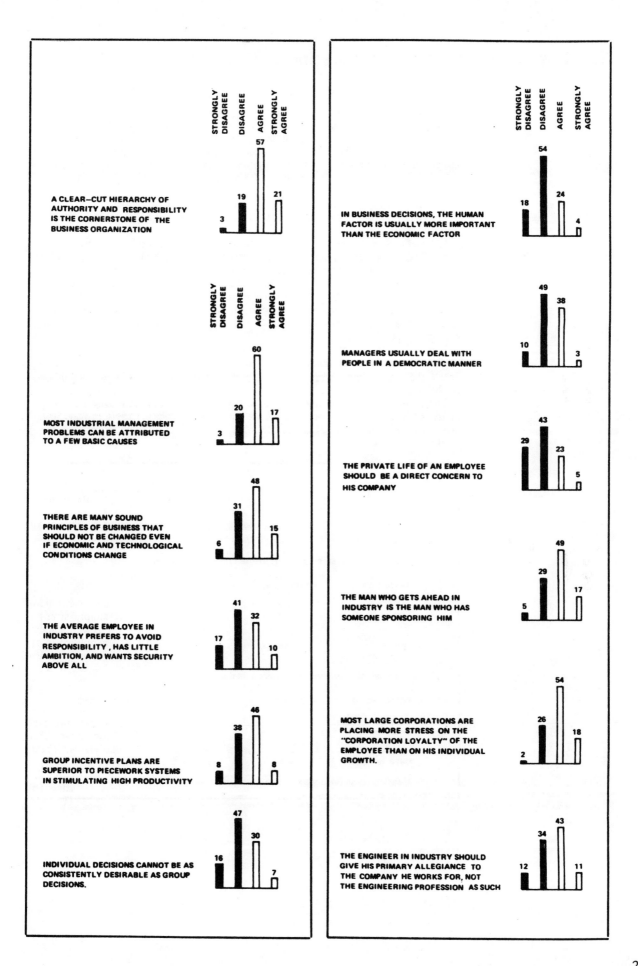

A CLEAR—CUT HIERARCHY OF AUTHORITY AND RESPONSIBILITY IS THE CORNERSTONE OF THE BUSINESS ORGANIZATION

STRONGLY DISAGREE: 3 | DISAGREE: 19 | AGREE: 57 | STRONGLY AGREE: 21

MOST INDUSTRIAL MANAGEMENT PROBLEMS CAN BE ATTRIBUTED TO A FEW BASIC CAUSES

STRONGLY DISAGREE: 3 | DISAGREE: 20 | AGREE: 60 | STRONGLY AGREE: 17

THERE ARE MANY SOUND PRINCIPLES OF BUSINESS THAT SHOULD NOT BE CHANGED EVEN IF ECONOMIC AND TECHNOLOGICAL CONDITIONS CHANGE

STRONGLY DISAGREE: 6 | DISAGREE: 31 | AGREE: 48 | STRONGLY AGREE: 15

THE AVERAGE EMPLOYEE IN INDUSTRY PREFERS TO AVOID RESPONSIBILITY, HAS LITTLE AMBITION, AND WANTS SECURITY ABOVE ALL

STRONGLY DISAGREE: 17 | DISAGREE: 41 | AGREE: 32 | STRONGLY AGREE: 10

GROUP INCENTIVE PLANS ARE SUPERIOR TO PIECEWORK SYSTEMS IN STIMULATING HIGH PRODUCTIVITY

STRONGLY DISAGREE: 8 | DISAGREE: 38 | AGREE: 46 | STRONGLY AGREE: 8

INDIVIDUAL DECISIONS CANNOT BE AS CONSISTENTLY DESIRABLE AS GROUP DECISIONS.

STRONGLY DISAGREE: 16 | DISAGREE: 47 | AGREE: 30 | STRONGLY AGREE: 7

IN BUSINESS DECISIONS, THE HUMAN FACTOR IS USUALLY MORE IMPORTANT THAN THE ECONOMIC FACTOR

STRONGLY DISAGREE: 18 | DISAGREE: 54 | AGREE: 24 | STRONGLY AGREE: 4

MANAGERS USUALLY DEAL WITH PEOPLE IN A DEMOCRATIC MANNER

STRONGLY DISAGREE: 10 | DISAGREE: 49 | AGREE: 38 | STRONGLY AGREE: 3

THE PRIVATE LIFE OF AN EMPLOYEE SHOULD BE A DIRECT CONCERN TO HIS COMPANY

STRONGLY DISAGREE: 29 | DISAGREE: 43 | AGREE: 23 | STRONGLY AGREE: 5

THE MAN WHO GETS AHEAD IN INDUSTRY IS THE MAN WHO HAS SOMEONE SPONSORING HIM

STRONGLY DISAGREE: 5 | DISAGREE: 29 | AGREE: 49 | STRONGLY AGREE: 17

MOST LARGE CORPORATIONS ARE PLACING MORE STRESS ON THE "CORPORATION LOYALTY" OF THE EMPLOYEE THAN ON HIS INDIVIDUAL GROWTH.

STRONGLY DISAGREE: 2 | DISAGREE: 26 | AGREE: 54 | STRONGLY AGREE: 18

THE ENGINEER IN INDUSTRY SHOULD GIVE HIS PRIMARY ALLEGIANCE TO THE COMPANY HE WORKS FOR, NOT THE ENGINEERING PROFESSION AS SUCH

STRONGLY DISAGREE: 12 | DISAGREE: 34 | AGREE: 43 | STRONGLY AGREE: 11

The best way to plan an engineering career

Summary. 60% of the respondents feel that small companies create more opportunities for the engineer to maximize his career than large corporations.

The responses were split regarding whether the best plan is for the engineer to move 2 or 3 times his first 5 years, and whether he should give his primary allegiance to his company or to the engineering profession as a whole.

Nearly everyone feels that product design excellence is often compromised to marketing expediency.

70% feel that the major stimulus to new design efforts is competition.

77% feel that the successful engineering design manager is a facilitator and not an initiator of design ideas.

60% of all respondents in all categories (salary, experience, number of subordinates and firm size) feel that small companies create more opportunities for the engineer to maximize his career. This is a surprising result. I would have expected that most would feel that large corporations provide the greater opportunities because they have greater resources.

A major concern in this area was that the large corporation would require too much specialization, so there would be less opportunity to have a well-rounded career.

The responses to this question should influence how firms organize their engineering activity. Optimally, the large corporation should try to organize to create the small company environment; perhaps the task team approach would be useful here.

The responses agreeing that moving to several jobs during an engineer's first 5 years is beneficial were about 50% for the categories of salary, experience and firm size, but they increased significantly with the number of companies that the respondent worked for.

NUMBER OF FIRMS WORKED FOR	% AGREEMENT	NUMBER OF RESPONDENTS *	% OF RESPONDENTS
1	40%	139	13.2
2–3	48%	456	43.3
4–5	59%	287	27.2
OVER 5	66%	172	16.3

(* THERE WERE 34 MISSING OBSERVATIONS FOR THIS DIMENSION)

EDUCATION	%AGREEMENT	NUMBER OF RESPONDENTS*	% OF RESPONDENTS
HIGH SCHOOL	66.7	45	4.2
LESS THAN BS	62.7	212	20.0
BS	55.5	474	44.6
MS	47.6	210	19.8
PE/PH.D.	41.6	113	10.6
2 GOOD DEGREES	25	8	0.8

(* MISSING OBSERVATIONS FOR THIS DIMENSION = 26)

EXPERIENCE	% AGREEMENT	NUMBER OF RESPONDENTS*	% OF RESPONDENTS
UNDER 5 YEARS	32.1	84	8.0
6–10 YEARS	44.0	191	18.2
11–15 YEARS	57.2	217	20.6
16–20 YEARS	61.2	175	16.7
OVER 20 YEARS	59.4	384	36.5

(* MISSING OBSERVATIONS FOR THIS DIMENSION = 37)

Apparently the people who have moved to several jobs have not been disappointed. The data also indicates that the vast majority of the respondents have worked for two or more firms; and nearly half have worked for four or more firms.

The responses were 50% in agreement that the engineer in industry should give his primary allegiance to the company he works for. This percent held for the number of subordinates, firm size and salary level, but varied significantly with education and experience (see chart).

91% of all respondents felt that in product design engineering excellence is often compromised to marketing expediency—this percentage did not vary by salary, engineering experience, marketing experience, or number of subordinates. 33% even feel "strongly" about this issue in all categories.

This strong response could be an expression of frustration. We "engineers tend to be perfectionists and are not satisfied until our work achieves its maximum potential"; and yet we are often forced to compromise to meet marketing or other requirements and constraints.

70% of all respondents feel that the major stimulus to new design efforts is to remain competitive rather than entering new markets. This response was the same for all salary and experience levels, as well as for those without marketing experience.

77% feel that the successful engineering design manager is a facilitator, not an initiator of design ideas. This percentage holds true for all levels of experience, education and number of subordinates. The job of the manager is to provide the environment wherein the designer can be creative. As we have discussed throughout this series, the management tasks are those of planning, organizing, staffing, communicating, conducting and decision making, not the preparation of actual designs. A manager may do some design work, but when he is, he is not doing management activity.

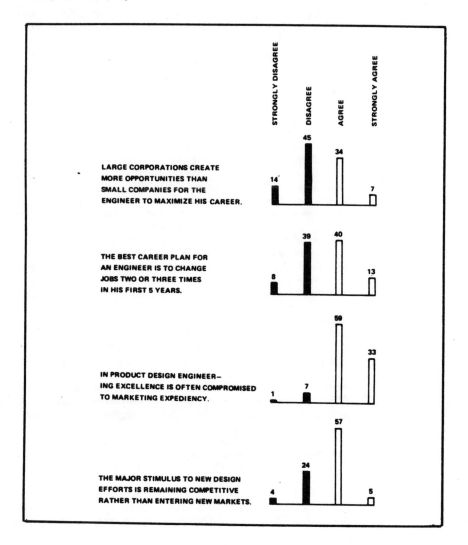

Dr. T.F. Gautschi, P.E.

The attitudes and values of engineers: a closer look

Our survey reveals why there are serious communication problems between engineers and their management

I'd like to begin this issue's Management Forum with a little reflection. This column has just gone into its third year of publication, and in over two years of publication I have had the good fortune to be a part of an exciting, growing, endeavor. In these past years, I have tried to present the subject of management in as simple and straightforward a fashion as I know how.

GROW TO SURVIVE

Just as a living organism must grow to survive, Management Forum must now grow in response to change. I mention this because we have now reached the point where the basics of management—communication, organization, and planning—have already been covered in previous Forum columns, and we are at the point where we must move on to new subjects with a new emphasis. This means that upcoming columns may assume a working knowledge of concepts covered in the past.

Although I try to keep each column understandable by itself, there may be unavoidable occasions where new readers will get "lost". At such times, I can only suggest they look at back issues or else buy a copy of the Design Management Forum book, which contains the past year's columns. For instance, I will soon start a series on Management By Objectives, and this series will assume a knowledge of organization theory, a subject I have covered in detail in past issues. In other words, we've covered the basics; now it's time to dig into the details. I hope you stay with me on this exciting journey.

RETURN TO A SURVEY

As a temporary respite from recent tutorial articles, I'd like to return in this column to some of the surveys we conducted. The Attitude and Value Survey presented in the 2/4/74 *DN* and reported on in the 5/20/74 *DN* has been analyzed in greater detail and I would like to share some new insights. These have been gained as a result of careful digging and cross-correlation by management students at the Sloan School of Management at M.I.T. This survey generated high interest among readers, and raised many questions.

Are engineers unique in their attitudes and values? Do they think like everyone else? The new data from the Sloan School compares your response to the survey questions with that obtained from top executives, middle managers, and students. I won't keep you in suspense: *significant* differences were uncovered, and I can now understand why most corporations have communications problems. Indeed, these survey results have broken fresh ground by exploring a long-neglected relationship—that between engineers and the companies they work for.

I. Business in society

The senior executives exhibited the greatest confidence in the management of private corporations; middle management next, design engineers next, and the graduate students had the least confidence. In fact, the engineers are more than 25 percentage points away from the senior executives in their answers to the first three questions and question 26.

Part of this difference can be explained by the possibility that subordinates evaluate management's performance as they perceive management operating under stress, and the managers evaluate their performance based upon what they believe to be their routine behavior.

However, we can't doubt there is a significant gap between the way executives and engineers view management actions. About 70% of all the engineers (regardless of salary level or years of experience) believe that pressure must be applied to management by unions or by the government, to assure that management will do what is best for its employees as a body. With white-collar employees constituting more than 50% of the workforce, I believe that pressure is building up for white-collar (including professional engineering) unions and/or some sort of government legislation to assure that management does do what is best for the employees. So if management believes that it is doing what is best for its employees without outside pressure, somehow it should be communicated.

For a given level of experience, those engineers who have achieved positions commanding the higher salaries have the greater confidence that corporate management will be responsive to the needs of its employees. This is also true for those who have more subordinates reporting to them. Engineers who fail to achieve financial success and authority tend to lose confidence in corporate management.

There was no evidence that engineers in small firms are any more, or less, confident of corporate management than those in large firms. Educational level achieved didn't have any effect upon a person's confidence in corporate management.

The data also reveals that engineers in government labs are more in favor of government competition with private enterprise than those in private sectors.

II. General Cynicism

The proportion of engineers who feel that management positions require a compromise of ethics is three times that of the senior or middle managers. This, along with the answers to the other questions, suggests that engineers do not identify very closely with the management of their firms. The interesting thing is that both groups are viewing the same activities, but from different perspectives. And each group believes it accurately perceives the situation.

No wonder we have communications problems.

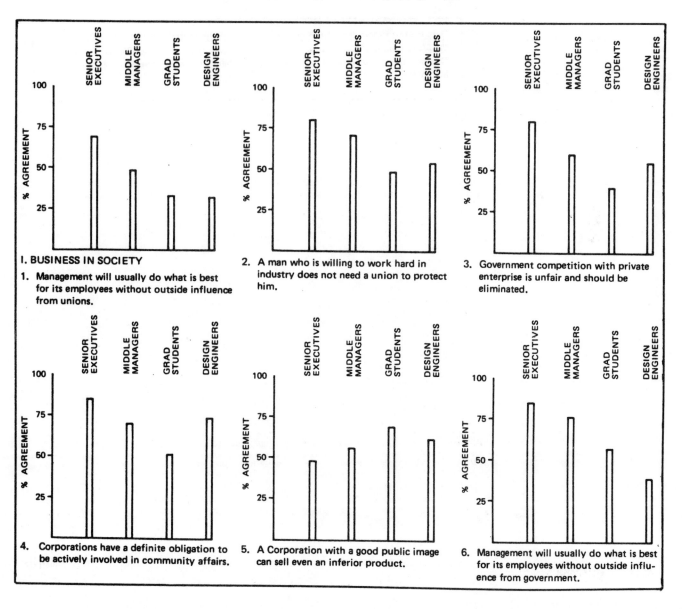

I. BUSINESS IN SOCIETY

1. Management will usually do what is best for its employees without outside influence from unions.

2. A man who is willing to work hard in industry does not need a union to protect him.

3. Government competition with private enterprise is unfair and should be eliminated.

4. Corporations have a definite obligation to be actively involved in community affairs.

5. A Corporation with a good public image can sell even an inferior product.

6. Management will usually do what is best for its employees without outside influence from government.

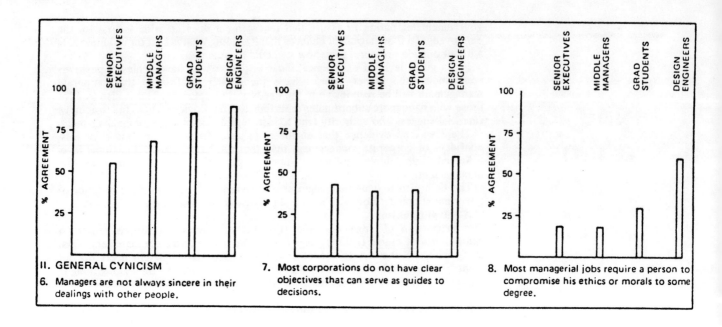

II. GENERAL CYNICISM

6. Managers are not always sincere in their dealings with other people.

7. Most corporations do not have clear objectives that can serve as guides to decisions.

8. Most managerial jobs require a person to compromise his ethics or morals to some degree.

Data for this report came from two sources: *A Survey of Attitudes of Engineers About the Management of Corporations,* Charles C. Holcomb, M.I.T., June 1975 and *Attitude Change During Management Education,* E.H. Schein, Administrative Science Quarterly, March 1967.

Dr. T.F. Gautschi, P.E.

The attitudes and values of engineers: a closer look (Part 2)

Why the engineer tends toward a professional rather than corporate identity

The comparison of the responses of the engineers with those of middle and top managers clearly indicate that the engineers have far less company orientation than the managers. Rather, the engineers exhibit a professional orientation.

Perhaps this can be explained by the fact that:

- Graduate education tends to increase the professional orientation among engineers.
- Exclusion from line management positions tends to increase professional orientation. Conversely, promotion to line management positions tends to increase company orientation.
- The professional orientation is more evident among those engineers who are enthusiastically involved in, and like working with, "things" and prefer not to manage people.
- As engineers are promoted up the ranks some become line managers while others become "staff engineers". For the most part, those that become staff engineers tend to relate more to their profession and view themselves as highly skilled professionals.
- Highly educated engineers tend to keep their professional orientation even if they become managers.
- Engineers who are dissatisfied with, or lack confidence in, the responsiveness of management to the needs of employees, usually also have professional rather than company orientations.

GROUP VS. INDIVIDUAL

Over 50% of the top executives believe that group decisions are consistently more desirable than individual decisions, whereas only 30% of the engineers feel this way. As we have discussed in previous articles, the higher level, more complex decisions do require the inputs from many people. (See *Design News* Management Forum article July 21, 1975 "Consensus Thinking").

It is interesting that 30% of the managers believe that the human factor is more important than the economic factor, whereas only 20% of the engineers feel that way. (See p. 159)

In statements 17, 18 and 19 the engineers exhibit a much more cynical view of the organization's relationship with its individual member than do executives. The higher-salary high-authority engineer's attitudes are less cynical than the average engineer, but even this group is far more cynical than the top or middle managers.

On the basis of these questions, the negative attitudes that the engineers have towards management would seem to be the result of their treatment as individuals by the firm rather than any fundamental difference in management theory or assumptions about individuals or groups in the firm.

PROFESSIONAL VS. CORPORATE LOYALTY

The responses to statement 19 further reinforce the notion that engineers tend to be more professional in their orientation, and they feel strongly that too much stress is placed on corporate loyalty, and not enough emphasis is put on individual growth. Perhaps the engineering professional feels the pressure of technological obsolescence more keenly than others in the organization. My guess is that this would be a good area for management to consider in their quest for improved organizational effectiveness.

The engineers view management practice quite differently from the way that the senior executives and mid-level managers do. This is consistent with the responses to the other questions. On this question the highest salaried segment of engineers had an agreement rate approaching that of middle-management.

CONCLUSIONS

The comparison of engineers' attitudes with those of top and middle management suggest several conclusions:

1. Engineers appear to have considerably less confidence in the responsiveness of management to the needs of its employees than do middle or top managers.
2. Engineers do not appear to have significantly different assumptions about management theories than those of middle and top managers.
3. Engineers view large corporations as less desirable to work in than do middle and top managers.
4. Engineers who hold management positions as indicated by high salary and high number of subordinates have less confidence in the responsiveness of management to the needs of its employees than do middle or top level managers.
5. Engineers who hold management positions as indicated by high salary and number of subordinates do not appear to personalize their management position. On questions #6 and #8 (last issue) these management level engineers exhibit more cynicism about the sincerity and ethical behavior of managers than do the middle and top managers.

FURTHER FINDINGS

Additional conclusions can be drawn from a statistical analysis of the question responses and the demographic variables.

1. Orientation to the engineering profession, as contrasted with orientation to the employer, increases with level of education.
2. Preference for individual decisions, as opposed to group decisions, increases with education level.
3. Size of the firm in which the engineer is employed appears to have no effect on his attitudes toward management. Engineers in smaller firms did show a tendency to view workers as less ambitious than those in larger firms.
4. The marketing orientation of the engineer does not appear to have any effect on his attitudes toward management.
5. The engineers' assumptions about the responsiveness of management to the needs of society do not appear to be affected by their work experience, salary level, or number of subordinates.
6. Large corporations appear to pay significantly higher salaries to engineers of the same education and level of experience than do small corporations.
7. Large corporations appear to hire a larger proportion of highly educated engineers than do small corporations.
8. The salary premium paid by industry for advanced education appears to increase as experience increases.
9. Engineers who do not have confidence in the responsiveness of management in the needs of its employees also tend to have professional rather than company orientations.
10. Engineers tend to increase their company orientation with increased experience.
11. Increased number of subordinates tends to increase the engineers' orientation toward the company and away from the profession.

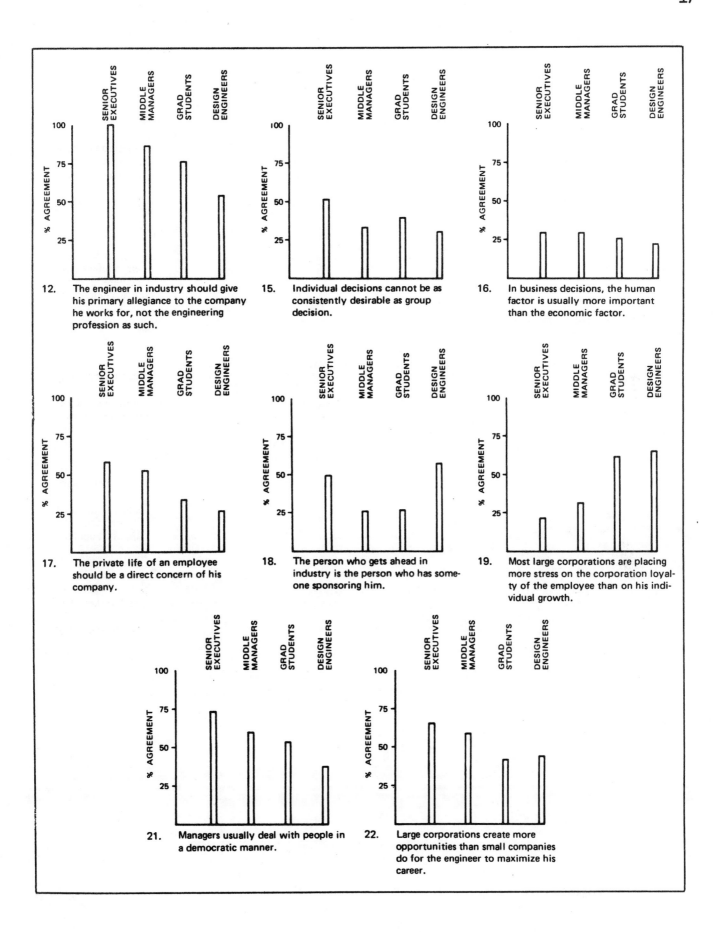

12. The engineer in industry should give his primary allegiance to the company he works for, not the engineering profession as such.

15. Individual decisions cannot be as consistently desirable as group decision.

16. In business decisions, the human factor is usually more important than the economic factor.

17. The private life of an employee should be a direct concern of his company.

18. The person who gets ahead in industry is the person who has someone sponsoring him.

19. Most large corporations are placing more stress on the corporation loyalty of the employee than on his individual growth.

21. Managers usually deal with people in a democratic manner.

22. Large corporations create more opportunities than small companies do for the engineer to maximize his career.

Improved safety pays dividends

Dr. T. F. Gautschi, P. E.

I have a little problem for you—I am sure that any of you can solve it. To make it a little more difficult, read it through once quickly without writing numbers down.

On a particular day a school bus was picking up its passengers. It holds 50 students when everyone is seated. At the first stop it picked up 7 students, at the next stop it picked up 9 more students, then it picked up 6 students. At the next stop it let off 5 students, then at the next stop it picked up 8 students, then it stopped to pick up 8 more students and at the final stop it picked up 13 students. How many stops did the bus make?

The answer is 7 stops, but most of you were probably trying to keep track of the number of students onboard! We call this *selective perception*—that is, we tend to perceive only those things that we are looking for, and we tend to reject the rest of the information.

SAFETY is like that. We often tend to think of our workplace as being a safe place to work and only see those things that make it safe—and tend to unconsciously reject those things which would make us feel otherwise. It is an easy trap to fall into. "After all, we haven't had a loss time accident in 2-1/2 years so our conditions and practices must be safe!"

I wonder if that is how the students at a college in Rhode Island felt until the night when they had a dorm fire and several women were killed,

. . . or the people managing those grain elevators that blew up with the resultant loss of many lives,

. . . or the fellow who lit a match to see if his gas tank was full, and was burned to death,

. . . or the operator who was killed when a machine guard was removed,

. . . or the man who was electrocuted when his electric drill was not grounded,

. . . or the man who thought safety glasses were for sissies and lost his sight in one eye.

The Bureau of Labor Statistics reports that 28 million workdays are lost each year in the U.S. due to job-related injuries or illnesses. This results in $2 billion lost production and $1.5 billion in lost wages.

In addition to saving lives and reducing pain and discomfort, good safety practice can result in higher productivity, higher employee morale and lower insurance rates. An effective safety program is *not* an additional cost to the company or additional responsibility for the supervisor.

On the contrary, an effective safety program will result in lower accident rates and employees who can work with greater confidence. The supervisor's role is critical to the success of any safety program. Just as the personnel function is *not* the ultimate responsibility of the personnel department, the safety function can *not* be the ultimate responsibility of the safety officer. Line management has this ultimate responsibility.

Your role as supervisor and manager is critical to the success of any safety program—most losses result from a failure of an employee to follow established safe practices.

Looking at safety from another point of view, the 1970 Occupational Safety & Health Act (OSHA) has added a new dimension to business and industry—that of enforcing a safe workplace for employees. It's now a federal offense to *not* assure safe and healthful working conditions for all employees.

In summary, improved safety can pay good dividends in terms of *reduced* pain and suffering, *increased* productivity, *increased* employee morale, *reduced* insurance rates and *compliance* with the federal law. It's all up to you.

To help focus your thinking on safety you may wish to review the safety check list and then initiate correct action as appropriate.

SAFETY CHECK LIST

1. Safety regulations are properly documented.
2. Safety efforts are coordinated.
3. Current info on injury and illness rates in the workplace are shared among everyone.
4. Supervisors practice safety.
5. Safety orientation for new employees.
6. Safety orientation for old employees on new job.
7. Safety meetings are held as required.
8. Workplace is inspected for safety violations (hazards) and prompt corrective action is taken.
9. All equipment is periodically checked for safety.
10. Complete and open investigations of all accidents where injury occurs.
11. Adequate medical equipment and facilities.
12. Adequate medical treatment and drills.
13. Management is concerned about safety.
14. Documented and understood emergency reporting procedures.
15. Rules are posted and enforced for specific hazard areas.
16. Supervisors receive training in safety (loss control).
17. Adequate safety promotion and publicity.

Basic facts about product liability

Info that can help you avoid a lawsuit

Dr. T. F. Gautschi, P.E.

In 1960, there were about 1,000 lawsuits for personal injury or property damage attributable to a product. In 1972, there were over 500,000 cases settled in court, with still more settled out of court. So the danger of a product liability suit should not be dismissed lightly anymore by an engineering manager.

This rapid increase in products liability activity is due to an increasing consumer awareness, a more sympathetic legal climate, and increasing product complexity. Plaintiff lawyers are also getting together, arranging clearing houses and exchanging information. Juries identify easily with the consumer and lawyers see the products cases as a new and potentially lucrative field. Furthermore, products liability cases that have been tried in courts have resulted in legislation that has greatly increased the protection to the consumer. As a result, the old guidelines have become obsolete.

CHANGING GUIDELINES

Old guidelines: A products liability case could only be made if the harmed person (1) had purchased the product directly without any intermediaries, (2) could prove a defect, not just a random failure and (3) the proven defect resulted from a negligent act.

New guidelines: A products liability case can now be made if the harmed person (1) is injured due to a defect or the defect makes the accident worse or (2) is injured from a forseeable misuse that the designer could have guarded or warned against.

The guidelines defining a defect are also much broader now. They include: a product failure, a product hazard, an attribute or condition of the product not contemplated by the consumer, and which would be unreasonably dangerous to the user (e.g. the lack of a properly worded or illustrated warning, or some sort of hidden hazard) or an attribute that made an accident worse than it could otherwise have been.

ADDITIONAL PRESSURE

The increasing number of products liability cases places additional pressure on the designer and the engineering organization to assure that their products are not defective. They must now anticipate possible misuses of the product. For, if by hindsight a court can determine that the designer might have guarded against the misuse, the company can be held liable for the injury. Anticipating possible misuses is a challenging exercise in creative, uninhibited thinking, and the designer needs as many independent inputs as can be enlisted.

To minimize product liability, design engineers should make the design of warning labels a part of their responsibility. They should be especially alert to having labels revised into ineffectiveness by some inventive sales or advertising person who wants to inject certain "minor" modifications to make the product less repugnant to the user. For example, the household cleaner that warns of a possible gas-generated explosion if subjected to elevated temperatures would not be as appealing to the user as would a product that did not have this warning. The electric motor with a warning that simply states, "**plug into 110 volts only,**" might have more appeal to the user than the one that states, "**plugging into voltages greater than 110 volts can result in a possible explosion of the motor due to excessive speed.**"

RUSSIAN RULES

I understand that products liability is taken very seriously in Russia. If a product is defective but does not cause an injury, the employee responsible loses 150% of his or her production credit on the quantity of the defective product that was produced. If the defect causes bodily injury, the person responsible is removed from the job. If the defect causes permanent damage, it is considered a criminal act and the employee responsible is prosecuted through the courts.

KEEP RECORDS

In addition to doing everything to assure that the product is not defective, the engineer and engineering manager should keep meticulous records just in case something does go wrong. These records should include: (1) any alternate designs that had a safety aspect (be sure to list why they were not used); (2) field test results on the warning labels used; (3) a history of the changes in design features or labeling that might bear on safety; (4) all product tests and their results; (5) a listing of anticipated and unanticipated misuses that were taken into account during the product safety evaluation; and (6) documentation regarding where the product stands vs. any ANSI Standard, Underwriter Laboratory Standard, Industry Standard, industry practice and Federal or State Standards.

CALL YOUR LAWYER

If by chance your product is involved in a liability case, there are some legal defenses that can be employed. Obviously, the first thing you should do is call your lawyer. He should use the following defense arguments: (1) proving misuses were not reasonably forseeable: (2) proving the defect that occurred was out of the manufacturer's control; (3) proving the risk was unknown at the time of manufacture due to limited available scientific knowledge; and (4) proving the manufacturer took proper precautions, had good quality control, followed up on complaints and made improvements to keep current in safety technology.

The Consumer Products Safety Act of 1972 is an outgrowth of previous liability litigation. The Consumer Products Safety commission that was created by this act has regulatory authority over all aspects of production and distribution of most consumer products. Commission officials have the power to establish and enforce rigorous safety standards on a national basis to provide protection for consumers against unreasonable risks of injury associated with consumer products.

Commission representatives may enter industrial and commercial establishments to inspect consumer products and determine compliance with a violation of federal safety standards. They may also ban hazardous products.

The full impact of this legislation is yet to be felt; however, the latitude given to the Commission represents a major force to be reckoned with in the future.

SET THE TONE

We as managers set the tone for our organizations regarding the reliability of our products. This tone is determined by how we handle tradeoffs between cost and reliability, and the amount of concern that we have for safety. We have the responsibility for assuring that our companies develop and produce reliable and safe products, so let's be sure that we do a good job in this increasingly important area.

Failure to recognize and understand the broadening scope of products liability today will surely manifest itself in products liability suits tomorrow.

Engineering manager's guide to Equal Opportunity

Dr. T. F. Gautschi, P.E.

A primer on the Equal Opportunity laws

Did you know that:

- Organizations such as the NAACP, NOW (National Organization for Women), and others may bring discrimination complaints against a company for an individual? And if found guilty, the company must pay the charging party's legal fees?

- You may incur a charge of discrimination by asking a female being interviewed questions on her marital status, if she has children or if she is pregnant?

- The U.S. government may suspend contracts with a company because of the actions of its subcontractors, vendors, employment or referral sources?

- The U.S. Department of Labor may suspend or delay all contracts pending for a company because of a non-compliance posture found at any branch?

DISCRIMINATION IS SERIOUS

- The odds against a company winning a discrimination complaint in court actions are about 20 to 1, and then only on technical grounds?

All of these examples are the results of two Executive Orders and the 1972 Employment Act. Legal machinery has been set in motion to eliminate discrimination in the U.S. work force—against women, and against racial and other minorities. From the point of view of both the employer and the employee, these actions are among the most significant taken in the past 30 years—and they will continue to have an expanding effect in the future.

INCREASING EMPHASIS

Unfortunately, most of us do not even have a basic familiarity with this activity. The purpose of this article is not to make experts of you, but simply to make you aware of this important area and to encourage you to learn more about it.

Equal rights legislation has two major channels—(A) the Equal Employment Opportunity Act of 1972 and (B) Executive Orders 11246 (1965) and 11375 (1968). The A channel is initiated by an employee complaint. The B channel applies to most companies that have contracts with the U.S. Government. Their intent is to assure that companies are not practicing discrimination.

A company can be found guilty of underutilization of minorities and females in the work force when it has:

SOME RULES

- a lower percentage in its work force than the population percentages

- the majority of its minority and female work force in lower-level jobs

- the majority of its minority and female work force in dead-ended jobs

The significance of this area was confirmed in 1973 when AT&T signed a consent decree with the EEOC for $38 million in back wages and future promotions for minorities and females.

AFFIRMATIVE ACTION PLAN

Today an Affirmative Action Plan (AAP) must be prepared by those companies that were initially in non-compliance. This document must indicate how the company plans to achieve and maintain the goal of removing discrimination in its employment practices. As a manager you should be aware of your company's AAP, and help implement it through your hiring and management practices.

Remember, companies do not discriminate, individuals do. Your company can have the best set of Affirmative Action Goals and Plans around, but the EEOC could still find you or one of your subordinates in violation of the Act. So think

BE SENSITIVE

Affirmative Action: be sensitive to discrimination; and learn more about the subject from your EEO representative.

I would like to thank Richard Keels of Mattapan, MA for his invaluable help and counsel during the preparation of this article.

THE MOST SIGNIFICANT EQUAL RIGHTS LEGISLATION

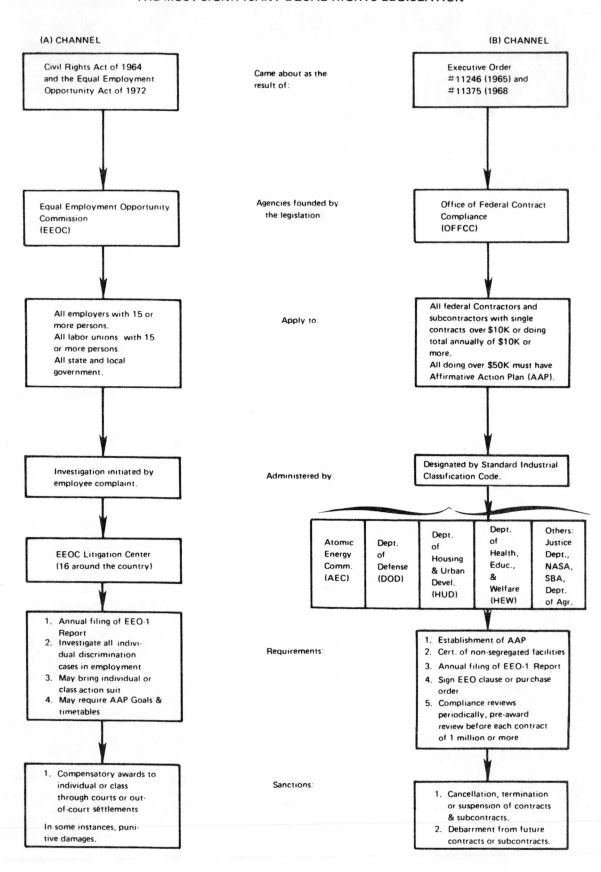

(A) CHANNEL

(B) CHANNEL

| Civil Rights Act of 1964 and the Equal Employment Opportunity Act of 1972 | Came about as the result of: | Executive Order #11246 (1965) and #11375 (1968 |

Equal Employment Opportunity Commission (EEOC)

Agencies founded by the legislation:

Office of Federal Contract Compliance (OFFCC)

All employers with 15 or more persons. All labor unions with 15 or more persons. All state and local government.

Apply to:

All federal Contractors and subcontractors with single contracts over $10K or doing total annually of $10K or more. All doing over $50K must have Affirmative Action Plan (AAP).

Investigation initiated by employee complaint.

Administered by:

Designated by Standard Industrial Classification Code.

Atomic Energy Comm. (AEC)	Dept. of Defense (DOD)	Dept. of Housing & Urban Devel. (HUD)	Dept. of Health, Educ., & Welfare (HEW)	Others: Justice Dept., NASA, SBA, Dept. of Agr.

EEOC Litigation Center (16 around the country)

1. Annual filing of EEO-1 Report
2. Investigate all individual discrimination cases in employment
3. May bring individual or class action suit
4. May require AAP Goals & timetables

Requirements:

1. Establishment of AAP
2. Cert. of non-segregated facilities
3. Annual filing of EEO-1 Report
4. Sign EEO clause or purchase order
5. Compliance reviews periodically, pre-award review before each contract of 1 million or more

1. Compensatory awards to individual or class through courts or out-of-court settlements

In some instances, punitive damages.

Sanctions:

1. Cancellation, termination or suspension of contracts & subcontracts.
2. Debarrment from future contracts or subcontracts.

A realistic decision-making game

Dr. T. F. Gautschi, P.E.

There are three strategies for resolving conflict: domination, compromise, and integration.

In the case of *domination*, one person forces his decision on the others—directly or indirectly—by "selling" his decision to the others.

Compromise is where each person involved in the situation gives a little and gets a little to arrive at a decision. No one loses, but on the other hand, no one "wins".

Ideally, *integration* will produce a solution that meets the constraints and objectives of each person involved in the situation. The integration process requires the achievement of mutual understanding of the facts, constraints and objectives; and then working out a solution that meets these factors. This process requires interaction skills such as: cooperation, objectivity and team work.

Realistic "management games" are often useful for improving interaction skills in decision making situations. The following is a description of such a game. To use it just get six people together and assign them the designated roles of Walt, George, Bill, Charlie, John and Hank. To get the most out of the game, allow at least an hour for the decision process and perhaps another half hour for discussing the process that took place.

The Research Fund Allocation Game

Everyone should be given copies of the General Description, the Fact Sheet and the Summary. The Special Instructions should be given *only* to the person designated—George, Bill, etc. There are no special instructions for Walt. Each participant should be encouraged to add any appropriate "facts" or other information in keeping with their special instructions and the role that they are playing.

FACT SHEET

GEORGE: *Cold Vaccine Project*

Original Budget, 12 months and $100K. No significant results to date. If this could be developed, it could become a major product line for the corporation and provide a large amount of sales and profit. In 10th month.

BILL: *Blood Disease Project*

This has been a continuing project for the past three years at an annual expenditure of $100K. This project has yielded information useful to several of the company's programs but has no particular end product in view. In 34th month.

CHARLIE: *Fuel Cell Research Project*

Original Budget $150K for a one-year literature research and the development of a research model of an organic fuel cell. This project deviates from the corporate image, but management feels that this is a field in which SA will eventually be involved. In 10th month.

HANK: *Pancreas Treatment Project*

It is well known that diabetes could be cured by rejuvenating or replacing the pancreas gland. Several of your customers are working in this field and SA feels that its research will enable SA to better serve its customers and perhaps even come up with a solution or technique for solving this problem. Budget $120K per year for three years. In 34th month.

JOHN: *Sugar Substitute Project*

Developing a sugar substitute that looks, tastes, and reacts like sugar, but has no calories and no adverse side effects. When perfected, this product would have a large market and replace the sugar substitute now available. This again deviates from the corporate image, but should be a real money maker. Original Budget $80K per year and it was scheduled for 24 months. In 22nd month.

S U M M A R Y

NAME	PROJECT	ORIGINAL 12-MONTH BUDGET	TO DATE	FUNDS REQ'D TO YEAR END
GEORGE	Cold Vaccine	$100K	$100K	$ 30K
BILL	Blood Disease	100K	75K	25K
CHARLIE	Fuel Cell	150K	110K	60K
JOHN	Sugar Substitute	80K	60K	40K
HANK	Pancreas Treatment	120K	75K	25K
		$550K	$420K	$180K

New Research Budget is $520K for this year

General Description

You are employees of Scientific Associates, Inc. Walt Marshall is the Director of Research and the others are project leaders. Each of you is vitally interested in your project and want to see it continued to what you feel is a logical conclusion. It has been Walt Marshall's practice to periodically review the progress on the various projects and to get all of the project leaders together every three months for a hard look at each project and to re-apportion funds as necessary.

Walt Marshall, this meeting is your third such meeting this year and to make matters difficult, top management must reduce your research budget to $520K for this year. Business has been a little slow and your sales and profit are below target so you feel fortunate to get this amount. Your original budget was $550K and you have expended $420K against it. So you now have $100K to cover your last three months of activity.

Your problem, Walt Marshall, is to determine what shall be done in the face of the reported progress and your funding situation.

SPECIAL INSTRUCTIONS

For GEORGE:

You have been trying to develop a cold vaccine. You submitted your original budget for 12 months, $100K, because you felt that the Research Director would be willing to fund that amount, and you were confident that you could show enough results to get more financing when needed. Things have not gone too well to date, but you feel sure that given a little more money and time—you will be successful. You need $30K for the next three months.

For BILL:

You have been investigating various blood diseases. You have not exceeded your funding for the past three years and your work has added to the company's profits. You have a good team and do not want it disrupted by a reduction in funding. Your project is not glamorous, but it is a consistent producer of useful information and techniques. You need $25K to complete the year.

For CHARLIE:

Your project has now been running for nine months and you feel that it is providing much useful information, and the demonstration model is nearly complete. You need $60K for the next three months to allow you to get some very important laboratory testing started. You feel sure that it will lead to several very profitable energy source products if you can just beat the competition to the market.

For HANK:

Your project is in its third year and has proved very valuable in helping SA provide service to its customers. You are under budget, and expect to spend only $100K this year. You feel that in a year or so SA could be leading the field in this area of research, and if this work were to be stopped at SA, you would go where you could continue this work. You would like authorization for an additional three years at $100K per year. You need $25K to complete this year.

For JOHN:

Your project is in the 22nd month and on budget, and success appears imminent. However, to properly continue your project you need about $20,000 worth of additional laboratory equipment. You are on your budget, so you need $40K to complete the year.

'Lost on the moon'

A number of our readers have inquired about the hypothetical case involving a spaceship crash landing on the moon that was mentioned in our 7-21-75 edition of Management Forum. It is interesting, and can be used to demonstrate the superiority of "consensus thinking".

Problem: You are a member of a space team on a trip to the moon. You and your team have just crash landed on the moon's surface. Your spacecraft was ruined and everything on board was destroyed except the 15 items below. You are scheduled to rendezvous with the mother ship, which is 200 miles away on the lighted surface of the moon.

Your survival depends upon reaching the mother ship. Rank the 15 items in order of importance to your successful and safe trip to the rendezvous location. Place number one (1) beside the item you consider most important, and so on through number 15, the least important item.

Process: Assemble a team of four or five people, and give each of them a copy of the list of 15 items. Ask each one to complete the priority ranking individually. Then, using the suggestions listed in the recap on Consensus Thinking, determine group priority rankings, and list them in the table below (or a facsimile) in the places indicated.

Item	Your Ranking	Group Ranking	
a. Box of matches			
b. Food concentrate			
c. Fifty ft of nylon rope			
d. Parachute silk			
e. Solar-powered portable heater			
f. Two .45 caliber pistols			
g. One case, dehydrated milk			
h. Two 100-lb tanks of oxygen			
i. Stellar map (of Moon's Constellation)			
j. Self-inflating life raft			
k. Magnetic compass			
l. Five gal of water			
m. Signal flares			
n. First-aid kit with injection needles			
o. Solar-powered FM receiver/transmitter			

Item	Correct Answer	Reasoning	Your ranking	Error points	Group ranking	Error points
a. Box of matches	13	No oxygen on moon to sustain flame; virtually worthless				
b. Food concentrate	4	Efficient means of supplying energy requirements				
c. Fifty ft of nylon rope	6	Useful in scaling cliffs, tying injured together				
d. Parachute silk	8	Protection from sun's rays				
e. Solar-powered portable heater	15	Cannot use without sunlight and not required when sun is shining				
f. Two .45 caliber pistols	11	Possible means of self-propulsion				
g. One case, dehydrated milk	12	Bulkier duplication of food concentrate				
h. Two 100-lb tanks of oxygen	1	Most pressing survival need				
i. Stellar map (of moon's constellation)	3	Primary means of navigation				
j. Self-inflating life raft	9	CO_2 bottle in military raft may be used for propulsion				
k. Magnetic compass	14	Magnetic field not polarized				
l. Five gal of water	2	Replacement for tremendous liquid loss on lighted side				
m. Signal flares	10	Distress signal when Mother Ship is sighted				
n. First-aid kit with injection needles	7	Fits aperture in space suit				
o. Solar-powered FM receiver/transmitter	5	Requires line-of-sight transmission and short ranges				

Items 13, 14 and 15 are all virtually worthless so priority is inverse order to their weight.

'Lost on the moon': the solution

In our last issue (12-8-75) we presented the "Lost On The Moon" problem. If for some reason you missed it, you might like to go back to it now before reading the answers, which are listed opposite.

Determine your error points and the group error points by taking the absolute difference between the correct answers and your answers (i.e. disregard $\oplus$ and $\ominus$ signs) and then total each column. Enter the results in the table below.

SCORING TABLE

Group	A Average Group Answer	B Best Individual Answer	C Consensus Decision By Group	Improvement Factor (A-C+(B-C)
1				
2				
3				
4				
etc.				

A = total of individual error points divided by number in group.

B = the lowest individual error total in each group.

C = error total using group answers.

Improvement Factor: the larger the number, the greater the improvement is of the group decisions over those of the individuals.

I have run this problem many times; the improvement factor is almost always positive in the range of 5 to 30.

Example:

Group	A	B	C	(A-C + B-C)
1	35	21	18	20
2	30	18	16	16
3	35	15	19	12

Management science turns to data processing

Dr. T. F. Gautschi, P.E.

User programs for decision-making

Initially, industry put primary emphasis on applying the computer to the business environment—basically to process business and accounting data and information. With the continuing reduction in processing time and costs, applications of computers have been expanding into such additional areas as engineering and development, scheduling, and manufacturing processes. It is therefore becoming more important than ever for the engineering manager to have a basic understanding of computers and what they can accomplish.

A computer data processing system can be viewed as a combination of hardware and software that accomplishes the four basic functions of input, processing, data storage and output, under the direction of user programs. These user programs are sets of instructions for performing specific data processing tasks. They are usually provided in a generalized form by the computer manufacturer, and are sometimes customized by the user to perform his tasks more efficiently.

A user may have access to a time-share system, he may have a small computer or he may have a large computer complex with extensive communication facilities to accomplish his data processing. In each situation he interfaces with the computational facility through his user programs.

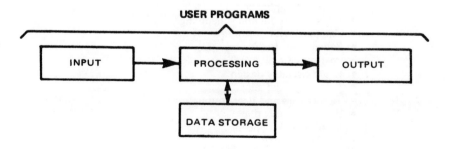

The purpose of this article is to acquaint you with two areas of user programs of particular importance to the engineering manager—management science and manufacturing programs. This will be accomplished by simply listing some of the programs that are available. The list is impressive and is continually being expanded by both computer manufacturers and users.

MANAGEMENT SCIENCE

Generally the term Management Science includes programs for: statistical analysis, mathematical calculations, simulation analysis, linear programming, network analysis and numerical control.

STATISTICAL ANALYSIS PROGRAMS

- Distribution functions
- Significance tests
- Analysis of variance
- Multiple linear regression
- Time—series forecasting
- Index numbers
- Statistical inference

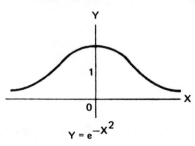

$Y = e^{-x^2}$

MATHEMATICAL PROGRAMS

Libraries are extensive and include:
- Numerical solution of differential equations
- Numerical integration
- Curve fitting
- Zeroes of polynomials
- Interpolation
- Solutions of systems of non-linear equations
- Solutions of systems of linear equations
- Matrix operations
- Random number generators
- Various functions such as Beta, Gamma, Bessel
- Fourier analysis

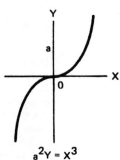

Cubical parabola

$a^2 Y = x^3$

There are also a wide variety of math programs in the engineering field including: structural design and analysis, many aspects of automation and computer-aided manufacturing and various engineering calculations. For example, programs are available for performing the following engineering analytical functions:
- Static response to concentrated and distributed loads
- Dynamic response to transient, steady-state, and harmonic loads, and random excitation
- Heat transfer calculations

SIMULATION ANALYSIS

Simulation programs solve problems by following the changes over time of a dynamic model of a system expressed in block diagram form. These programs have a wide area of application, including:
- Job shop production scheduling
- Computer system studies
- Power plant fueling logistics
- Post office mail handling
- Logic circuitry design
- Airport ground support
- Tanker cars and fleet routing
- Warehouse locating
- Lumber mill modeling
- Pipeline loading
- Materials inventory modeling
- Bank paper work flow

LINEAR PROGRAMMING

Linear programming is used for:

- Capital budgeting
- Resource allocation
- Facilities location

Unfortunately, although each of us as managers could improve our performance through the use of computer management science programs, few of us have done so to date. Whatever the reason, the total impact of management science has been rather small.

Bridges must be built that will close the gap between the cultures of the management scientist and the practicing manager, and that will encourage the manager to complement his intuitive decision-making with management science concepts and analysis.

The above should give you an appreciation for the breadth of what's available in the management science program field. Hopefully, you as managers and practicing engineers will be motivated to look into this area more deeply.

A listing of manufacturing programs

There are a number of application programs designed for use by manufacturing industries. As the automated factory becomes more of a reality these programs will be more closely integrated to provide effective control over the entire manufacturing process.

To indicate the extent of such programs they will be listed in seven major categories: marketing management, engineering data management, inventory management, production management and control, procurement management, financial management systems and manufacturing management sciences.

Marketing management:
- Order entry
- Customer service
- Order billing
- Market analysis

Engineering data management:
- Standards maintenance and summary reporting
- Engineering drawing control
- Engineering project control (see 'Network analysis' later in this article)
- Engineering design simulation
- Bill of material management

Inventory management:
- Product identification data creation and maintenance
- Inventory control
- Demand forecasting
- Order/demand data
- Material control
- Material requirements planning

Production management and control:
- Data maintenance
- Capacity requirements planning
- Order release planning
- Operation sequencing
- Completion time estimates
- Production reporting
- Numerical control (see discussion on NC later in this article)

Procurement management:
- Vendor data control
- Buyer activity reporting
- Purchase order processing
- Receiving and receiving inspection processing
- Quality assurance—purchased material
- Plant services and supplies administration

Financial management:
- Accounts receivable
- General ledger
- Payroll
- Cost of sales/productions
- Standard cost generation and analysis

Manufacturing management science programs:

Network analysis programs are used to assist in solving management problems in project control.

They include:
- PERT
- Time and cost
- CPM
- Resource allocation

Typical uses are:
- Long-range planning
- New product introduction
- Drug (chemical) testing
- Construction/installation of plants
- Conversion/maintenance of plants
- Development of computer systems
- Work studies
- Road and/or pipe-line construction

Numerical control (NC) involves the control of machine tools and equipment by numerical input. NC programs transform mathematical and geometric descriptions as expressed in APT language into a medium acceptable for operating the machine tool. The program output describes all the motions and actions necessary to produce a given part. These include such factors as feeds, speeds, distance, coolant, etc.

NC is commonly used in manufacturing to remove metal in such industries as automotive, aerospace, consumer goods, ship building, electrical equipment and computers. It is also used for pattern cutting in textile and furniture industries.

NC eliminates the requirement for hard tooling and also makes the fabrication of complex shapes possible directly from mathematical formulations. An example is the fabrication of torpedo or boat propellers.

My intent with this and the previous article has been to give you some idea of the breadth of what's available in the management science and manufacturing fields. Hopefully they will motivate you to learn more about computers and their application to your job.

A roadmap of the computer industry

Looking ahead to the next decade

Dr. T. F. Gautschi, P.E.

As managers we should have a perspective of where the computer has been and where it is going.

Although it is one of the major driving forces in our dynamic environment, it is really a very young industry. In 1955 there were less than 300 U.S. computers installed on a world-wide basis. Today over a quarter million units are installed, and by 1980 over one million units are projected to be installed!

FIRST GENERATION

I recently came across an interesting chart called "Generations of Progress", prepared by International Data Corp. It's not precise, but it does provide a useful management overview. Across the top, the history of the computer industry is broken into time periods, or generations, of roughly five years each. In general, the "named" machines—large, slow, clunky monsters—ushered in the age of the computer. Each had a personality; few were built.

SECOND GENERATION

These scientific wonders—with names like Eniac and Alwac and Univac—were replaced by the business-oriented second generation computers that brought data processing to many businesses. Then families of machines followed. Looking to the future, it appears the concept of network computers—and networks of computers—will introduce even further changes.

In the past 20 years electron or vacuum tubes were replaced by transistors and then by integrated circuits. The drive to make circuits smaller and faster is continuing.

NEW MEMORY

In main memory, delay lines quickly gave way to rotating drums. In the late 1950's the magnetic core was introduced to hold the computer's information, and this was the norm (in improved versions) until the last few years, when semiconductor memories of various types were introduced.

Auxiliary memory—used to hold information that is needed only on an occasional basis—has progressed from decks of punched cards to tapes, to large disc stacks to mechanized tape libraries. On the horizon are very large auxiliary storage devices such as the Bell Lab invention called the "bubble memory".

NEW DATA ENTRY

Data entry has gone from the card punch (which will remain the most popular input method for another few years) to various key-capture units to the concept of direct data entry.

Output has progressed from the "flashing light" era of the early computer to faster and faster printers. In the future, management by exception techniques will be applied to the computer. Reams of printout will be replaced by meaningful documents or displays only. Necessary data may be "dumped" directly onto microfilm for look-up when needed. And, paralleling the development of exception reporting will be action output—such as direct control of machines or automatic transfer of funds.

NEW ARCHITECTURE

The architecture of computer systems—the way their elements are put together—will continue to move away from the classical combination of a processor, a memory, some control circuits, and an input/output unit. Instead, a network oriented around a large memory using many processors will be configured by the operating system—the instructions that tell the computer how to work with the various elements that make it up.

Throughout all of this movement, the emphasis will be on transparency—the provision to the user of a system he can't see—a system that provides answers.

"GENERATIONS" OF PROGRESS*
A MANAGEMENT OVERVIEW

GENERATION	EARLY	SECOND	THIRD	TODAY	FUTURE
DATES	1951-1958	1959-1964	1965-1970	1971-1976	1977 - - - -
PRODUCTS	"Named" Machines	Business Oriented	Families - Networks - - - - -		
ELECTRONICS	Vacuum Tube	Transistor	Hybrid Circuits/Integrated Circuits/Large Scale Integration		
MAIN MEMORY	Delay Line/Drum	Magnetic Core	Core/Plated Wire	Semiconductor	
AUXILIARY MEMORY	Punched Cards/Tape	Drum/Tape/Disc	Improved Disc/Tape	Advanced Disc/Tape Library/Bubble Memory	
DATA ENTRY	Paper Tape and Punched Cards		Punched Card/Key-to-Tape/Shared Processor/Direct Data Entry		
OUTPUT	"Flashing Lights"/Slow Printers/Line Printers/Tape/Display/Disc/High-Speed Printer/Documents/Action				
ARCHITECTURE	Logic + Memory + Control + Input/Output		+ Larger Auxiliary Memory + Teleprocessing + Multi-Processors		
PROGRAMMING	Brute Force/Assembly Language/Compilers/Operating Systems/Emulation/Data Base-Network Processing		Software Packages	On-Line Guidance Transparency	
USES	Computation	Financial DP	Information Processing	On-Line IP	Answer-Orientation
ACQUISITION	Purchase -				
	Rent -				
			Third-Party Lease (Short- or Long-Term - - - - - - - - - - - - - - - - - - -		
ALTERNATIVES	"Borrow"	Service Bureau	Time Sharing/Remote Service/Minicomputer/Turnkey System		

*Taken from EDP Industry Report and Market Review, International Data Corp., Waltham, Mass.

Appendix I: Ethics survey questionnaire

Dr. T.F. Gautschi, P.E.

SURVEY - Problems of ethics in engineering management. Design Management Forum will be a regular feature of *Design News.* To test yourself and give us information on the opinions of the design engineer, please read each case history carefully and mark the alternative that best describes what you would do. Then mark the alternative that best describes what you think others would do in the same situation.

Case 1

Imagine that you are the president of a company in a highly competitive industry. You learn that a competitor has made an important scientific discovery that is not patentable and which will give him an advantage that will substantially reduce the profits of your company for about a year. There is some hope of hiring one of the competitor's employees who knows the details of the discovery.

—— Alternatives	You	Others
a) Probably would try to hire him.	☐	☐
b) Probably would not try to hire him.	☐	☐

Reason————————————————————

Case 2

Should corporation executives act solely in the interest of the stockholders without regard to the interest of employees and consumers?

—— Alternatives	You	Others
a) Yes, because maximizing profit is management's responsibility.	☐	☐
b) No, some consideration should be given to the employees and customers.	☐	☐
c) As much as possible without creating employee or customer problems.	☐	☐

Reason————————————————————

Case 3

An engineering manager earning $20,000 a year has been padding his expense account about $1,000 a year.

—— Alternatives	You	Others
a) Acceptable if other executives in the company do the same thing.	☐	☐
b) Acceptable if the executive's superior knows about it and says nothing.	☐	☐
c) Unacceptable regardless of circumstances.	☐	☐

Reason————————————————————

Case 4

Sam works for you. He is technically capable and a good worker, but he does not get along well with the others in your group. So when Sam has an opportunity for a transfer, you encourage him to take it. What would you say to Sam's potential supervisor when he inquires about Sam?

—— Alternatives	You	Others
a) Stress Sam's strong points and avoid his personality problem.	☐	☐
b) Stress Sam's strong and weak points.	☐	☐
c) Try to be neutral.	☐	☐

Reason————————————————————

Case 5

When it becomes necessary to reduce the work force,

—— Alternatives	You	Others
a) Separate older, less efficient employees.	☐	☐
b) Separate the younger, lower-paid employees.	☐	☐
c) Separate solely on seniority.	☐	☐

Reason————————————————————

Mark the alternatives and mail survey page to:

Dr. T. F. Gautschi
Design News
221 Columbus Ave.
Boston, MA 02116

Case 6

You are an engineer, but you are not directly associated with the DOT project. The other day you overheard a conversation in the cafeteria between the program manager and the project engineer that makes you reasonably sure that a large contract will soon be given to the ABC Company to develop and manufacture a key DOT subsystem. ABC is a smaller firm and its stock is traded over the counter. You feel sure that the stock will rise from its present $2.25 per share as soon as the DOT contract is let.

—— Alternatives	You	Others
a) Do nothing.	☐	☐
b) Buy stock.	☐	☐
c) Tell friends.	☐	☐
d) Tell broker.	☐	☐

Reason _____

Case 7

You are the project engineer working on the development of a small liquid rocket engine. You know that if you could achieve a throttling ratio greater than eight to one, your system would be considered a success and continue to receive funding support. To date, the best you have achieved is a four to one ratio. You have an unproved idea that you feel has a 50% chance of being successful. Your project is currently being reviewed to determine if it should be continued. You would like to continue it. How optimistically should the results and the new ideas be presented?

—— Alternatives	You	Others
a) Realistically, even if funding is cut off.	☐	☐
b) Optimistic enough to assure obtaining funding.	☐	☐

Reason _____

Case 8

What should one do about employees with long good records, whose work becomes inefficient?

——Alternatives	You	Others
a) Carry until retirement.	☐	☐
b) Lay off.	☐	☐
c) Reduce salary.	☐	☐

Reason _____

Appendix II: Attitude and value survey questionnaire

Dr. T. F. Gautschi, P. E.

A corporation with a good public image can sell even an inferior product; managers usually deal with people in a democratic manner; the man who gets ahead in industry has someone sponsoring him

Do you agree with these statements? Our survey aims to find answers to questions like these

Even though I interact with engineers and engineering managers every day, and teach courses in engineering management, I have always had trouble understanding management values and attitudes. The fact is, we know a great deal about the knowledge a manager has, and the skills he uses to apply that knowledge, but we're dismally ignorant of the attitudes and values that define how and when and for what ends the manager intends to use his knowledge and skills. Yet this is vitally important to his success.

If you study the literature you will soon realize very little has been done in this area, and the survey that follows is an attempt to shed some light on questions that have remained unanswered too long. We'll have a survey report on your responses within two months, aided by analysis from a student assistant from the Sloan School of Management at MIT. Survey questions have been adapted from "Attitude Change During Management Education" by E.H. Schein, *Administrative Science Quarterly*, Vol. II, 1967.

Instructions for Attitude and Value Survey

Please check the appropriate column for your response to each question—whether you **strongly disagree, disagree, agree,** or **strongly agree** with the statement. Then answer each question in the **Dimension** column (please be assured this information will remain *strictly* confidential). Then cut off the page at the line and mail it to me, **Ted Gautschi, 221 Columbus Ave., Boston, MA 02116.**

I recommend that you keep a record of your answers. Mark the questions with the numbers one through four to code the four options.

QUESTIONS	STRONGLY DISAGREE	DISAGREE	AGREE	STRONGLY AGREE	DIMENSIONS
1. Management will usually do what is best for its employees without outside influence from unions. Comment:					1. Indicate type of industry: Fabricated metal products Machinery except electrical Electrical equipment and supplies Transportation equipment Instruments & related products Ordnance and accessories Business & engineering services Federal government
2. A man who is willing to work hard in industry does not need a union to protect him. Comment:					
3. Government competition with private enterprise is unfair and should be eliminated. Comment:					
4. Corporations have a definite obligation to be actively involved in community affairs. Comment:					
5. A corporation with a good public image can sell even an inferior product. Comment:					
6. Managers are not always sincere in their dealings with other people. Comment:					
7. Most corporations do not have clear objectives that can serve as guides to decisions. Comment:					2. Years experience: Under 5 6-10 11-15 16-20 over 20
8. Most managerial jobs require a person to compromise his ethics or morals to some degree. Comment:					

DIMENSIONS	STRONGLY DISAGREE	DISAGREE	AGREE	STRONGLY AGREE	QUESTIONS
3. For how many companies have you worked including present job? 1 2-3 4-5 Over 5					9. A clear-cut hierarchy of authority and responsibility is the cornerstone of the business organization. **Comment:**
4. How many people do you supervise? None 1-3 4-7 8-12 13-20 Over 20					10. Most industrial *management* problems can be attributed to a few basic causes. **Comment:** 11. There are many sound principles of business that should not be changed even if economic and technological conditions change. **Comment:** 12. The engineer in industry should give his primary allegiance to the company he works for, not the engineering profession as such. **Comment:**
5. Annual salary range: 10,000-15,000 15,001-20,000 20,001-24,000 24,001-28,000 Over 28,000					13. The average employee in industry prefers to avoid responsibility, has little ambition, and wants security above all. **Comment:** 14. Group incentive plans are superior to piece work systems in stimulating high productivity. **Comment:**
6. Academic achievement: high school 1-3 years college Bachelor's Master's Professional Engineer or PHD					15. Individual decisions cannot be as consistantly desirable as group decisions. **Comment:** 16. In business decisions, the human factor is usually more important than the economic factor. **Comment:** 17. The private life of an employee should be a direct concern to his company. **Comment:**
7. Are you or have you had any marketing or sales responsibility? Yes No					18. The man who gets ahead in industry is the man who has someone sponsoring him. **Comment:**
8. Do any hourly wage employees work under you or with you? Yes No					19. Most large corporations are placing more stress on the "corporation loyalty" of the employee than on his individual growth. **Comment:** 20. The successful engineering design manager is a *facilitator* vs. an *initiator* of design ideas. **Comment:** 21. Managers usually deal with people in a democratic manner. **Comment:**
9. Size of company you work for: Less than 100 employees 101-500 employees 501-1000 employees 1001-5000 employees Over 5000 employees					22. Large corporations create more opportunities than small companies for the *engineer* to maximize his career. **Comment:** 23. The best career plan for an engineer is to change jobs two or three times in his first 5 years. **Comment:** 24. In product design engineering excellence is often compromised to marketing expediency. **Comment:**
10. Are you a member of any minority race group? Yes No					25. The major stimulus to new design efforts is remaining competitive rather than entering new markets. **Comment:**
11. Religion: Catholic Jewish Protestant Other None					26. Management will usually do what is best for its employees without outside influence from government. **Comment:**

Dr. T.F. Gautschi, P.E.

Career Path Survey

One of the most crucial decisions we make in life is the choice of our jobs and our career. Few of our activities occupy as much time, or require a greater investment of energy and motivation than does our work activity. This survey attempts to probe the intriguing area of engineering career paths, and the dynamic relationship of person to job in the changing technological environment. As with previous surveys in this series, we will tabulate and interpret your responses and report the results as soon as possible in a future issue of Management Forum.

Please be assured that all questionnaires will remain strictly confidential. Check or fill out the answers and mail the completed questionnaire to me, Dr. T. F. Gautschi, *Design News*, 221 Columbus Ave., Boston, MA 02116.

1. Please indicate the year that you received your *educational degree(s)* and enter the numerical code that corresponds to your field of specialization in the spaces below.

High school   ___ ___
Associate Degree   ___ ___
Bachelor's Degree   ___ ___
Professional Registration (P.E.) ___ ___
Master's Degree   ___ ___
Professional Certificate   ___ ___
Ph.D.   ___ ___

1. Aeronautical Engineering
2. Biomedical Engineering
3. Chemical Engineering
4. Civil Engineering
5. Electrical Engineering
6. Environmental Engineering
7. Industrial Engineering
8. Mechanical Engineering
9. Management or Business
10. Psychology, Sociology, Personnel Relations
11. Arts and Humanities
12. Other (specify) _____
13. Other (specify) _____
14. Other (specify) _____

The following items ask questions about the jobs you've held during your career. A job is defined as a change in employers or a move to a different division in the same company. Starting with your present job, indicate your response to each question, for each job, by an X in columns 1-5 at the right. Your responses to questions pertaining to your present job should be in column one, your next previous job in column two, and continue as such through your first job. If you have had more than five jobs in your professional career, check the box below and give responses for the *last* five jobs you've held.

☐ I have had more than five jobs in my career.

2. A. For each of your jobs, indicate whether your major job function was engineering or management

	Present Job	1st Previous Job	2nd Previous Job	3rd Previous Job	4th Previous Job
	1	2	3	4	5
1. Engineering					
2. Management					

2. B. 1. For those jobs that you checked the major job function as being *engineering*, indicate the field of specialization for *each* job.

1. Aeronautical Engineering					
2. Biomedical Engineering					
3. Chemical Engineering					
4. Civil Engineering					
5. Electrical Engineering					
6. Environmental Engineering					
7. Industrial Engineering					
8. Mechanical Engineering					
9. Other (specify)					
10. Other (specify)					
11. Other (specify)					

2 B.2. For those jobs in which *engineering* was your major function, indicate (with an X) the type of engineering work you did.

1. Research					
2. Development					
3. Product Design					
4. Production Engineering					
5. Sales					
6. Field Engineering					
7. Purchasing					
8. Quality Assurance					
9. Testing					
10. Technical Documentation					
11. Other (specify)					
12. Other (specify)					

2. C. 1. For those jobs in which *management* was your major function indicate (with an X) the area of management practice you were involved in.

1. Technical Management					
2. Personnel Administration					
3. Financial Management					
4. Production Management					
5. Marketing					
6. Sales					
7. Other (specify)					
8. Other (specify)					

2. C. 2. For those jobs in which *management* was your major function write the number of people supervised in each of these *management* positions in the boxes at right which correspond to that job.

3. Check the reason for leaving each job (other than, of course, your present job.) Omit this question if you have held only one job.

1. Left to assume another position within the same company					
2. Left to assume a position with a different company					
3. Was laid off					
4. Was fired					
5. Other (specify)					

4. Defining a promotion to be an increase in responsibility or status, indicate with an X how many promotions you received in each job.

1. No Promotions					
2. One Promotion					
3. Two Promotions					
4. Three or more promotions					

5. For each job, indicate the degree to which your salary changed between jobs by checking the appropriate box. (Omit if you have held only one job.)

1. Salary increased by more than 15% _____
2. Salary increased by 5-15% _____
3. Salary remained essentially the same _____
4. Salary decreased _____

6. Indicate the type of industry in which you were employed in each of the above jobs. If you were also self-employed in that job, check the box in row 6, corresponding to that job.

1. Education (universities, technical schools, etc.) _____
2. Utilities (non-profit) _____
3. City, state, or federal government _____
4. Private sector (business, industry, profit-making utilities) _____
5. Private consulting engineering firms _____
6. Self-employed _____

7. What is/was the size of the organizations you've worked for? (Place X's in the appropriate spaces.)

1. Less than 100 employees _____
2. 100-499 employees _____
3. 500-999 employees _____
4. 1000-4999 employees _____
5. more than 5000 employees _____

8. How many years did you stay on each job? (Write the number of years in the boxes at right.

9. A. By inserting a 4, 3, 2 or 1 in each job column on the right, indicate your level of satisfaction, on each job, with each factor below.

> Very Satisfied   4   3   2   1   Very Dissatisfied

9 B. Then in each column on the right, circle the three most important factors that caused you to change from one job to another (for each job except the present).

9 C. Then in the column indicated on the left, insert a number for the 1st through the 5th most important job factor for you.

___ 1. Opportunity for promotion _____
___ 2. Job security _____
___ 3. Company prestige _____
___ 4. The people you work with _____
___ 5. Physical working conditions _____
___ 6. Opportunity to do challenging work _____
___ 7. Job prestige _____
___ 8. Opportunity for professional development _____
___ 9. Earnings _____
___10. Opportunity to do creative, innovative work _____
___11. Opportunity to spend time with your family _____
___12. Recognition for your contributions to the organization _____
___13. Opportunity to exercise leadership _____
___14. Amount of stress and strain _____
___15. Personal enjoyment you receive from your work _____
___16. Chance to work on socially relevant projects _____
___17. Fringe benefits _____
___18. Opportunity for retirement _____
___19. The amount of information available on career paths and promotional opportunies _____

	Definitely Unimportant	Somewhat Unimportant	Somewhat Important	Definitely Important
20. Your opportunity to influence decisions at higher levels				
21. The amount of information you receive about what is going on in the company				

10. Career Ambitions. Rate the importance to you of the following career ambitions. Indicate your response by an X in the appropriate box at right.

	Definitely Unimportant	Somewhat Unimportant	Somewhat Important	Definitely Important
A. Invent something new				
B. Become president of my company				
C. Work on projects that fulfill basic human needs				
D. Make a great contribution to my profession				
E. Make a great contribution to my employer				
F. Become wealthy				
G. Start a business of my own				
H. Publish my work so that it will be widely read				
I. Teach my profession to others				
J. Become powerful and influential				

Dr. T.F. Gautschi, P.E.

Five laws for the manager

None can stand up to scientific analysis . . .
yet each has a ring of truth!

PARKINSON

In recent months I have run across five 'laws' or principles that should be of interest to the manager. Parkinson's Law, formulated by C. Northcote Parkinson, is probably the best known: *"Work expands so as to fill the time available for its completion.*

More than once I have attended meetings that started at 9:30 a.m. and stretched out until noon. The same amount, or more, could have been accomplished in a meeting that was started at 11:00 a.m. and still finished at noon! Perhaps the message here is that if we want a meeting to be short, start it just before lunch, or just before quitting time (this later ploy works especially well when the attendees are in different car pools).

The same principle applies to master schedules involving the coordination of a number of tasks being performed by different people. Everyone seems to jockey for the next to last position. No one wants to be blamed for holding up the overall program, but at the same time each participant wants to use as much time as possible to complete their task. This game is often used in a space launch countdown—there it's called playing the game of "chicken".

Another aspect of Parkinson's Law can be summarized as follows:

There need be little or no relationship between the work to be done and the size of the staff to which it may be assigned. This is especially true when the "work" is mostly paper work.

Also, in time, a staff organization tends to increase in size regardless of the size of the organization that it is serving. In general, in large organizations, this rate of increase is between 5 and 10% per year unless some specific management action is taken to reduce it.

MURPHY

We are all familiar with, and have experienced, Murphy's three laws:

- *Nothing is as easy as it looks.*
- *Everything takes longer than you think it will.*
- *If anything can go wrong, it will.*

I recently came across a fourth element in Murphy's Law that should have a special interest for the manager:

- *There is no way at all to please everybody any of the time.*

In the early part of the nineteenth century a German physiologist, Ernst H. Weber, came up with Weber's Law:

WEBER

In any given kind of perceiving, equal relative (not absolute) differences are perceptible.

This law can be applied to length, weight, brightness of light, intensity of sound, products and packages—and even for individual or group performance evaluations.

Weber's law can be expressed as $\Delta I = K I$

where K is a constant ratio, I is the stimulus and ΔI is the "just noticeable difference".

This law indicates that psychophysical experiments can be run to establish the constant (K) for different stimulae. Typical applications would be to use Weber's law to determine just how much difference there would have to be between two products to be perceived by someone in terms of one being lighter, milder, sweeter, larger, cheaper, safer, heavier, louder, softer, etc., from the other.

PETER/PAUL

Lawrence J. Peter formulated the Peter Principle: *In an hierarchy every employee tends to rise to his level of incompetence.* James Healey[1] proposed the Paul Principle:

For every employee who rises above his level of competence, there are several whose full talents are not utilized.

He supports this contention with four factors:

- People get locked into particular pyramids (organizational structures) and promotions or transfers are often difficult because of the requirement for high technical specialization.
- Supervisors tend to recognize only the immediate, and observable talents that a person has, and don't appreciate total capability.
- A person often does not commit his total capabilities to the organization because he cannot identify with its goals or objectives.
- Poor supervisory practice can submerge much of the talent that a subordinate possesses.

PARETO

In 1897 Vilfredo Pareto formulated Pareto's law: *Significant items in a given group normally constitute a small portion of the total items in the group and the majority of items in the total will, in the aggregate, be of minor significance.* Roughly this works out to be an 80-20 pattern.

For example:

- 20% of a salesperson's customers usually account for 80% of the sales.
- 80% of complaints will come from 20% of the customers.
- 20% of the items in an inventory will account for 80% of the total cost.
- 80% of a manager's problems will be associated with 20% of his subordinates.
- 20% of the people in a volunteer organization do 80% of the work.
- 80% of the contributions come from 20% of the contributors. etc.

This law can be extended to a 15-30 pattern and a 5-50 pattern as shown below:

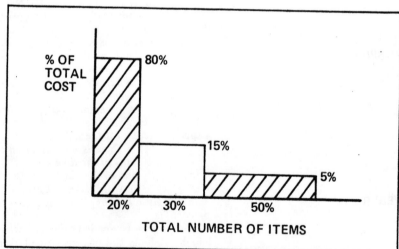

Here, 20% of the items account for 80% of the total cost.
30% of the items account for 15% of the total cost.
50% of the items account for 5% of the total cost.

We managers could make better use of our most limited resource—time—by using Pareto's law as a guide when we select priorities.

[1]Healey, James H., "Why not a Paul Principle?" *Business Horizons,* December 1973.

The Scanlon Plan — a strategy for increasing production

Dr. T. F. Gautschi, P.E.

All principles of management that encourage people to identify with their work group, that encourage people to participate as much as they can, and that continually focus on equitably rewarding all members of the organization are seen as ways of applying the Scanlon Plan philosophy.[1]

Many organizations in the U.S. do *not* operate at their peak productivity. Some feel that the basic reason for this situation is the lack of commitment on the part of the worker, which in turn results from the fact that management has created "theory X" controls and job specifications to go along with their "theory X" view of the workforce. That is, the prevailing practice seems to be one of specifying completely what the worker is to do, and then setting up controls to assure that he does it. The person in this situation is thought of basically as a programmable robot that should be programmed by management to do certain tasks in specified ways, and as long as he does the required number of tasks per day he is doing an acceptable job. No more is required, or asked, of him. This is a dehumanizing view of a person, and with a workforce that has increasingly higher expectations than workers had in the past, it can and does result in a great deal of dissatisfaction and alienation.

Clearly, if the worker wants to be involved and be effective in the work situation, this pattern of operations ignores a vast and ever increasing reservoir of worker talent that could be used to increase productivity, and at the same time increase worker satisfaction and reduce alienation.

Business, government, and academic leaders along with a more educated workforce are urging that both productivity and the quality of life be raised. The purpose of this article is to present a strategy for accomplishing this goal. This strategy, referred to as the Scanlon Plan, has proven useful over the past 30 years in small and large organizations, with and without unions. It is really a philosophy, a theory of organization and a set of management principles all rolled into one. It has two main elements, which when combined can produce ideas and procedures that can start where an organization, and its people, are, and grow with them to provide a viable framework for the future as well as for the present.

Element 1. TEAMWORK. A system must be established for coordinating the efforts of labor and management in the identification, development and implementation of improvements that will make life at work more satisfactory and more productive; and at the same time preserve management authority and responsibility.

Element 2. REWARDS. A related system must be worked out which will distribute the economic (and psychological) rewards resulting from the improved productivity among everyone in the organization. Although the Scanlon Plan is often viewed as a structure of participative committees and a particular type of performance measurement, it is basically a mixture of philosophy, theory and application that cannot be reduced to one universal formula.

Teamwork. The way most organizations are currently established there is no strong motivation toward cooperation and teamwork among the various departments. To the contrary, each department tends to optimize its response to its own problems without any particular concern for the pressures on the other departments. (This approach is termed suboptimization.) This generally applies to all of the departments in an organization including: production, engineering, procurement, accounting, inspection, maintenance and industrial engineering. What is required is some technique, or process, that focuses everyone's attention—from the floor sweeper to the president—on the same goal: increasing productivity. Then decisions will be made that are best for the total organization and interdepartmental cooperation and concern will be enhanced.

To accomplish this teamwork the typical Scanlon Plan has two main features—an open suggestion system and a committee structure for encouraging, evaluating, acting on, and communicating the actions taken on the suggestions. (Remember, the important motivating factor is that *everyone* shares in the rewards that result from the increased productivity that is made possible by the implementation of the suggestions.)

The committee structure has two levels.

At one level is the PRODUCTION Committee—one for each department, or appropriate sub-unit. It usually has the department supervisor and one or more elected employee representatives. The Production Committee meets at least monthly to discuss ways of reducing waste and identifying more efficient ways of doing the job. They discuss the monthly schedule and process the various suggestions. Some suggestions can be acted upon directly, others are forwarded to the Screening Committee for action. Minutes are kept for each meeting.

The SCREENING Committee is composed of the general manager and the heads of the major functional units, and an equal or greater number of elected, non-managerial, non-supervisory people (these members are rotated periodically). This committee meets monthly just prior to the time when the bonuses are paid. This committee seeks to operate by consensus and tries to avoid binding votes or unilateral action by management. It is responsible for acting upon all suggestions that are forwarded by the Production Committees, reviewing the financial results and determining what bonuses should be paid for the month just completed. They also identify problems and encourage everyone to make suggestions for their solution. Detailed minutes are not usually prepared, but the disposition of all suggestions is recorded.

All rejected suggestions are discussed with their originator by a member of either the Production Committee or the Screening Committee as appropriate. As the committee members become more proficient in processing suggestions, they also learn to trust each other, and as a consequence they

1. *The Scanlon Plan for Organization Development: Identity, Participation and Equity*, C.F. Frost, J.H. Wakeley, R.A. Ruh, Michigan State University Press, 1974.

A

become a valuable communication network. It should be emphasized that the committees deal exclusively with operating improvements, and are not concerned with grievances, wages, etc.

Rewards. To promote cooperation, the Scanlon Plan provides a financial reward to everyone in the organization based upon the performance of the total organization. This encourages every worker to do his or her bit to improve productivity and to view their activities from the perspective of the total organization.

The reward system must be easy to understand, the bonuses should be paid monthly and the system must fit the company situation. In its simplest form the reward (bonus) computation formula is: total labor costs ÷ total value of production. It is important that this ratio be an accurate representation of the organization's operations because it is used for determining the monthly bonus.

For example, suppose that for a particular organization: the ratio is 0.35, that is: Labor cost ÷ Monthly shipments ± inventory change = 0.35
Then if the monthly shipments are $100,000, and the inventory change is + $20,000, the "normal payroll" would be:

0.35 (100,000 + 20,000) = $42,000.
Then if actual payroll was only $40,000, the difference of $2000 would be the bonus to be divided up. Obviously, the value of "The Ratio" is very important and should be established jointly and be based upon past actual performance. Generally, the ratio should not be changed very often.

Depending upon the industry, the bonus is usually divided between the company and the workforce on something like a 25% to 75% basis. The workforce share (75) is then distributed in proportion to the gross income for each worker each month. Those firms using the Scanlon Plan pay the standard industry wage and the bonus is paid in addition—it typically runs between 5% and 20% of the payroll.

The common goal is to "beat The Ratio". Everyone in the organization knows that by improving his individual productivity he helps to beat the ratio, and that this will result in financial reward. Because of this essential feature, I believe that the plan works best in organizational units where the size is not so great that it completely overwhelms the contribution of any one individual.

Better leadership. The Scanlon Plan is *not* a substitute for good leadership, but it might make good leadership even better. It should not provide a *sense* of participation; it should provide opportunities for *real* participation. To work there must be a strong management commitment to the total philosophy and a desire to work out an equitable arrangement both on the part of the employees (often a union) and management.

Its implementation requires superior management performance, especially in areas pertaining to the adequacy and utilization of all human and material resources. It also requires aggressive participation, involvement and commitment by everyone to the organizational goal of increased productivity.

REFERENCES
1. *The Scanlon Plan for Organizational Development: Identity, Participation and Equity*, C.F. Frost, J.H. Wakeley, R.A. Ruh, Michigan State University Press, 1974.
2. The Scanlon Plan, edited by F.G. Lesieur. M.I.T. Press, 1958.
3. "The Scanlon Plan Has Proved Itself" *Harvard Business Review*, F. G. Lesieur and E.S. Puckett. September/October 1969.
4. "Enterprise For Everyman", *Fortune*, January 1950.

Dr. T.F. Gautschi, P.E.

Major R & D management responsibilities

Balancing cost, performance & schedule; evaluating R & D effectiveness

The three principle dimensions of every R & D project are performance, schedule and cost, and there is a definite relationship between these three variables for each project. Performance is generally proportional to the product of time and cost. Thus, the achievement of improved performance usually requires some combination of additional time and cost, or the reduction of cost requires a reduction in peformance, or perhaps in schedule.

CONSTANT ASSESSMENT

A major project management responsibility is the proper balancing of these three variables by means of review and assessment. To keep this balance current, management must frequently analyze its decisions relating to performance, schedule, and cost to assess their current validity in relation to project results and the total environment within which the project is being conducted. For example, in some situations, schedule and perhaps performance should be sacrificed in order to reduce the development cost to a minimum. In other situations performance may be the most important factor, and time and cost may be of secondary importance.

CUSTOMER IS NOT ALWAYS RIGHT

A pitfall that has trapped many companies attempting to engage in the field of systems development is the temptation to accept the customer's own appraisal of his technical needs and to exert an extensive effort in an attempt to design equipment to meet the furnished specifications, e.g. to achieve a specified guided missile accuracy the resultant weapon may be too heavy, too complicated and too costly. This excessive cost may pertain to the development cost as well as the production of a system.

Highly technical and complex non-technical operational considerations are all mixed together in the essentially economic appraisals that underlie the establishment of sound specifications for a development program. This problem is not confined to the initial phases. It recurs continually throughout a program.

REAPPRAISAL

Every time new information is discovered as to what can or cannot be done in the development of one of the major subsystems, a reappraisal of what changes ought to be made in the other major subsystems is required. The resulting system will thus be optimized as effectively as possible, in terms of the overall requirements and the non-technical aspects of the problem.

PLAN REALISTICALLY

Another factor that tends to complicate the performance, schedule, cost picture is that experience has shown that the estimated cost and planned time scales for development effort are often unrealistic. The error tends to be larger for systems incorporating many new ideas and major improvements in performance than for less ambitious projects.

A recent example of this is the Black Mesa and Lake Powell railroad in Arizona. It was built at a cost of $54 million to operate one train that would haul coal between silos near Black Mesa to the Navajo generating station. It was intended to operate without a locomotive engineer. Engine operations were to be controlled by an onboard computer, directed by wayside transmitters. The cars were to be loaded and dumped automatically, the road to use concrete ties, the rails to be continuously welded. Even the whistle was to be triggered automatically. In short, it was intended to bring 21st century technology to a 19th century industry.

To date there are a number of problems—two engineers and an electrician ride the train and control it manually, it cannot haul as much coal as intended, the concrete ties are chipping and cracking, the rails and locomotive wheels are wearing out at a high rate, even the automatic whistle had to be disconnected when it began triggering on beer cans between the rails.

Undoubtedly, these problems, and others yet to be identified, will be solved with the application of enough money and time and some change in performance requirements. However, the combined effect of a tight schedule and pushing limits of technology in some areas has caused a serious situation.

The perfectionist can also be a problem. The more theoretically inclined scientists and engineers are often more interested in putting out a "perfect" product instead of meeting a schedule or budget with an acceptable product. Meeting any delivery schedule involves a compromise with perfection. We should not strive to develop the best design, but strive to develop the best design within time and resources available.

MANAGEMENT DISCIPLINE ACHIEVES BALANCE

These are difficult decisions for many engineers and scientists because they are generally most concerned with developing maximum performance. Left to themselves, the engineer and scientist might never get their product into production and on to the customer, because there are always a number of ways one can find to "improve" upon the current design. Thus, a major management responsibility is to provide the discipline that determines the proper balance between performance, cost and schedule.

Every management needs to know whether it is getting what it should out of R & D for the money invested; whether the research yield is good or bad; and by what standards the judgment is to be made. There are two aspects of R & D activity that make this evaluation particularly difficult: Uncertainty of how individual projects and complete research programs will come out—ranging from the question of the cost and time required for a project or a program to be successful to the question of whether it will turn out to be successful at all; and the difficulty of determining how successful a project is after completion. Even in private industry where R & D can affect profit and loss, there seems to be no consistant criteria for such evaluation.

EVALUATING R & D

The evaluation of R & D is somewhat like trying to measure the length of an ill-defined object with a rubber ruler. It is more subjective than objective, and yet major decisions are of necessity based on such evaluations. There are three typical types of questions that the R & D manager must answer: (1) How can one judge whether or not the expenditures are not twice as large as they should be or perhaps only half as large as they should be? (2) How can one tell if others are getting more for their R & D dollar? (3) How can one tell if the program is loaded down with frills, or is too practical and near term?

These are difficult questions, yet their answers are vital to the proper execution of any R & D program. For the most part they are the same kinds of questions that should be applied to any activity dealing primarily in intangibles; for example, the personnel development program, or general management itself. While management science is not sufficiently developed to permit the same precise measures of research effectiveness that cost accounting can provide for measurement of manufacturing effectiveness, criteria like the following can be applied:

1. What percentage of earnings is derived from new products developed by research within the last five or ten years?
2. What does customer experience indicate regarding the quality standards of the various products for the applications at which they are directed?
3. What has been happening to our company's share of the market?
4. How does our ratio of patent grants compare with competition?
5. To what extent has R & D been instrumental in cost reduction programs? In increasing productivity?
6. What is the quality and extent of the advanced product planning program?
7. Is there a stamp of innovation and creativity within the organization?
8. Are the key people strongly motivated?
9. Is there a depth of personnel behind the key positions and an organized personnel development program?
10. Is there confidence in the individual heading the R & D activity?
11. Are effective techniques being used to get the most value from the whole R & D organization?

All of these tests are useful over a long-range, but they are difficult to apply to the individual project on a short-range basis.

SUBJECTIVE JUDGEMENT

The difficulty of developing good numerical criteria for output of a research and development organization is one of the prime difficulties in any estimate of efficiency of operations. However, subjective judgements, which a group of people form on the basis of visiting several laboratories, can turn out to be reasonably consistent and can therefore be expected to have some validity even though the criteria for measuring success are not defined. It is suggested that criteria for judging whether an R & D laboratory is doing good work might be if the laboratory people are enthusiastic about their jobs, understand what they are doing, and seem to be having a good time carrying out their operations. On the other hand, they are probably not making much progress if they are worried about administrative problems, concerned about money and are not interested in discussing the technical aspects of their work.